AMERICAN LABOR

FROM CONSPIRACY
TO
COLLECTIVE BARGAINING

THE MODERN FACTORY

SAFETY, SANITATION AND WELFARE

George M. Price

 ARNO & THE NEW YORK TIMES
NEW YORK   1969

Reprint edition 1969 by Arno Press, Inc.

Library of Congress Catalog Card No. 74–89758

Reprinted from a copy in
The New York State Library

Manufactured in the United States of America

THE MODERN FACTORY

SAFETY, SANITATION AND WELFARE

THE
MODERN FACTORY

SAFETY, SANITATION AND WELFARE

BY

GEORGE M. PRICE, M.D.

*Director, Joint Board of Sanitary Control in the Cloak, Suit and Skirt
and the Dress and Waist Industries, New York City
Formerly Director of Investigation, New
York State Factory Commission*

FIRST EDITION

FIRST THOUSAND

NEW YORK
JOHN WILEY & SONS, Inc.
London: CHAPMAN & HALL, Limited
1914

THE SCIENTIFIC PRESS
ROBERT DRUMMOND AND COMPANY
BROOKYLN, N. Y.

TO

Mary E. Dreier

THE HEART AND SOUL

OF THE

NEW YORK STATE FACTORY COMMISSION

THIS BOOK

IS DEDICATED IN APPRECIATION AND RESPECT

PREFACE

THERE were in the United States, according to the census of 1909, 268,491 industrial establishments in which there worked 6,615,046 persons. These figures do not include a great many smaller workshops in stores, separate parts of industrial establishments and small domestic workshops.

The modern factory is, therefore, a paramount economic force in the social and industrial life of the country and the nation.

Factory and labor legislation, industrial relations between capital and labor, improvement of factory conditions and amelioration of the conditions of the large mass of American workers are the burning questions of the day and the most vital problems of the hour.

The Federal government, the legislatures of individual states and many private social organizations throughout the country vie with each other in numerous inquiries, conferences, investigations, commissions, exhibits, etc., all bearing on the subject of industrial and factory conditions.

The time is ripe for a treatise on the modern factory; for, in spite of all the intense interest in the subject of industrial and factory conditions, there is as yet no special book on this subject in the English language.

An attempt is made in this book to give a comprehensive, although necessarily brief, review of the safety and sanitary conditions of factories and workshops as they are, and to indicate the methods of safety, sanitation, efficiency and welfare of factories and workshops as they should be.

As sanitary inspector of the New York Health Department for a number of years, as student and teacher of sanitary science, as practitioner for twenty years in the most crowded section of the East Side in New York City, as author of a number of books on general sanitation and hygiene, the writer has had special opportunities for studying industrial workers and industrial conditions at first hand.

Since 1910 the author has been and still is the Director of the Joint Board of Sanitary Control in the Cloak, Suit and Skirt and the Dress and Waist Industries, this new experiment in the sanitary control of an industry by those most interested in the industry itself: viz., organized employers, organized workmen and representatives of the public. In 1912 and 1913 the author was the Director of the investigations of the New York State Factory Commission, during which time he made extensive tours of inspection throughout the state, visiting hundreds of establishments in this as well as in other states. During the summer of 1913 he made for the United States Department of Labor a study of factory inspection in England, France, Germany, Austria, Belgium and Switzerland, the result of which has been published in a report issued as Bulletin No. 142 of the Bureau of Labor Statistics.

Acknowledgment is due to the Honorable Robert F. Wagner, State Senator of New York and Chairman of the New York State Factory Commission, and to the Honorable Abram I. Elkus, Counsel for the Commission, for permission to use many of the illustrations which have appeared previously in my official reports to the Commission. Thanks are also due to the many industrial corporations and private individuals who have kindly loaned me illustrations, full credit for which has been given in the text of the book.

Grateful acknowledgments are due to the following gentlemen: Professor C.-E. A. Winslow for reading the chapter on " Ventilation "; Messrs. J. K. Freitag and H. F. J. Porter for reading the chapter on " Fire Protection "; Mr. William Newell of the New York Labor Department for reading the chapter on " Safety and Accident Prevention "; and Mr. Norman Macbeth for revising the chapter on " Light and Illumination."

I cheerfully acknowledge my gratitude to Miss Violet Pike, my literary assistant and secretary, for her most efficient, faithful and industrious help in looking up literature, in reading manuscripts and proofs, in gathering data and general help in the laborious work of writing and bringing the book to press.

The book has been written and prepared for press within less than six months. It is inevitable that in such a hasty preparation there will be found a number of errors of omission and commission, for which indulgence is craved and which will be corrected in future editions if such are called for.

31 UNION SQUARE, NEW YORK.

CONTENTS

CHAPTER I

THE FACTORY, ITS RISE, GROWTH AND INFLUENCE

CHAPTER II

THE WORKPLACE

CHAPTER III

FACTORY FIRES AND THEIR PREVENTION

CHAPTER IV

FACTORY ACCIDENTS AND SAFETY

CHAPTER V

LIGHT AND ILLUMINATION IN FACTORIES

The Importance of Light in Factories. Inadequate Light in American
and European Factories. The Relation of Factory Lighting to Clean-
liness of Shop. Light and Efficiency Production. Relation of Adequate
Light to Accident Prevention. Eye Strain, Eye Diseases and General
Impairment of the Health of the Workers. What is Adequate and
Proper Light? Quantity and Intensity of Light. Surface Brightness.
Definition of a " Foot-Candle." German and Other European Stand-
ards on Light. Definition of " Glare." Prevention of Glare. Daylight.
The Factors upon which It Depends. Standards Adopted in Different
Countries. The Importance of the Window and Its Proper Construc-
tion. Artificial Illumination. Requirements for Efficient Illumina-
tion. Color. Uniformity. Products of Combustion. Sources of
Artificial Illumination. General Illumination. Localized Illumina-
tion. Localized-general Illumination. Tungsten Lamps. Reflectors.
Standards of the Wisconsin Industrial Commission................. 232

CHAPTER VI

FACTORY SANITATION

Classification of Factory Sanitation. General Cleanliness. Water
Supply for Drinking Purposes. Washing Facilities. Dressing-rooms.
Bathing Facilities. Plumbing and Plumbing Fixtures. Toilet Accom-
modations. Lunch-rooms. Sewage Disposal. Noises, Odors, Smoke,
Gases and Fumes. Disposal of Factory Wastes................... 259

CHAPTER VII

EMPLOYERS' WELFARE WORK

CHAPTER VIII

AIR AND VENTILATION IN FACTORIES

CHAPTER IX

INDUSTRIAL DUSTS AND DUSTY TRADES

CHAPTER X

INDUSTRIAL POISONS, GASES AND FUMES

CHAPTER XI

FACTORY LEGISLATION

CHAPTER XII

FACTORY INSPECTION

APPENDICES

LIST OF ILLUSTRATIONS

THE MODERN FACTORY

CHAPTER I

THE FACTORY, ITS RISE, GROWTH AND INFLUENCE

Industrial Evolution. The world is a huge workshop,—a scene of intense industrial activity for the satisfaction of human needs. And so it was from time immemorial. For industry is as old as the human race. Perhaps older. In the vast maze of antiquity, ages before any recorded events, there must have existed immense industrial activity among prehistoric peoples,—activities of which at present we gain only a faint conception from the few records that remain, but which left their strong impress upon those ages and constituted the germ from which our industrial system has evolved.

Industry being so necessary and so constant a factor in the life of man and in the development of the race, the methods of economic production and the stages of industrial evolution may therefore be viewed as the basis of the progressive development and history of civilization.

Viewed in this light industrial production has, roughly speaking, passed through three stages of development. Each of these stages may be characterized by the prevailing method of industrial production. These three methods are *domestic production, handicraft production* and the modern *factory system*.

" *Domestic production* is production in and for the house from raw materials furnished by the household itself. In its purest form it presupposes the absence of exchange and the ability of each household to satisfy by its own labor the wants of its members. All that it has, it owes to its own labor, and it is scarcely possible to separate the operations of the household from those of production." *

Handicraft production is that carried on within or outside of the house, usually by free workers, and is characterized by what we call " custom production." " The handicraft man always works for the consumer of his product; the region of the sale is local, namely, the town and its immediate neighborhood. . . . Whenever one line of handicraft threatens to become too large, other new handicrafts split from it." †

The modern factory system presents an entirely different method of production. By this system the economic wants of large communities, groups of persons and whole nations are satisfied by wholesale production on a large scale in specially constructed plants by means of so-called free wage labor and by the help of machinery and motive power.

It must be remembered, however, that this classification of the stages of industrial evolution simply indicates the prevailing method of production. At no time did one method exist to the exclusion of all others. To-day there exist side by side important variations from the prevailing factory system; domestic production in many peasant communities; handicraft and house industries even in advanced industrial centers. " No single element of culture that has once entered into the life of man is lost. Even after the hour of its predominance has expired, it continues in some more modest position to co-operate in the realization of that great end in which we all believe, the helping of mankind towards more and more perfect forms of existence." ‡

Whatever the system of production, the industrial factor is the predominating one. Its paramount influence is impressed upon all the forms of human progress, and upon it moral, religious and intellectual evolution is necessarily based.

Many of the forms of industrial activity depend upon climatic conditions, upon the nature of the soil and upon the character of the physical surroundings which determine the modes of procuring food and the manufacture of the necessities of life.

The place of work itself is of great importance in all stages of industrial evolution. The character of the workplace naturally differs with the stages of industrial development and depends upon many factors, not the least of which are (1) the general progress in

* Buecher, Industrial Evolution, p. 155.
† Ibid., p. 170.
‡ Ibid., p. 184.

housing conditions and (2) the stage of industrial production itself. In the domestic system of production, for instance, the workplace is within the house, usually not separated from the general living quarters. Certain forms of activity must be carried on within the house, others may be performed outside of the house, especially where climate permits. The construction and internal arrangement of the workplace will depend upon the state of housing progress.

Industry, the Workplace and Their Influence in Ancient Times. From what is known of Egyptian civilization, it is evident that there was a high state of industrial organization during the periods of which we have historical traces. That Egyptian industry was founded on slave labor is evident not only from the monuments remaining but also from the biblical stories of Genesis which show that the ruling class made their slaves do most of the work. The hard labor imposed upon the slaves led to frequent revolts, a number of which are mentioned in very early days and the greatest of which is described in the story of the Exodus of the Hebrews.

Little is known of the character of the workshops in Egypt. The fine pottery and utensils, some forms of which are still found in archaeological excavations, show that there was much domestic and handicraft production which must have been carried on in special places, for the most part out of doors, owing to the climatic conditions of the country.

The wages of the workers were almost always paid in kind— in wheat, oil or wine. The foremen or taskmasters had for their emblem a whip. The Egyptian proverb ran, " Man has a back and will not obey until it is beaten." It was the whip that built the pyramids, dug the canals and carried through most of the monumental works, which remain until to-day in Egypt. The workers considered it a necessary evil; from Pharaoh's minister down to the lowest of the slaves, none might escape it. The man who had never in all his life been beaten was considered as honorable as if he had obtained a decoration or special favor from the king.

In the working districts of Egyptian cities each shop was separate from the rest of the house and was rented separately. It was a small square room, often only a niche, open to the street, closed at night with wooden shutters. A typical shop would be furnished with one or two mats, low tabourettes and shelves. Sometimes behind the shops were small rooms kept locked for precious wares.

The merchants were also artisans; employed apprentices and worked themselves between the intervals of making sales. There are many bas-reliefs and ancient paintings which show the workers employed at their different crafts, from the shoemaker to the goldsmith.*

Industry in early Greece was carried on by free men, and only later was it given over to slaves. " In the days of Homer and Hesiod work was considered not only necessary but honorable. Manual labor, in the time of Homer, was the employment of princes and nobles and it was an honor to be a good worker. For cattle raising, agriculture and manufacture only the greatest respect and admiration were expressed. These vocations were preservers of life, and their best form was as yet too new and attractive to be regarded with indifference and contempt." †

The gods themselves set the mortals an example of industry. Hephæstus was a smith and served all the gods on Olympus; he made the arms of Achilles and the door for Hera's room. Athena wove her own peplum. Paris built his own house. Ulysses, before leaving Ithaca, made a wonderful bed adorned with silver and ivory.

After the Doric invasions, with the multiplication of slaves as the result of military conquest, work came to be considered shameful. According to the philosophers, the ideal life was lived without labor and spent in contemplation or service to the state. As most of the labor was done by slaves, handworkers were in the lowest grade, because, according to the accepted ideas of the time, " trade dulled the spirit and body and left no time to fulfil the duties of citizenship." Herodotus also remarks that " traders are hated by the Egyptians, Thracians, Scythians and Persians; " that he regards " handworkers as next to slaves if not below them, since while the slaves served one master, the handworkers served many." In spite of the large number of slaves, many hand-workers still existed who by the Solonic law were given the right to organize and form guilds and other organizations, most of them secret and some of them having large political interests.

There is little data on the character of the workplace in Greece. There seems to have been small interest in this matter and only casual references to it are found. A leather workshop with nine or ten slave workers is mentioned by Æschines. The father of Demosthenes was the owner of a large knife workshop in which

---

* Maspero, G., Au temps de Ramses et Assourbanipal.
† Keller, Homeric Society, p. 85.

thirty slaves were employed. The orator Lysias and his brother had, at the Piræus, a shield workshop with one hundred and twenty slaves as workers.

The construction of Greek workshops, like their dwellings, was simple, and suitable to an air-loving people. The rooms faced open courts or peristyles with blank walls outside. Houses were of one story; windows were absent; the doors opened on narrow streets. The workshops were open to all passersby. In cold weather many citizens entered to warm themselves at the craftsman's forge. Sometimes in the smithy the poor would sleep all night. The Greek craftsmen worked naked, and employers mingled with their workers and busied themselves with the same tasks.

That many of the Greek philosophers and physicians recognized the influence of industry and the workshop upon health is certain, although their references to it are few and scattered. Aristotle mentions the diseases of the " runners " and prescribed certain diet for gladiators. Hippocrates remarks: " There are many handicrafts and arts which cause those who exercise them certain pains and plagues." He speaks of the specific diseases of miners and burden carriers, of gardeners, riders, etc.

Plato considered philosophy unfit for those " whose bodies are not only deformed by their arts and handicrafts, but whose souls are also in like manner confused and crushed by their life of labor. What sort of race must such as these produce? Must it not be bastardly and abject? "

Little attention was paid to the influence of labor on health for the reason that the lives of the slaves were of no great consideration. Indeed, the increase in the number of slaves became an important state problem which the Spartans, for instance. tried to solve by exercising their youths in the art of killing off and slaughtering the innocent helots.

In Rome associations of free wage-workers existed from the earliest times. Mommsen states that there were eight guilds of craftsmen in Rome under Numa Pompilius, one of the first rulers of whom we have an account. They were the following:—flute-blowers, coppersmiths, fullers, potters, goldsmiths, dyers, carpenters and shoemakers. Mommsen adds, however, that there is no aspect of the life of the Roman people respecting which information is so scant as that of the Roman trades.

Later the law of Constantine gives thirty-five guilds existing at one time, including associations of builders, fishermen, gold-work-

ers, fullers, armorers, cooks and waiters, basket-makers, weavers
and clothing makers. These handicraft workers were all free.
The inscriptions found among the ruins of Pompeii show that
these organizations were much interested in politics and took part
in the local elections. Little is known of the lives of these ancient
workers. Those who belonged to the guilds undoubtedly had certain
privileges and comparatively secure positions, but much of the
lower kind of work was done by slaves and hirelings. T. Pampa,
quoted by Buecher, enumerates one hundred and forty-six different designations for the functions of slave laborers as well as for
the free handworkers. These early craftsmen lived in special
quarters in the city, and many of the streets were named after the
industries carried on in them.

The Roman workshops, even the largest, were situated within
the houses belonging to the rich or in shops located in the poorer
quarters. "With scarcely an exception, all houses of Pompeii
were only one story in height. All the rooms were therefore on the
ground floor; they all faced inwards and were lighted from the
court or atrium and not from the outside. For with a people who
had no glass with which to close their windows, it was impossible
to enjoy security without excluding light and air, otherwise than
by lighting rooms from the interior." *

In most instances the outside of the better class of houses was
given over to shops and smaller workplaces which opened on the
streets, while residences were wholly hidden from view by them.
Rome contained a dense population and the shops in the poor
quarters must have been small, dark and unsanitary. A great number of slaves were not housed at all, but spent their miserable lives
in mines, on the galleys, in the cellars, or were exposed to the vicis-
situdes of the climate. Thus, we find that an ancient tribune
speaks of the Roman proletariat as follows: " The wild have holes
and for everything there is some shelter, some retreat; but the poor
who struggle and die for Italy, they have light and air and nothing
more. *Houseless* and *homeless* they wander with their wives and
little ones. The poor must struggle and die for the blustering
drunkards and corrupted wealthy, called nobility, whom their
labor creates and sustains." †

At a later time there must have been great congestion of population in Rome and in the large cities of Italy. Houses were from

* Ferguson's History of Architecture.
† Plutarch's Lives, The Gracchi.

ten to twelve stories in the front and from twelve to fifteen stories in the rear. The height of ceilings from the floor was ten to twelve feet on the lower stories, but this height decreased, so that in the upper stories, designed for poor tenants, the ceilings were less than five feet from the floor, and in Pompeii a house four feet and three inches high was found. The poorest class of workmen lived in the upper stories and also in cellars and sub-cellars, which were filled with paupers whose condition may be better imagined than described.

Of course, with the contempt of the Romans for the lives of the slaves and manual workers, no attempt was made to better the conditions of the people or to study the influence of industry upon their health. That it was known admits no doubt. Pliny reports the dangers of workers with sulphur and zinc. The satirists Martial, Juvenal and Plautus speak of the " blear-eyed smith," " lame tailors," etc. Galen also makes observations on the diseases of certain workers.

Great sufferings from want among the slaves of Italy are mentioned in Pliny's Natural History. The slaves, who were not killed off directly by their masters, were condemned to early graves by plagues and epidemics which were then so frequent. The laborers were held to be the lowest in the rank of human beings next to the slaves, and the life of a laborer was considered a mean and unmanly occupation. The hordes of barbarians who fell prey to the arms of Rome and were then enslaved, performed most of the manual labor, and the frequent and desperate revolts of these slaves, as exemplified in some of the ancient insurrections like that of Spartacus, and the bloodthirsty way in which they were put down, show how little slave-owners cared for the lives, health or comforts of their workers.

Industry and Workplace in the Middle Ages. The overturn of ancient civilization by the Germanic invasions, the introduction of Christianity and the fall of Rome had a profound effect upon the system of industrial production of the ancient *regime*. In the frequent dynastic upheavals during the decline of the empire, the end of slave production became imminent. The rise of the new religion imbued the slaves with a new spirit. The breaking up of the empire led to economic isolation. Great markets disintegrated, and international trade came to an end. The barbarian invaders of the empire brought with them their primitive domestic economy as well as their political institutions, so well described by Tacitus.

The industrial unit was the family, whether the simple grouping
of parents and children or the larger households of manorial overlords or monasteries, with their serfs and dependents.

The transition from domestic production to the handicraft or
guild system was gradual. The rise and growing economic impor-

After Jobst Amman

A Mediæval Bake-Shop

tance of the mediæval towns fostered the development of handicrafts, and during the twelfth century, guilds, or associations of
workers in similar crafts banded together for mutual protection,
began to appear. Among the first craft guilds were those of the
weavers and fullers of woolen cloth. These guilds were especially protected by the cities and had practically a monopoly of

labor. No one could work at a craft without admission to the guild; the limitation was exacting and the rules were very severe. An apprenticeship of seven years was usually necessary before a worker could start for himself. The guilds assumed the responsibility for the quantity and quality of production, and craftsmen deviating from these regulations were severely punished.

There was no large class of wage-workers under the guild system. Each worker having passed through his years of apprenticeship could become a master of the craft, sometimes after having spent a few years as journeyman. The cloisters and monasteries were seats of great industrial activity. Trade was carried on in fortified cities by means of markets and fairs. The exchange of commodities was limited to the city or to a group of cities and there was little inter-city communication and hardly any international communication until a much later period.

It is to the guild system of production that we owe the wonderful cathedrals and abbeys of the middle ages, the stained glass, sculptures and carvings that adorn them, the tapestries, pottery and metal work that are the despair and admiration of modern craftsmen.

But during the sixteenth century, the power of the guilds began to decay. Their decline followed the development of capital and the growth of trade, due to the improvement of the means of communication and the great discoveries of the fifteenth century explorers. The expansion of the market demanded increased production, which the guilds, with their restrictive regulations on the numbers of apprentices and quantity and quality of the product, were unable to supply. To meet this demand, extra-town and extra-guild production sprang up all over Europe, and the capitalist or *entrepreneur* began to make his appearance in industry. A form of production developed under which the master worker or merchant, who had accumulated some capital, bought the raw materials and distributed them to the workers in the country and on the outskirts of the town, later collecting and selling the finished product either directly to the consumer or to the merchants in the towns During the sixteenth and seventeenth centuries and the early part of the eighteenth century, this method prevailed in the manufacture of staple commodities and became the forerunner of the modern factory system. It is sometimes called the cottage industry because of the industrial activity of the workers spread in so many cottages outside of the towns.

Of course, in the latter part of the middle ages after the fifteenth century, there were a number of large industrial establishments

Dyeing and Spinning Wool in the Eighteenth Century

in various countries, besides the small workshops in the cities or those shops attached to the great monasteries or baronial manors. As early as the beginning of the sixteenth century, there is a description of a factory of an important merchant, John Winchcombe, called Jack Newbury, whose manufacturing establishment seems to have been well known throughout England. The following quotation from Fuller's "Worthies," giving a glowing account of his plant, is of interest:

" Within one room, being large and long, there stood two hundred looms full strong; two hundred men wrought in these looms in a row. By every one a pretty boy sat making quills with mickle joy. In another place hard by, one hundred women merrily were carding hard with joyful cheer, and in a chamber close beside, two hundred maidens did abide; and in another room seventy children picking wool—forty men in the dye works—twenty fullers—nearly a thousand workers in all."

According to Wilhelm Stieda,* there was in 1573 a large sugar refinery in Augsburg; in 1592 a gold and silver place at Nuremburg; in 1593 a soap factory in Augsburg; in 1649 a blue-dye factory in Annaberg; in 1686 a " tuch fabrik " in Halle where fifty weavers and three hundred spinners were employed. Some time later a wool and silk factory was established in Magdeburg where five hundred workers were employed. In 1710 a porcelain factory was established in Meisen; in 1718 a porcelain factory was established in Berlin; in 1764 a linen factory was established in Tournai, Belgium, where eight hundred workers were employed; and a woolen factory was established in Mechlin employing four hundred and thirty-four workers.

According to Stieda, there were in Germany before 1801 at least twenty factories, each employing between one hundred and five hundred persons.

There must, therefore, have been some large establishments throughout European countries during the latter part of the middle ages just before the beginning of the factory era, but most of the work was done either by artisans, who were members of the guilds, in little shops in their own houses, or by the house-workers, who lived on the outskirts of towns and in agricultural settlements and were commissioned by the large capitalist to do certain work, especially spinning and weaving. These people worked in their own houses, alternating this work with agriculture. It was only with the advent of the modern factory system that a great change took place in the construction and character of the workshop.

* Article " Fabrik " in Conrad's Handwörterbuch der Staats Wissenschaften.

The workshop of the craftsman in the mediæval period was located on the first floor of the tall houses, in the narrow streets of mediæval fortified cities. One who at the present time passes through some of the narrow streets of Cologne, Ghent, Nuremburg and other ancient towns may easily imagine the conditions of the houses and work-

After Jobst Amman

The Master Shoemaker and his Journeymen (16th century)

shops, when every town was a fort and every city a citadel. In many of the cities the crafts were huddled together in special quarters and many streets took their names from the crafts which were carried on in them; such as the Rue de la Cordonnerie in Paris, where the shoemakers lived, and the Rue Pot de Fer, where the iron-workers lived.

The shops where the craftsman, his apprentices and journey-men worked were small and dark; the floor was of earth; the windows frequently of oiled paper, as glass was too expensive.   The shops opened on narrow streets.   There are still some old towns where typical mediæval streets can be seen, the second story jutting over the first story and the third story again over the second, so that the passerby in the street or the workers in the rooms on the first story, were as badly off for light as those living at the bottom of modern canyons formed by high buildings in twentieth century cities.

The workshop served also as a salesroom and opened on to the street.   Pigs, chickens and other animals could wander freely in and out.   In rainy weather the mud and filth from the streets was tracked in the workshops.   All refuse and sewage was of course emptied into the streets and the smells must have been indescribable.

The fact that the houses were draughty and that unless the windows were opened there was very little light to work by, was probably the salvation of the workers of those early times.   They had perforce to live a good deal in the air.   With no sanitation and with the often very crowded condition prevailing even in small towns, it is no wonder that the ranks of the workers of the middle ages were frequently decimated by the plagues which swept over Europe from the thirteenth to the seventeenth centuries.

Brizon gives the following description of some mediæval workshops:*

" The bakeshop was a low room which opened on the street; at the back of the room was the black hole of the oven.   Well in sight was a wooden sideboard on which bread and rolls were displayed.   Near the window was a pair of scales on which the bread for customers was weighed.   Beside the scales were the tallies on which the baker marked bread sold on credit; for credit had already become a custom.   Here and there against the wall were baskets, rolling pins, wooden mallets and great wooden shovels.   Often the baker himself bolted his wheat with a bolting mill."

" The pastry cookshops were almost always numerous and attractive.   They were very much the fashion during the century of Gargantua.   In Paris, these shops were the admiration of Lippomana, the Venetian Ambassador.   ' If you want,' said he, ' your food completely ready, cooked or baked, in less than one hour, the cooks and pastry cooks will prepare for you a dinner or a supper for fifteen, twenty or one hundred persons.   The rotissier will give

* Pierre Brizon, Histoire du Travail et des Travailleurs, p. 69–73.

you meats; the patissier, pastry, tarts, entrées and desserts; the cuisinier, jellies, sauces and ragouts.' "

" In the rear of the shop of the pastry cook was the gaping mouth of the oven; in the front were windows of oiled paper. Within the shop were the implements of the trade and cooking utensils. These utensils were often of very fine materials. There

After Jobst Amman

A Printing Shop in the Sixteenth Century

were boilers for fish, cake dishes and baking dishes of copper, all shining, and rolling pins, graters and moulds covered with silver. Near the window the cakes were displayed, while the pastry cook himself stood in front of the scales."

" The workers who were occupied with the manufacture of clothes and clothing materials all worked seated. The noise of the weaver's loom would come from the cellar or from a room on the ground floor or on the first story. The master workman worked alone or with his apprentices, often in the country in the homes of the peasants, who furnished him with wool. He might, however, pursue several trades either in his home or with his workers in a workshop. He seldom sold the material he wove directly to customers, but rather to merchants."

"Here is a picture of a hat maker who lived at Troyes on a bridge which crossed a branch of the Seine. His workshop was on the river in a little room where there was a copper boiler, steam casts, mortar, wooden mallets and a hundred and one different forms for making hats. There he made hats of felt or of wool which were afterwards dyed. He did not have many in stock, for when he died in 1693 there were only thirteen in his shop, valued at twenty livres."

With the general neglect of sanitation and disregard of health peculiar to the middle ages, the study of the influence of occupations on the health of the serfs and villains, or even upon the lives of the free members of the guilds was naturally neglected, for the masters fared as badly as the apprentices and journeymen with whom they worked. There are, however, records left of the awakening of some physicians and scientists to the importance of health and sanitation during the latter part of the middle ages.

During the fifteenth, sixteenth and seventeenth centuries a number of physicians began to recognize the effects of industry on health and from time to time gave expression to their knowledge in reports and monographs. In the transactions of the Royal Society of England of the sixteenth and seventeenth centuries we occasionally come across references to the effects of coal and lead mining, the manufacturing of mirrors, the detrimental influence of dust, etc.

Not, however, before the end of the sixteenth century did the knowledge of industrial diseases and occupational influences become crystallized. This was done in the great work of the father of modern industrial hygiene, Bernardino Ramazzini. Ramazzini was born in Capri in 1633. In 1659 at the age of twenty-six years he received his doctor's diploma. That he must have practised among workers, and that he must have had great clinical experience, and been an original and deep thinker is shown by his works which were published from time to time, the first in 1685. His greatest work on industrial hygiene, written in 1690, was not published until 1700 and bears the following title: "De Morbis Artificium Diatriba," and is the first work on industrial hygiene based upon rich clinical experience, and deep knowledge and insight into human nature and industrial activity.

The work consists of forty chapters, which were later supplemented by twelve more chapters. In the introduction, Ramazzini

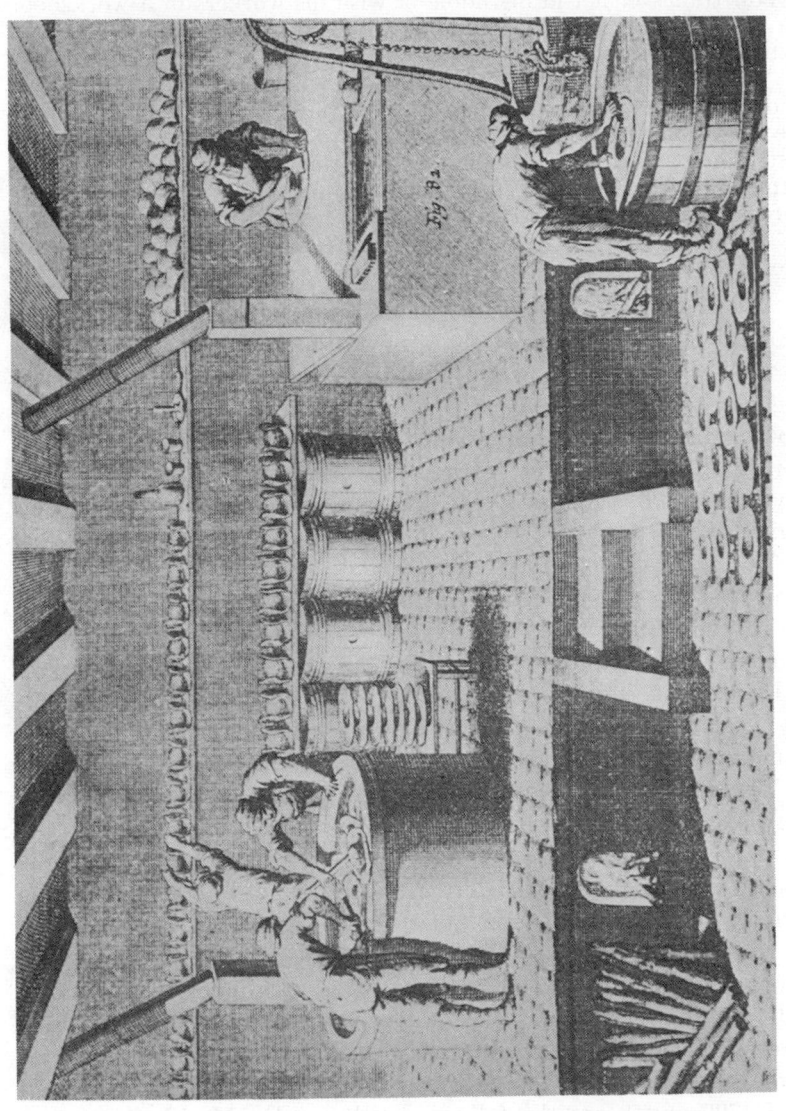

Making Hats in the Eighteenth Century

speaks of the importance of industrial hygiene and the need for the physician always to ask the occupation of the patient, especially among the manual workers. The work fully describes the processes of a great number of industries:—miners, mirror-makers, chemists, potters, glass-makers, painters, sofa-makers, smiths, lime-workers, fullers, tobacco workers, beer brewers, bakers, millers, starch-makers, laundry workers, etc.

Each chapter describes a group of works, goes deeply into the industrial activities, the injurious influences of each activity, the character of the work itself and the workplace, and mentions the ills and diseases to which the workers are subject. In the supplement added in the second edition there are chapters on the typographical workers, on textile workers, wood workers, polishers, brick workers, well diggers, marine workers, etc.

During his fruitful life Ramazzini continued to work along the same lines and published numerous editions and papers on subjects of industrial hygiene. Ramazzini gave the first impetus to the study of the influences of industrial activities and the diseases of occupations. For nearly one hundred and fifty years the classic work of Ramazzini was the one chiefly used throughout the civilized world. It was reprinted and republished in many tongues and countries, and has inspired a great number of his successors. This work was not surpassed until the works of Thackrah of England, Layet of France and Hirt of Germany, at last put industrial hygiene upon a firm scientific basis.

The Modern Factory System. The discovery of America and other new lands, the breaking down of inter-city barriers, the development of international and intercontinental communications, the expansion of commerce and trade, the creation and large undertakings of the great commercial companies, all led to dissatisfaction with the guild system of production, which was no longer able to supply the rapidly increasing demands of trade and commerce. During the seventeenth and eighteenth centuries, it became more and more evident that industrial production by the means of handicrafts or cottage industries was inadequate, and that the burden of limitations imposed by the guild organizations upon industry was hindering the development of industrial organization.

It is customary to date the birth and rise of the modern factory system from the middle or latter part of the eighteenth century. As a matter of fact, the germ of the new economic system could be found in much earlier methods of production, and the rise of capitalism in the sixteenth and seventeenth centuries can be justly regarded as the forerunner of the modern factory system. During these centuries antedating the factory system the distribution of wealth, commercial enterprises and international trade were gradually modernized and concentrated in the hands of capitalists. Industrial production, although occasionally concentrated in large communities or even in large establishments, was still in the main carried on on a small scale, so that no great increase in the quantity of commodities was possible. This necessary increase in production and wealth could only be attained by the aid of the wonderful inventions and discoveries that were made during the eighteenth century.

Among the multitude of human wants there is perhaps not one so closely interwoven with human progress as the production and

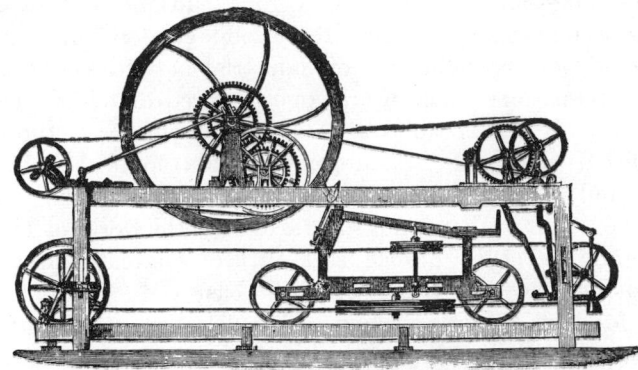

From " The Industrial Evolution of the United States." by Carroll D. Wright, LL.D.; copyright, 1895, 1897. By permission of Charles Scribner's Sons.

Crompton's Mule-Jenny (Specification Drawing)

manufacture of clothing. The spinning of yarn from cotton, flax, hemp, silk, etc., has been from time immemorial accomplished by the crude means of distaff and spindle, and later by the spinning wheel. That the quantity and quality of material produced by this elementary method could not be great, and that it required the work of many persons for long periods to satisfy increasing wants, is obvious.

The fly shuttle was known for quite a long time and increased the possibility of weaving cloth without, however, increasing the amount of yarn that could be spun. During the early part of the eighteenth century, the weavers complained bitterly of having to remain idle through inability to obtain sufficient yarn from the spinners. This inequality was removed with the invention of the spinning jenny, which was due to the genius of Thomas High, a Mr. Kay, and James Hargreaves. It is usual to give the credit for the invention of the spinning jenny to Hargreaves, who made the first machine in 1767 and patented it in 1770. It is a fact, however, that the clockmaker Kay, who afterwards was employed by Arkwright, and Thomas High, a reed maker of Leigh, made the first machine and set it up in High's house. It was even named in honor of Jane, the daughter of Mr. High. The jenny was perfected by Hargreaves, who failed at first to obtain a patent for it, but used it for his own purpose. So great was the production of yarn by this invention that the spinners resented its efficiency and a mob stormed his house and destroyed his first machine.

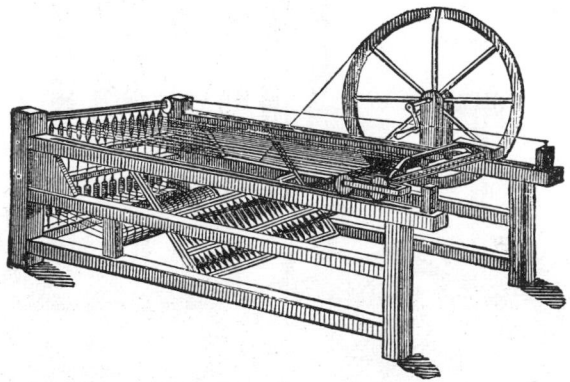

From "The Industrial Evolution of the United States," by Carroll D. Wright, LL.D.; copyright, 1895,1897. By permission of Charles Scribner's Sons.

Hargreave's Spinning Jenny

Nevertheless, the process of spinning by machinery was only really begun when the barber, Arkwright, saw the great promise of Kay's and High's invention and made or had made for him important improvements resulting in his so-called water-frame, patented by him in 1771. Not only had Arkwright the ingenuity to adapt the invention of the spinning jenny, but he also had the daring to embark in large manufacturing, and with several partners established the first cotton spinning mill, which at first gave work only to about a dozen workers. The machinery of this mill was turned by horses. In his later factory at Cromford it was run by water power, and hence his spinning machine came to be called the water-frame.

The invention of the spinning jenny and the water-frame had not completed the improvements for spinning yarn in large quantities and of good quality. This was made possible by the invention of Samuel Crompton, who constructed his mule in 1779, so called because in it the principles of High's jenny as well as Arkwright's water-frame were combined. These inventions made possible an enormous increase in the quantity and an improvement in the quality of spinning yarn; and it was now the process of weaving that lagged

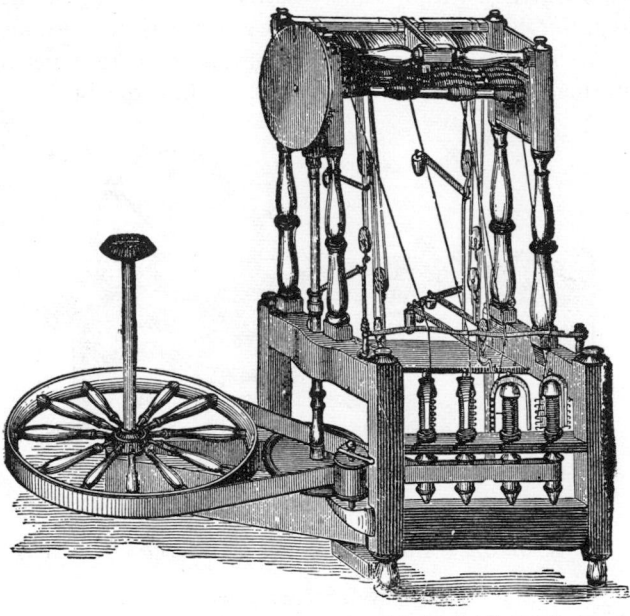

From " The Industrial Evolution of the United States," by Carroll D. Wright, LL.D.; copyright, 1895, 1897. By permission of Charles Scribner's Sons.

Arkwright's Spinning Machine.   From the original drawing

behind until the invention of Edmund Cartwright's power loom, which he patented in 1785. Yet in spite of these inventions, as long as there was no possibility of utilizing any other power except horse or water power, large scale production was still an impossibility. It was only after the discovery by Watt of the steam engine and its application to factories in 1785 that the real revolution began in the method of cotton cloth production. Henceforth, an impetus was given to industry that could not be stopped, and the results of which could hardly be foreseen at that time.

The enormous increase in cotton production may be somewhat judged by the following: In 1775 the amount of raw cotton imported into England was only 5,000,000 pounds. It increased as follows:

1785	17,992,882 lbs.
1790	31,447,605 "
1801	54,203,433 "
1811	90,309,668 "
1821	137,401,539 "
1831	273,249,653 "
1841	437,093,631 "
1849	775,469,008 " *

The increase of production in the cotton industry was naturally followed by increased production in many other industries. In 1701, England's woolen export amounted to 2,000,000 pounds; in 1770, to 14,000,000 pounds. The following table shows the increase in industrial production in the export of British cotton goods:

1741	£ 20,709
1751	45,986
1764	200,354
1780	355,060
1791	1,875,046
1833	18,486,400 †

With increased production came also a great increase in the population under the factory system, especially in certain districts. In 1700, Lancashire numbered only 166,200 inhabitants; in 1750 the population was 297,400; in 1801 it had grown to 672,565; in 1831 to 1,336,854; being an increase of more than eightfold in one hundred and thirty years.‡ Not only in England but in other countries and also in the United States there was great increase in industrial production.

In 1775, the first spinning jenny ever seen in America was exhibited in Philadelphia. The first experiments, embodying the principles of Arkwright's inventions in the erection of a primitive cotton factory, were made in Massachusetts, but it was in Rhode Island that the first factory was started in which perfected machinery, made after the English models, was practically employed. This was begun by Samuel Slater, the " father of

* Innes, Arthur, D., England's Industrial Development, p. 233.
† Baines, History of the Cotton Manufacture, pp. 111 and 349.
‡ Ibid., p. 360.

American manufactures," who came over from England for the purpose, and started his mill with three cards and seventy-two spindles in 1790. A man in South Carolina (mentioned by a writer in the *American Museum*, for July, 1790) completed and had in operation on the Santee, ginning, carding, and other machines driven by water; and also spinning machines with eighty-four spindles each. In 1814, the first power loom was set up at Waltham, Mass. This factory was the first in the world, as far as records show, in which all the processes involved in the manufacture of goods from the raw material to the finished product, were carried on in one establishment.*

Within the first fifty years of the eighteenth century, the quantity of cotton wool imported seems to have little more than doubled; within the last twenty years it multiplied more than eightfold. The rate of progression, therefore, was ten times as great in the latter period as in the former.

Within the first fifty years of the eighteenth century the value of cotton exports nearly doubled; within the last twenty it multiplied fifteen and a half fold. The rate of progression, therefore, was nearly twenty times as great in the latter period as in the former. Such are the effects of machinery! †

The following table shows the early cotton manufacture in the United States as regards the number of spindles:

1805	4,500
1807	8,000
1809	31,000
1810	87,000
1815	130,000
1820	220,000
1825	800,000
1831	1,246,703

The following table shows the growth of the factory system as illustrated by the cotton industry in Great Britain and the United States:

	Year.	No. Est.	No. Spindles.	No. Looms.	No. Employes.
Great Britain:	1833	1,151	9,333,000	100,000	237,000
	1878	2,671	39,527,920	514,911	482,903
United States:	1831	801	1,246,703	33,433	57,466
	1880	756	10,653,435	225,759	172,544 ‡

* Carroll D. Wright, Industrial Evolution of the United States, p. 130.
† Baines, History of the Cotton Manufacture, p. 216.
‡ Carroll D. Wright, The Factory System in the United States, p. 6.

From Baines' "History of the Cotton Manufacture."

Mule Spinning about 1830

The Industrial Revolution and its Influence. The Industrial
Revolution, partly described above, impressed itself upon all
branches of human activity and produced vast changes in the economic and political as well as the intellectual development of mankind.

The first results of the Industrial Revolution were the enormous expansion in trade and commerce, and the great increase in
the wealth of nations, the rise of capitalism and the capitalistic
system of production, great expansion in commercial undertakings,
the hunt for domestic and foreign markets, the increase in wealth
and manufactures, and the general increase in the wealth of nations.
Some of the above statistics show the enormous development of
production in England (imports and exports) as well as in the
United States due to the changed mode of production. In 1793
the value of exports in England amounted to £17,000,000; it was
doubled in 1800, and more than trebled in 1815, reaching the sum
of £58,000,000.

In 1700, an estimated population of England and Wales, based
upon the parish registers, showed a total of 5,000,000. In 1750, the
population increased to 6,000,000, and according to the first census
in 1801 it had increased to 9,000,000. The population increased
approximately twenty per cent the first half of the eighteenth
century, and approximately fifty per cent during the last half. During the nineteenth century the population quadrupled itself. The
first thirty years of the nineteenth century added more than the
whole of the eighteenth century; and the acceleration in the increase
of the population appears to have set in in the latter part of the
eighteenth century.*

The following table shows the growth of capital and population in England and the property per head:

	Population.	Property.	Property per head.
1720	6,500,000	£ 370,000,000	£ 57
1750	7,000,000	500,000,000	71
1800	9,000,000	1,500,000,000	167 †

It was also during this period that the great redistribution of
population set in. It may be illustrated by noting that the northern and north midland counties, which to-day contain one-half
of the population of England, in 1700 contained less than one-

* Innes, p. 225.
† Porter, Progress of the Nation, p. 696.

quarter. It was mainly during that last quarter of the eighteenth century that the center of gravity was decisively shifted.

Reference has already been made to the concentration of population in industrial cities and in industrial centers, and a table was cited showing the increase of population in the Lancashire district. The invention of machinery necessitated the concentration of capital, construction of large factories and congregation of a large number of workers within them. The utilization of steam power made manufacture independent of watercourses and concentrated industry near the coal fields and in large industrial centers. The decrease in domestic production led to depopulation of the agricultural districts, the abandonment of the farm cottages, and the massing of a large working population in towns and around large establishments. It was due to the economic expansion that foreign markets, colonization, and the conquest of new markets became so necessary.

At the root of all the English wars during the last part of the eighteenth century and the beginning of the nineteenth century were economic causes. The wars were necessitated by England's endeavor to gain commercial supremacy of the world, after she had invented the means of supplying the world's markets to overflowing. The American Revolution was brought about through attempts of the home government to keep the colonies as markets for English products and prevent development of colonial manufacture and trade with other countries.

A wide cleft was made in the relations of employer and employé. A new class, that of wage workers, was created. The whole industrial framework of society was changed. The means of production, formerly in the hands of each worker, through application of steam power was taken away from him and concentrated in the hands of large capitalists, dividing the industrial world into two sharply defined classes of employers and employés, with the class of employers possessing the means of production and the workers competing with each other and struggling for existence, forming a new class whose numbers continually increased, as machinery and steam invaded one industry after another.

The output of factories increased a hundred and thousand fold; manufactures grew with unheard of rapidity; but the modern factory system also supplanted the old amicable and personal relations of master, journeyman and apprentice. It made it difficult for the journeyman and apprentice to ever become a master; it

From Baines' '' History of the Cotton Manufacture.'

A Cotton Factory in 1830: Carding Room

compelled the worker to change his employment with the exigencies of industry and to run the risk of losing his trade with each new invention and discovery.

With the advent of improved methods of spinning and weaving, the importance of the skilled craftsman declined, as the simplified machinery made it possible for an unskilled laborer, a woman or even a child to perform the simple operations necessary, and thus to supplant the skilled and adult laborer. The displacement of a large number of adult workers, their flocking to the industrial centers, made competition among them so great that wages fell to a minimum. The division of labor in factories made possible by improved machinery, made of the worker a simple appendage to the machine, who could be replaced at the whim and will of the employer.

Aristotle dreamed that " if the weavers' shuttles were to weave of themselves there would be no need either of apprentices for the master worker or slaves for the overlords." One part of the dream came true. Weavers' shuttles almost wove of themselves and still the golden age was beyond the ken of man. The application of machinery to spinning and weaving created a greater and greater demand for apprentices and for the utilization of the youngest children in industry. While wealth increased enormously, poverty increased by still greater strides. From 1760 to 1818 the poor rate grew from three shillings sevenpence per head to thirteen shillings threepence per head.

As Carlyle expressed it, " England is full of wealth, yet England is dying of inanition." The golden age of the cotton trade marks the advent of the dark age of starvation and wage slavery. The changed form of manufacture introduced competition not only among the workers but also among employers. There ensued a fierce struggle between the factory owners to undersell each other, to cheapen production, to gain a foothold in the market. Success became dependent upon rigid economy in methods of production and in the manufacture of wares at a minimum cost. It was hardly possible for the manufacturer to economize much in the quality of the material, for the sale of his goods depended on this quality. He could not economize on machinery, for his output greatly depended upon the efficiency of his machine. The line of least resistance was to economize at the expense of the workers, who, under this competitive system were so anxious for a job that they cared not where they worked or how they worked

From Baines' History of the Cotton Manufacture."

A Cotton Factory in 1830: Weaving Room

so long as they did work. Economy therefore ruled in the construction of the factory, in the lack of provision for health and comfort, and in the wages paid to the workers. In fact, the employer considered the condition of the employés no affair of his.

Radcliffe says that from 1788 to 1803, at the beginning of the expansion in the cotton trade, "barns, cart houses and old buildings of all descriptions were repaired, windows broke through old blank walls and were fitted up for loom shops." The worker was drawn away from his peaceful cottage in the agricultural district, with his alternating work at the loom and in the fields, and was transplanted into the poisoned and foul air of the mill, with its whizzing machinery and maddening speed, which petrified his soul and atrophied the organs of his body, and shortened his days by the cruel haste of the machinery.

But perhaps the greatest evil which followed the inception of the modern factory system was the terrible exploitation of child labor in the factories. Children have always participated in industry. Reference has already been made to the extensive employment of children in some of the industrial establishments during the middle ages; but it remained for the modern factory system to exploit systematically the labor of children, to make it a necessity of manufacture and to use and abuse a large part of the growing generation within the factory and mill.

When the early manufacturers could not get a sufficient number of children or free workers to feed their machines and tend their looms, they trafficked with the poor-law officials, who sold the children of paupers in a form not different from the methods of ancient and modern slave dealers. No one nowadays, even those who have read the lurid reports of some of the labor committees of the present day, can imagine the horrors which existed in England and other countries toward the end of the eighteenth century and in the first quarter of the nineteenth century with respect to child labor. Some of the accounts of the condition of the industrial population in England as well as in other countries may be found in the reports of the official committees, which began their work in 1776 in Manchester and continued their efforts practically throughout the course of the nineteenth century. In some of these reports are found accounts by eye-witnesses of conditions which spread horror in the minds of all concerned, except those who directly profited by the labor of children.

In Alfred's " History of the Factory Movement," volume i., pages 21 and 22, is the following summary:

" In stench and heated rooms, amid the constant whirling of a thousand wheels, little fingers and little feet were kept in ceaseless action, forced into unnatural activity by blows from the heavy hands and feet of the merciless overlooker, and the infliction of bodily pain by instruments of punishment.   They were fed upon the coarsest food, often with the same as that served out to the pigs.   They slept by turns and in relays in filthy beds which were never cooled. There was often no discrimination of sex, and disease, misery and vice grew as in a hotbed of contagion.   Those who tried to run away had irons riveted to their ankles with long links reaching up to the hips and were compelled to work and sleep in these chains. Many died and were buried secretly at night and many committed suicide."

Gibbins, in his " History of England," in discussing the early factory investigations, says:

" Terrible evidence of overwork was given before the committee, but the grasp of Mammon was cruel and relentless, and now that social reformers were in earnest, the inevitable opposition of capitalistic greed rose up in all its power to block the path of humanity— the surest block was delay.

It is unnecessary to go further into a description of the abuses at the beginning of the present industrial system or to cite the complaints and inquiries which were made in England and other countries on the condition of the laboring class and of the children in the factories.   Much of this data may be found in Engels' " Condition of the Laboring Class in England,"   in Chadwick's " Report on the Condition of the Laboring Class in England," and in the other reports named in the Appendix.   It is sufficient to say here that the discovery and disclosure of the evils of child labor and other abuses of modern factory production led to popular demands for redress and improvement and for the curbing of the power of the capitalists by factory legislation, which will be described in a later chapter.

The evidence adduced by the reports of investigating committees in different countries, as to the effect of the modern factory system upon the health and the lives of the workers, and the industrial population, served to prove the contention of the earlier hygienists since Ramazzini, that intimate relations exist between occupation and health, and that industry and industrial mortality are interdependent.   The real proof, however, could only appear after vital statistics became a science, when general vital registration was introduced in England and other countries, when mortality statistics were taken in connection with the occupations of the population, and when it became apparent that there was a great difference in the mortality rates between industrial and rural districts and between the inhabitants of one district and those of another.   Until the beginning of the nineteenth century vital statistics were practically unknown in their present scientific form, and all calculations as to the number of population, death rate, disease rate, etc., were based simply upon guesswork.

When, in 1801, the first census of population in England was made and statistics were gathered from the towns and outlying districts, when some order was brought into the registration of deaths and their causes, then only could some deductions be made from the figures thus obtained.   Even so, it has only been within the last few decades of the nineteenth century that occupational statistics in relation to mortality have been gathered in such a form as to make their scientific use possible.

Even now, however, mortality statistics are neither accurate nor definite and the pitfalls of those who seek to base deductions upon the figures obtained are many.   We have as yet no scientific classification of occupations, nor is there any universal uniform registration of deaths or classification of the causes of deaths. Occupational mortality statistics are therefore still full of errors and the deductions obtained from them still problematic.

Aside from all these considerations, there are a number of added factors which make the value of occupational mortality statistics uncertain.   The questions of the selection of a trade and occupation by individuals, the shifting of population from one trade to another, the dropping out of persons from especially hazardous and dangerous trades so that their deaths occur while pursuing an entirely different trade from that in which they are engaged most of their lives, and similar factors, play a most important rôle in the uncertainty of occupational mortality statistics.

Nevertheless, granting all the objections made to the deductions obtained from occupational mortality statistics, there is undoubtedly much evidence in the statistics of a great many countries, evidence which is practically the same in all countries in spite of the differences in climate and conditions, to prove, (1) that the mortality of persons living in industrial districts is much greater than the mortality of persons living in agricultural districts; (2)

that the mortality of persons in certain general occupations, such as farmers, fishermen, clergymen, etc., is much lower in comparison to the mortality of persons pursuing industrial occupations; and (3) that the mortality of persons in certain occupations, is much lower than the mortality of persons who pursue occupations which contain elements of danger and are of an unhealthful character for one or more reasons.

There is also abundant statistical data in the records of the sick benefit and insurance societies and especially in the records of the State Sickness Insurance Office in Germany from which the following conclusions may be drawn:

(1)   That the morbidity rates are greater in industrial populations than among agricultural populations.

(2)   That the morbidity rates of persons in certain occupations are much higher than among persons in other occupations.

(3)   That persons working in certain dusty trades suffer from a higher tuberculosis morbidity rate than those who work in occupations where there is no dust.

(4)   That there are certain diseases of the nerves, skin, eyes and ears as well as infectious diseases which may be directly traced to the occupations of the workers suffering from these diseases.

The health factors of occupations may be classified as follows:

GROUP I. FACTORS DUE TO THE PERSONALITY OF THE WORKER:

(a) Initial health of the worker.
(b) His susceptibility, vitality and resistance.
(c) Nutrition, personal hygiene, etc.
(d) Temperament, education, etc.
(e) Choice of vocation and trade.
(f) Sex.
(g) Age.

GROUP II. FACTORS DUE TO CONDITIONS OF WORK:

(a) Character of work; active or sedentary.
(b) Attitude and position.
(c) Duration and pauses.
(d) Fatigue, tension and responsibility.
(e) Wages, compensation, etc.
(f) Extremes of climate, temperature and humidity.

GROUP III. FACTORS DUE TO THE MATERIALS AND PROCESSES:
- (a) Dusts.
- (b) Poisons.
- (c) Gases and fumes.
- (d) Infectious material.
- (e) Dangerous machinery and appliances.

GROUP IV. FACTORS DUE TO THE PLACE OF WORK:
- (a) Outdoor and indoor.
- (b) Construction of workplace.
- (c) Type of workplace.
- (d) Location of workplace.
- (e) Light and illumination.
- (f) Air and ventilation.
- (g) Sanitary care and comforts.
- (h) Fire protection.

In studying the modern factory we shall give a detailed account of the industrial etiological factors, especially in Groups III. and IV., embracing important parts of industrial hygiene.

Definitions of Factory, Workshop, etc. The conception of the words " factory " and " workshop " has somewhat changed from the meaning generally given them at the inception of the modern factory system. At the beginning the word " factory " meant a trading establishment in a distant country. It was defined by Wright and Webster as a " house or place where factors do reside; a house or district inhabited by traders in a distant country." This meaning still survives in the case of the Hudson Bay Company, whose trading posts in the Canadian Northwest are still called factories by the older generation of traders. Such "factories" are stations for the Indians, trappers, guides, and other inhabitants of the Northwest, to which they bring their skins and other produce and exchange them for merchandise.

The change in the meaning of the word " factory " began with the eighteenth century. Baines, in his " History of the Cotton Manufacture," refers to the use of the latter term as a modern invention. Of course, the modern use of the term is justified by its derivation, but the word " factor" was in earlier times rendered " agent " in the sense of deputy or manager.

The word " fabrika " is often mentioned in the middle ages and was applied to paper, glass, iron, copper, and other manufacture done in cloisters and monasteries. In Adrian Beyer's "Algemeine Handlexicon," the word "fabrika" is defined as "fabrika, officina, namentlich,—eine Werkstätte, die eine gewisse Art vom aller hand Waaren verfertigt wird."

Ure, in his "Dictionary of Arts and Manufactures," has no article on the word "factory." Carroll D. Wright's definition is often quoted as a classic. It is as follows:

"A factory is an establishment where several workmen are collected for the purpose of obtaining greater and cheaper conveniences for labor than they could procure individually at their homes, for producing results by their combined efforts which they could not accomplish separately, and for preventing the loss occasioned by carrying articles from place to place during the several processes to complete their manufacture." *

The etymological and general definitions of the word "factory" are rarely taken into consideration in attempts at legal definition made in various countries with the beginnings of factory legislation. These definitions were made at different periods and were changed according to the exigencies of the times and to developments in legislative control.

The first Factory Act passed in England used the words "mill and factory" without definition, simply applying them to certain kinds of textile establishments. In the Act of 1844 the words "mill and factory" were defined as "all buildings and premises situated within any part of the United Kingdom of Great Britain and Ireland, wherein or within the close or curtilage of which, steam, water or any other machinery is employed in preparing, manufacturing or finishing; or in any process incident to the manufacture of cotton, wool, hair, silk, flax, jute or tow, either separately or mixed with any other material or any fabric made thereof, were used." †

At this time therefore the expression "factory" meant any place devoted to spinning or weaving fabrics by power. As industrial establishments came more and more under the control of the inspectors of factories, other works were added. In 1860 bleach works, in 1861 lace works and in 1864 a number of miscellaneous industries in no way connected with textiles or necessarily using power machinery were added to the definition of "factory and mill."

In time the word "factory" had come to mean an extraordinary variety of things. It meant "not only every place wherein

* Carroll D. Wright, Report on the Factory System of the United States, p. 533.
† Cooke-Taylor, Introduction to a History of the Factory System, pp. 3–4.

power other than manual was in use in any process connected with the production of textile fabrics, together with bleach, print and dye works and a great variety of other products specially named under the Act of 1864 as well, but also " any premises, whether adjoining or separate, in the same occupation, situated in the same city, town, parish or place and constituting one trade establishment, in, on or within the precincts of which fifty or more persons are employed in any manufacturing process," thus reintroducing the criterion of number of employes. *

Until 1878, this remained as the legal definition of a factory in England, and all establishments with less than fifty persons were considered workshops and not factories. Other countries as well have attempted to define the word " factory " by the number of employés within the establishment. Thus, the French Law of 1841, the Austrian Industrial Code of 1859, the Italian Code of 1886 regarded a workshop as a place with more than ten workers therein. The Industrial Code of Saxony of 1861 regarded a factory as one employing more than twenty workers. In the German law the expression " Fabrik " is left out entirely and establishments of ten workers or more are considered only as " Fabrikmässig."

A more scientific definition of factory and workshop was first established in England by the Act of 1878, which, while not giving a specific definition of a factory, makes a distinction between a factory and a workshop based upon the fact that in the former machinery worked by steam, water or other mechanical power is used, while a workshop is a place where work is done without the help of motive power. There are some exceptions to this rule, and there are also special definitions for textile factories, non-textile factories, domestic factories, workshops, domestic workshops, etc.

The present New York Law gives the broadest definition of a factory and it has been judicially decided that for the purposes of protection of workers, it shall be construed to mean " any place where goods or products are manufactured or repaired, cleaned or sorted, in whole or in part, for sale or for wages."† The following is the definition given in the New York Law:

" The term factory shall be construed to include any mill, workshop, or any other manufacturing or business establishment and all buildings, sheds, structures or other places used for or in con-

---

* Cooke-Taylor, Introduction to the History of the Factory System, p. 6.
† Ritchie vs. People, 40 N. Y., pp. 454-455.

nection therewith, where one or more persons are employed at labor, except power houses, barns, storage houses, sheds and other structures used in connection with railroad purposes, other than construction or repair shops, subject to the jurisdiction of the Public Service Commission's law. Work shall be deemed to be done for a factory within the meaning of this chapter whenever it is done at any place, upon the work of a factory or upon any other materials entering into the product of the factory, whether under contract or arrangement with any persons in charge of, or connected with such factory directly or indirectly through the instrumentality of one or more contractors or other third person."

The following are definitions of a factory in other states:

Pennsylvania: A factory is a building, the main or principal design or use of which is a place to produce articles as products of labor.*

Massachusetts: The term " factory " means any premises where steam, water or other mechanical power is used in aid of any manufacture or printing process there carried on.†

Minnesota: The term " factory " or " mill " means any premises where steam, water or other mechanical power is used in aid of any manufacture or printing process there carried on.‡

The following tables show the number of industrial establishments classified as factories and workshops in the United States, several large states, and in six European countries:

MANUFACTURING ESTABLISHMENTS IN THE CHIEF INDUSTRIAL STATES, ARRANGED ACCORDING TO THE NUMBER OF WAGE-EARNERS. (U. S. Census, 1909.)

State.	Population.	No. Establishments.	Wage-Earners, Average Number.
New York	9,113,614	44,935	1,003,981
Pennsylvania	7,665,111	27,563	877,543
Massachusetts	3,366,416	11,684	584,559
Illinois	5,638,591	18,026	465,764
Ohio	4,767,121	15,138	446,934
New Jersey	2,537,167	8,817	326,223
Michigan	2,810,173	9,159	231,499
Connecticut	1,114,756	4,251	210,792
Indiana	2,700,876	7,969	186,984
Wisconsin	2,333,860	9,721	182,583
Missouri	3,293,335	8,375	152,993
North Carolina	2,206,287	4,931	121,473
California	2,377,549	7,659	115,296
Rhode Island	542,610	1,951	113,538
Maryland	1,295,346	4,837	107,921
United States	91,972,266	268,491	6,615,046

* Franklin Fire Insurance Co. vs. Brock, 57 Pa., pp. 74, 82.
† Rev. Laws Mass., 1902, p. 916.
‡ Gen. St. Minn. 894, Par. 2264.

Number of Industrial Establishments and Workers in England. According to the statistics gathered in 1907, found in Table III., p. 289, of the Annual Report of the Chief Inspector for Factories in 1911, there were the following number of workers in British factories:

	Males.	Females.	Total.
England and Wales................	2,736,214	1,500,836	4,227,050
Scotland.........................	423,392	236,664	660,056
Ireland..........................	125,262	114,741	240,003
Total in United Kingdom..........	3,274,868	1,852,241	5,127,109

According to the report of 1912 there were 117,275 factories and 155,697 workshops, 272,972 establishments in all.

Number of Industrial Establishments and Workers in France. According to a census made in 1911 there were in France a total of 507,557 industrial establishments, classified as follows:

No. of Persons.	No. of Establishments.	Per Cent.
Establishments having from 1 to 5 persons.....	402,186	79.25
Establishments having from 6 to 20 persons....	74,567	14.68
Establishments having from 21 to 100 persons...	24,763	4.88
Establishments having from 101 to 500 persons.	5,433	1.07
Establishments having more than 500 persons...	608	0.12

The following table shows the age and sex of the 4,258,617 workers and employes in establishments subject to the supervision of the inspectors of labor:

Males under 18 years.....................	336,140	7.8
Females under 18 years..................	286,578	6.7
Females over 18 years...................	914,214	21.4
Males over 18 years.....................	2,721,785	64.1
Total..................................	4,258,617	

Number of Industrial Establishments and Workers in Austria. The industrial population of Austria was in 1901, 4,149,320. The total number of establishments was estimated at 1,000,000 in 1909, with a total working population of 2,351,446 in 1901. There were, however, only 151,903 industrial establishments subject to inspection in 1911, of which only 16,181 were designated as factories.

Number of Industrial Establishments and Workers in Belgium. In Belgium there are about 80,000 industrial establishments with over 800,000 workers.

Number of Industrial Establishments and Workers in Prussia. In Prussia there were 169,606 industrial establishments in 1912, with at least ten workers in each establishment. In these establishments there were working 3,579,771 persons.

Number of Industrial Establishments and Workers in Germany. According to a table of the International Labor Office, there were 264,431 factories and 93,871 workshops in the whole of Germany in 1909, with a working population of nearly five and one-half million persons.

CHAPTER II

THE WORKPLACE

TYPES, CONSTRUCTION AND MODEL FACTORIES

Types. A century and a half of the new economic system of production has passed and has inevitably brought about profound changes in the industrial and political development of the civilized world. During this period giant strides have been made in industrial expansion, and wonderful discoveries in the domain of the physical sciences. Invention has been followed by invention and greater economic progress made within this comparatively short period than during the whole history of mankind. Methods of production have been completely revolutionized and industrial control concentrated in the hands of a special class; while a large portion of the population has been converted into a great standing army of a new class—that of the industrial proletariat.

Since the birth of the new era many changes have taken place in the character of industrial control, in the methods of competition, and in the very conception of industry and trade. Feverish activity, fierce competition, the idea that the whole scheme of industrial activity was destined to pass like a nightmare, fear of state interference, and the philosophy of *laissez faire* have given way to a profound conviction that the new system has come to stay, that the largest, most concentrated and most efficient forms of industry are bound to survive, and that industry may prosper and trade succeed quite as well under state control as without it.

This changed attitude has been reflected in important changes in the character of the workplace itself, in the development of large industrial establishments, and different conceptions of the requirements of the modern factory and workshop.

The petty stinting and miserly economy of the first factory owners are no longer considered indispensable to industrial success. The herding of workers in dingy, dark, dreary shops, in flimsy and

39

An Early American Factory: Lowell Cotton Mills in 1828.

Courtesy of the Macmillan Co,

An English Cotton Factory, about 1830.

From Baines   History of the Cotton Manufacture."

ramshackle structures is no longer considered economical. The
new science of " industrial efficiency " teaches that there was no
economy in the previous methods of treating factory workers; that
industrial prosperity and commercial success are compatible with
decent workplaces, humane working conditions, and considerate
treatment of employes.

This latest conception of the workplace is unfortunately not
universal; and among the thousands and hundred thousand workshops and factories, there is great diversity in the type of construction and the character of the workplace. Side by side with the
model factory, with all the latest improvements and the most
recent examples of welfare work, we still find the ancient handicraft workshop in the tenement or converted building, and nearby,
perhaps also an example of the primitive loom shop in the tenement
districts of European cities.

There are four distinct types of workplaces which may be distinguished in industrial centers in all countries. These are (1)
the domestic workplace, (2) the handicraft workshop, (3) the multiple workplace or so-called loft building, and (4) the special factory.
Each of these types of workplace deserves separate consideration.

The Domestic Workplace. The domestic workshop, variously
designated as sweatshop, home or tenement shop, consists of a room
or rooms or places where any work for outsiders is done by members
of the family living therein, with or without the aid of their
dependents and children.

There is a great difference between the character of the modern
domestic workshop and the domestic workplace of primitive economy,
or even the industrial cottage of the pre-factory period. In the
primitive domestic workplace, work was carried on by the members
of the family, slaves and dependents, only for the satisfaction of
the family needs. In the old cottage industries of England and
other countries the work was done for capitalists who furnished the
material; but the methods of work, of distribution, and wage payment, were totally different from those prevailing in the sweatshop.

The sweatshop is the overflowing cesspool of modern factory
production. In it are performed the finishing touches and processes,
which, by reason of their simplicity or cheapness, may be done in
the home by children, by women or by men thrown upon the industrial scrap heap.

The work performed in the home workshops is usually limited
to certain industries and branches of trade. The lace homework

of Brussels, the embroidery industry of Switzerland, the tobacco, cigar and cigarette homework of certain parts of Germany, the sweatshop belt of London, and the tenement homeworkers in the clothing trade of the East Side of New York are examples of industrial homework. There are, however, few branches of industry in which there is not more or less homework existing side by side with general factory production.

In a thorough investigation made by the New York State Factory Investigating Commission, the following six classes of industry

N. Y. Factory Commission.

A Home Workshop: Picking Nuts for the Trade.

are mentioned as those in which homework was found: (1) clothing, millinery, including artificial flowers, feathers, etc., (2) textiles, (3) fur and leather goods, (4) paper boxes, etc., (5) food and tobacco, and (6) miscellaneous industries.*

" Homework has been discovered in some process of manufacture in each of these large divisions. The extent of it cannot be stated, but it is of the utmost significance that the system has found its way in so many industries."

* Second Report of Factory Investigating Commission, 1913, vol. i., p. 92.

In the last report of the chief inspector of England, the following trades are mentioned as those in which "outworkers" were found: wearing apparel, household linen, lace curtains, etc., furniture and upholstery, lacquer plating, file making, brass and brass articles, fork tuning, cables and chains, anchors and grapnels, locks, latches and keys, artificial flowers, nets, tents, rackets and tennis balls, paper bags and boxes, brush making, feather sorting, carding of buttons, stuffed toys, basket making, etc.

As to the extent of homework, the number of domestic workshops and the total number of persons engaged in homework, only a general estimate can be made, as there is little reliable data and no general statistics. One of the investigators of the New York State Factory Commission, states that

"At the present time it is impossible to estimate with any degree of accuracy the number of people engaged in homework in New York City. If the figures obtained form any basis for computation, the number of homeworkers must run into the hundreds of thousands." *

According to the same report, New York State permits forty-one articles to be manufactured in tenements, and sixty-six additional articles were found made in tenement houses without the sanction of the law.† There are at present over 15,000 licensed tenements in New York State, in every apartment of which homework may be done. According to Miss Van Kleek, "there are 7000 homeworkers in the artificial flower and feather trade, and they are more numerous than employes in the shops." ‡

In eighteen embroidery firms investigated, an average of 103 homeworkers per firm was found. On this basis there are 51,500 embroidery workers in New York City alone.§ According to a Federal report,

"Nowhere are there accurate statistics to indicate the extent of home finishing or other homework. It is resorted to more extensively in New York and more proportionately in Chicago than elsewhere. There are solid blocks in New York where by actual count more than three-fourths of the apartments contain home finishers." ||

* Second Report of the Factory Investigating Commission, vol. ii., p. 677.
† Idem, p. 678.
‡ Van Kleeck: The Artificial Flower Trade, p. 90.
§ Second Report, Factory Investigating Commission, vol. ii., p. 677.
|| Report on Condition of Women and Child Wage-Earners in United States, vol. ii., p. 218.

Nor is the extent of homework limited to large cities only. Smaller cities and even rural communities are not free from it. In the New York investigation, referred to before, homework was found in small communities like Little Falls, Gloversville, etc., and there are many places outside of large cities where homework is prevalent.

In England, figures are given showing 103,958 outworkers for the year 1912, who are employed by 12,111 employers.* In France, in Belgium, in Austria and other countries where home-

N. Y. Factory Commission.

A Home Workshop: Wrapping Candy in a New York Tenement.

work is entirely uncontrolled, no data exists to show the extent of homework or the number of domestic workplaces.   In Germany, where a law has lately been passed regulating homework, no general census has as yet been made.   The Hirsch Dunker Unions, with a membership of about 100,000, report 4800 homeworkers.† About 35,000 homeworkers in the tobacco trade are organized in unions, and between 2000 and 3000 in the metal trades of Solingen.‡

* Annual Report, Chief Inspector of Factories and Workshops, 1912, p. 247.
† Kaethe Gaebel, Die Heimatarbeit, p. 77.
‡ Ibid, p. 72.

The character of the home work-place has been vividly described in the many reports made of sweatshop work within the last decade. The workplace is usually one of the two or three rooms of a tenement house, the kitchen or bedroom, as a rule, where the family not only works, but eats, sleeps at night, and sometimes harbors lodgers and boarders. The light, ventilation and cleanliness of these home workshops are those of all tenement rooms and apartments in overcrowded and unsanitary districts.

Among the thoroughly substantiated evils of homework are the following: unsanitary condition of the premises, infection of the workers and their families by the materials and articles on which they work, the possibility of contamination of these articles by the germs and diseases so prevalent among the families of homeworkers, and the spread of infection by these means to the public, the unrestricted hours of work for women, the frequent prolonged and arduous work at night, the participation of the children in the work, the competition with factory work and consequent lowering of the wages of the workers in the regular factory and workshop.

The English report states that in 2478 instances the premises were unwholesome, and in 768 cases the premises were infected with disease.*

The report of the New York Factory Commission already referred to, cites examples of work participated in by whole families, some members of which were stricken with scarlet fever and other infectious diseases. Tuberculosis, the scourge of the tenement house, is often found among homeworkers. Mortality and morbidity statistics distinctly show the greater death and disease rate among the tenement-house population, especially in overcrowded homeworking districts.

The evils of homework and the foul conditions of domestic workshops present important problems to the legislatures of civilized countries. Drastic remedies are sought, and the abolition of the whole system of homework has been advocated.

The Workshop. From statistical data it appears that the whole industrial activity of the present time, apart from homework, is not concentrated in the large factory, but is also carried on in the small workshops so prevalent in every industrial community.

Some of the statistics quoted in the last chapter showed that in England the majority of workplaces belonged to the "work-

* Annual Report of Inspector of Factories, 1912, p. 247.

shop" class; that there were 155,697 of these, or over 57.03 per cent of the total number of industrial establishments.

In France, out of the 507,557 industrial establishments, there were not less than 402,186 or 79.25 per cent of workshops having only between one and five persons working therein, showing the overwhelming number of industrial establishments belonging to the so-called " Petit Industrie."

In Austria, out of 151,903 industrial establishments subject to

Picking Rags in a Cellar Workshop.

inspection in 1911, only 16,181 or 10.65 per cent were designated as factories.

In Prussia, the industrial establishments which are regarded as subject to inspection are only those which have at least ten workers; and in the whole of Germany there were 93,871 workshops, with the probability that a large number of small workshops were not included in the enumeration.

The small workshop, therefore, is more frequently found than the large factory, and a large part of industrial activity is being performed outside of the large modern factory.

The type of the workshop differs according to the industry, locality and many other factors. Few of the workshops are of a character similar to the old handicraft workshop, so characteristic of the guild era. In the large cities as well as in smaller communities, workshops are found located in little shops on the ground floors or in basements and cellars of houses in which one man, sometimes with an apprentice, is doing his own work for his own customers. This is the case with the cobblers, dressmakers, custom tailors, blacksmiths, etc. There are also other shops where work is carried on for large manufacturers in which a number of workers are employed. This is found in clothing, baking and kindred industries, in which the shops occupy stores or ground floor apartments of tenements and small buildings.

Most of these workshops, whether they belong to the first or second type, number but few workers, and contain little machinery. The principal evils of these small workshops are the difficulty of their control, the adverse economic conditions under which the operatives work, and bad sanitary conditions.

It is a most difficult matter to control the smaller kind of workshop, since in most cases the authorities know nothing of their existence. They grow like mushrooms, change and disappear with a kaleidoscopic rapidity, and their control is one of the most difficult problems of modern factory inspection.

However, apart from the difficulty of control, which is merely a question of the efficiency of the inspection service, conditions in the small workshop may be as excellent as those in the largest model factory. In many ways, indeed, the small workshop has its advantages. There is less monotony in the work, more chance for the worker's initiative and an absence of that military discipline necessitated by large scale industry. Friendly relations are apt to exist between the workers, and the workers and the employer, who shares in their labor. In the small shops in skilled trades, where skill and finish rather than speed and quantity are required, the wages are high and hours not excessive.

By far the largest number of these workshops are located on the ground floors of tenements and dwellings in the busy streets of industrial centers, in the dark and dingy rooms back of stores and salesrooms, and frequently indeed in the cellars and basements. This is especially characteristic of certain industries, notably the bakery and confectionery trades. In all cities a large number of bakeries and confectionery shops are found on the ground floors,

N. Y. Factory Commission.

A Cellar Bakery: Underground Shops are apt to be Dark and Unclean.

and the manufacture for these shops is, as a rule, done in underground bake-houses in the basements and cellars under the stores. In my investigation of bakeries in New York State, I found nearly four thousand bakeries in New York City located in cellars and low basements, and the same conditions prevail, though not quite to such an extent in Berlin, Vienna, London, Brussels, and especially Paris, where baking is done not only in cellars, but in deep sub-cellars. This evil is perhaps characteristic only of the large cities, like Chicago, New York, etc. Nevertheless, the number of basement and cellar workshops in the bakery and confectionery trade as well as some other trades is exceedingly large.

The reasons for considering underground workplaces unsanitary have been set forth in many official reports, and may be summarized as follows:

" A cellar is an unfit place for the manufacture of food stuffs, or for the habitation of workers. There cannot be any natural light in a cellar under the most favorable conditions, and no place can be sanitary that lacks sunlight. Cellars are the most difficult places to ventilate unless mechanical ventilation is installed, which is out of the question in the ordinary small bakery. Cellars in which bakeries are located cannot have a temperature which is healthy for workers; they are too near the ground and the emanation from the ground, and the ovens and the heated atmosphere needed for dough raising, make it almost impossible for cellar bakeries to have a moderate and equable temperature in the absence of proper ventilation. Cellars cannot be kept clean as other parts of the house, for they are semi-dark, contain most of the plumbing pipes and fixtures, and are, as a rule, the dumping ground of the whole house. Cellars are also the natural habitation of insects, rodents, etc., and are also in proximity to breeding places of flies, which are attracted to the food stuffs." *

Tenant Factories. In large industrial centers a number of workplaces are located in the so-called multiple workshop buildings, which have developed within the last decade or more. These workshops consist of separate floors or parts of floors, located in buildings which contain a number of workshops. Sometimes the building in which these workshops are located is one that was formerly used as a tenement or dwelling, and which has become too dilapidated for living purposes; and has then been converted, by breaking up the partitions and altering the construction, into a workshop building. More frequently these shops are located in

*New York State Factory Investigating Commission, First Report. Vol. i., p. 235.

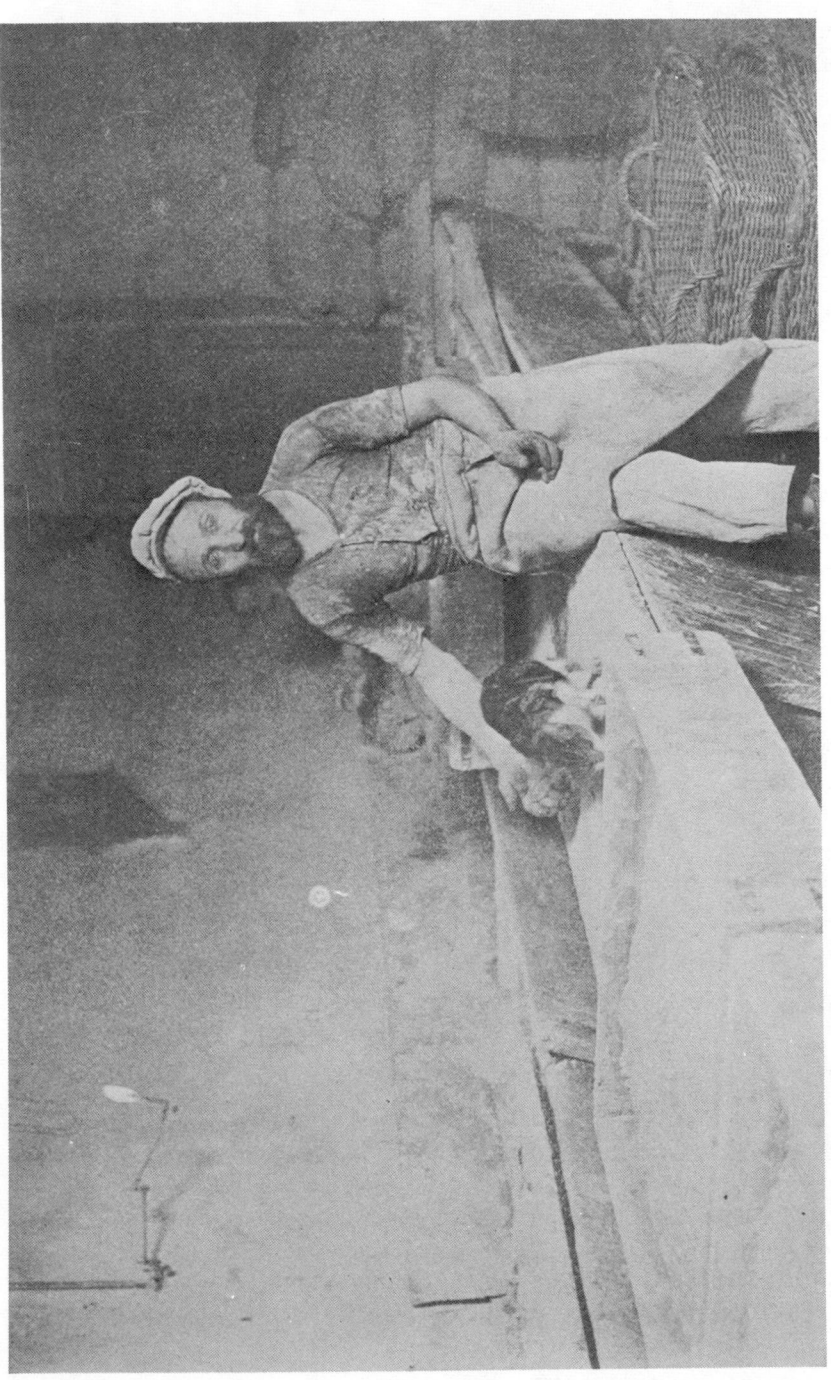

N. Y. Factory Commission.

Unclean Conditions in a Cellar Bakery.

buildings specially constructed for this purpose, which are known as loft buildings.

Loft construction is a recent development in the industrial

A Cloak and Suit Shop, East Side, N. Y. City.

Joint Board of Sanitary Control.

life of a city. It is a result of the congestion of an immense population on a small area. In New York City alone, between 1901 and 1910, on Manhattan Island in a certain limited district, not less than 800 loft buildings were erected from eight to twenty stories in height.

The loft building is found not only in New York, but is beginning to make its appearance also in smaller cities; and cities of the first and second class are now beginning to consider the problem of curbing and controlling loft building and multiple shop construction. Of the thirty thousand odd industrial establishments in New York City, by far the largest number are located in loft buildings. Whole industries of a certain character are almost entirely located in loft buildings. Thus, 83.80 per cent of all the shops in the cloak and suit industry, and 94.34 per cent of all the workers are found in loft buildings. This is even more the case in the dress and waist industry. Almost 96 per cent of the shops, and not less than 98.57 per cent of the workers in this industry, are in the same kind of building.*

How large a percentage of the workshops of industries, especially in New York City, are located in loft buildings may be gathered from these facts as well as from the figures in the table given below:

Clothing shops in lofts........................ 74.8%
Fur shops in lofts............................. 58.9%
Printing in lofts.............................. 57.5%
Paper bags and boxes in lofts 54.3%
Tobacco in lofts.............................. 52.6%
Flowers and feathers in lofts................. 52.0% †

The problem of loft shops has been the theme of recent investigations in New York State, and the subject was brought to the attention of the world by the shocking catastrophes of Newark, the Asch Building fire and the Binghamton calamity, all of these occurring between 1911 and 1913.

The fire dangers and lack of fire protection in the loft buildings are perhaps the most damning objections to multiple shops. This form of workshop, however, is characteristic only of a few large industrial cities, and there are indications that its spread will soon be limited.

Special Factories. In the largest and most important industrial countries, by far the greater percentage of industrial activity and production is carried on in the modern factory. By the term modern factory is meant " a structure or building which is constructed and maintained for the special industrial activity to be carried on therein." Statistics are lacking as to the proportion

---

* Third Annual Report of the Joint Board of Sanitary Control, pp. 55 and 59.
† Second Report of New York Factory Investigating Commission, vol. ii., pp. 423-424.

of industry carried on in the special factory, although there is some information as to the number of special factories as distinguished from the smaller workshops. In an investigation made in New York State, it was found that of the 2500 investigated establishments in the different industries, the following per cent of industries were carried on in special factory buildings:

Gloves.................................... 90.9%
Textiles.................................. 84.0%
Chemicals, paints and illuminatives............. 83.5%
Woodwork................................ 82.0%
Stone and glass........................... 78.9%
Hats and caps............................. 65.7%*

The carrying on of work in special factories by the aid of machinery and motive power is, of course, largely determined by the industry itself and by the character of the industry. Wherever in an industry no large machinery or permanent plant is necessary, where individual machines are used, where the division of labor is not too great, and where the material production is not too bulky the work may be carried on in smaller shops, and not necessarily in specially constructed or fitted workplaces. Certain industries, such as textiles, large metal industries, flour and paper mills, are carried on largely in special buildings and factories.

It is difficult to obtain a census of the industrial plants in a state or country. There is, as yet, especially in the United States, a general neglect of this important subject. Nor is there any general system of registering industrial plants; and most of the statistics of industrial establishments are based upon the decennial census enumerations, which are not always reliable. It is only lately that several states, notably New York, Pennsylvania and Massachusetts, have passed laws requiring the registration of all industrial establishments; and it was only during the latter part of 1913 that New York State issued an industrial directory.

In some European countries this work is thoroughly organized. England has a complete registration of all factories and workshops; Germany, Belgium and Austria have not only a registration law, but also an authorization or licensing provision for certain kinds of industrial establishments.

In most countries, the evils of unrestricted and unregulated construction of dwelling and tenement houses have already been

* Second Report of New York Factory Investigating Commission, vol. ii., p. 434.

Bush Terminal Company.

Modern Factory Buildings.

fully recognized. The unregulated construction of habitations, especially in the large industrial centers, has led to a great many abuses; to the crowding of houses upon full lots, leaving no space for light and ventilation, and to so many great evils that for the last decade or more serious attempts have been made in most of the cities of the civilized world to curb the cupidity of landlords, to regulate construction of tenement houses, and to compel all builders of new houses to present their plans to the city authorities and to follow certain stipulated rules and regulations for house building, as well as to compel them to make improvements in houses already constructed. As a rule, the local authorities in each town or city supervise the construction of tenement and dwelling houses. There are strict regulations as to the height of the building, percentage of lot it may occupy, percentage of lot which is to be left entirely free and unbuilt upon, the strength of walls and floors, the size of the rooms and apartments, the installation of sanitary conveniences within the house, the size of the windows, etc. All these regulations naturally have led to great improvements in housing conditions in the large cities, and have been of incalculable benefit to the town population, especially the working class.

There is as yet hardly any regulation in reference to the building of factories and industrial establishments. This is left to the whim and will of the owner and his more or less competent architect.

In some countries, notably in Germany and Austria, each manufacturer in certain specified industries must receive an authorization before beginning work in a particular establishment. There is then an earnest scrutiny made of the kind of building intended for such an establishment; and architects, physicians and factory inspectors are obliged to go over every detail of the plans for construction and installation and point out to the owner and his architects the requirements necessary to the health, comforts, and lives of the workers. This is a wise procedure, based upon the well-known adage of the superiority of an ounce of prevention over a pound of cure; for it is evident that a great many of the evils found in most industrial establishments could have been easily prevented by taking a little care before beginning to build.

Certain specially dangerous industries, particularly those where explosives are manufactured, must be located in an isolated spot. Other industries, especially those which, for one reason or another, may become offensive to the neighborhood, must be located at a distance from habitable quarters of cities and towns; while others must be located near sources of power or within the city or towns because of the peculiar requirements of the industry.

Hence, on examining the factories and workplaces of different industries, one is struck by the general diversity of structures peculiar to each industry; factories and mills belonging to the textile trade are entirely different in their characteristics and type of construction from chemical establishments, or metal, or woodworking establishments; not only each industry but each city, each country and each locality presents its own type of factory, mill or workplace.

The site of a special factory depends in each case upon the needs of the particular establishment to be constructed. Among the many factors which are of importance in the location of a factory are the means of transportation, the proximity of markets, the provision for expansion, the sources of power, and the presence of a working population.

The surroundings of a factory are of some importance, although this is a matter which has been greatly neglected in the past. Factories have hitherto been constructed with the sole idea of utility, and with no thought of beauty in architecture. The factories of the past, and too many at the present time, have no claim whatever to any beauty in their surroundings. Many of them look like penitentiaries, prisons and barracks, huge, somber, dark and forbidding, darkening the surroundings with a pall of black smoke.

Fortunately, a great change has taken place in the conception of factory construction and surroundings. Some of the modern factories built within the last ten years present a pleasing appearance, and a great effort seems to have been made by the architects, builders and owners to tone down the forbidding aspect of the factory and make it look more pleasant and beautiful, and to surround it with trees, parks and gardens.

It is now not exceptional to see splendid examples of factory architecture, model in surroundings, location and plant. Some of the shining examples in this respect are the well-known large industrial plants of the Shredded Wheat Company at Niagara Falls, the National Lamp Company at Cleveland, Ohio, the United Shoe Machinery Manufacturing Company at Beverly, Mass., the National Cash Register Company at Dayton, Ohio, the Heinz factories at Pittsburg and many others.

The Patterson Bros., of Dayton, Ohio, while constructing their factory, called in a landscape expert to help in planning its grounds.

They had their walls colored bright buff and machinery painted in light colors instead of black. They put palms in the factory and planted shrubbery on the grounds. The General Electric Light

Entrance to Kodak Park Works, Rochester, N. Y.

Company in Schenectady, decorated the main entrance to their works with tubs of flowers, and Boston ivy was planted about the principal buildings near the entrance.*

* Tolman, Industrial Betterment, p. 5.

Abroad, there are also a large number of industrial establishments well known for their beautiful appearance and pleasant surroundings. At Messrs. Boden's net factory in Derby, though in the heart of the town, the windows look out on courtyards containing well-kept gardens and a gymnasium, " the former of which," writes Lord Meath, " would have done credit to a nobleman's château, so neat and well kept were their flower borders."

The factory of Messrs. James Templeton & Company, carpet manufacturers in Glasgow, has been rendered a thing of beauty and an added attraction to the neighborhood, by being faced with colored bricks after the design of the Doge's Palace at Venice.*

The Hammerbrot works near Vienna I found in a pleasant spot several miles distant from the city, with beautiful surroundings. The Leverkusen factory of the Beyer Chemical Company is also very beautifully located.

Factories may be classified, according to the materials used in construction, as follows: (1) wood or frame, (2) wood and brick, (3) steel frame with brick or concrete walls, (4) reinforced concrete.

There are still many special factories made entirely of wood although happily this is prohibited in most industrial towns and cities. The frame factories we find at present—and there are still too many of them—are structures built many years ago, which have changed their tenants many times, and in which the poorer industries and smaller establishments are housed. One industry especially seems to have a special predilection for frame factories: this is the chemical industry. Many of the processes in this industry require separate buildings; a number of these processes are dangerous on account of dealing with explosives, powerful acids, etc.; so that there seems to be some advantage in housing them in separate buildings. It is pleasant, however, to note that most of the newly constructed chemical factories have departed from this practice and are being built of a more durable material.

The second type of construction of special factories is called " mill construction," which consists of a frame of wood with brick walls. The particulars of mill construction are as follows: the frame joists and floors are made of heavy timbers, the floor timbers being heavy and spaced eight to twelve feet apart, the floors made of three to four-inch blocks with single or double top boarding. The floors are made tight and heavy and there are no openings in the floors between one story and another, all such openings being

* Tolman, Industrial Betterment, p. 80.

placed in specially constructed separate towers. This so-called "mill construction" has been frequently used, and is especially characteristic of the New England textile mills as well as some of the mills in the middle and far west.

With the increased cost of lumber and with the decreased cost of steel, mill construction has largely given way to the type of construction which consists of a steel frame with brick or concrete walls. In respect to fire protection, steel-frame construction is not much superior to mill construction, although more suitable to factories in large towns and cities. A material largely used in model factories is reinforced concrete, which is so far the best for industrial buildings.

The history of plain concrete dates back to prehistoric times. It was used in the ancient cities of Egypt, Greece and Rome; for Roman aqueducts and Roman roads, and its great durability is proved by the remains existing up to the present day.

Reinforced concrete, meaning by this the introduction of iron and steel into the aggregate of the concrete, is said to be about seventy years old, although commercially it is only for about fifteen or twenty years that industrial buildings have been constructed of reinforced concrete. One of the reasons for using reinforced concrete is the necessity for fireproofing structural steel, such as is found in the modern skyscraper office and loft buildings in the large cities. A great many factories are constructed almost wholly of reinforced concrete, which is at present accepted as the ideal material for this type of structure. The cost of reinforced concrete is considerably less than structural steel. Concrete buildings are more fireproof than buildings made of any other material; they are strong, safe, fire and vermin proof, may be adapted for various designs and requirements, and can be so constructed as to give the most light, best heat and be exceedingly sanitary in all respects. Factories made of reinforced concrete carry a lower accident insurance rate than buildings of other materials, and their fire-resisting character has been proven many times. One of the construction firms doing considerable work in erecting modern factories of reinforced concrete, has the following to say as to the advantages of this form of building:

"In the design of factory buildings of reinforced concrete, the following points are generally taken care of: actual fire prevention; as far as modern knowledge goes, notably smokeproof stairways, concrete or tile partitions around all stair and elevator walls; concrete, brick, or tile fire walls, reducing the floor space areas to operating minimum, concrete stairs, etc. The floors of concrete are clean, not especially hard to work on, are sanitary in that cement is a lime product and, therefore, inherently sanitary. The floors may be

Concrete and Glass : The Adler Clothing Factory at Rochester, N. Y.

washed down weekly. Vermin are excluded. Ventilation and light are at the maximum, owing to the adaptability of concrete to any kind of a design. One of the greatest benefits rendered the owner is the reduction of any tendency toward panic on the part of the employes.

It has been found that in these model fireproof buildings, the employes come to have confidence in the fire resistance and load carrying capacity, and consequently are more calm in emergencies than in other types of buildings." *

The number of stories, the width, length and size of the building intended for a factory or used for such purposes are determined by the needs of the industry and the many factors enumerated above. It is worthy of note that European industrial establishments are never more than five stories in height, mostly two or three stories, and that many of them are only one story high. Such a form of construction is, of course, possible only where land is cheap and expansion possible; but the benefit derived from such construction as far as light, ventilation and safety from fires is concerned, is incalculable.

I have seen a number of factories abroad one story in height, presenting a beautiful and comfortable appearance, with the skylights giving splendid light inside. One of the largest industrial establishments of its kind is that of the Provodnik factory at Riga, Russia, which occupies many acres of ground and which consists of a series of one-story buildings, so arranged that the raw product comes in by trains on one side, and the manufactured product is shipped from the last building on the other side.

Even in the largest cities and capitals of Europe, industrial establishments over five stories in height are seldom to be seen, the height being regulated by the government. In the absence of statistics it is impossible to state the number of special factories in the United States above five stories, but there must be a great many of them. Mention has already been made of the many-storied loft buildings. The width and length of a building are important in relation to fire prevention and protection; and the necessity of intervening fire walls for certain spaces will be spoken of in the next chapter.

Without going into the details of building construction of factories beyond the scope of this work, the importance of the walls, ceilings and floors in industrial buildings should be noted apart from their load carrying capacity, fire protection, thickness, and materials of construction. Of greater importance in relation to industrial hygiene is the inner decoration and finishing of the walls and ceiling surfaces, especially in industries where a large amount of humidity is present, or where steam is generated. An absorbent surface will take in much moisture and will be always

* Turner Construction Company.

damp, while a smooth surfaced wall or ceiling will cause condensation
of moisture and dripping on the floors or on the workers.   Where
there are means of quickly drying the walls and ceilings, it is perhaps
better to have an absorbent surface than a condensing one.   On the
other hand, where such means are absent, the evil of condensation
can only be overcome by thorough ventilation or by frequently
mopping up and wiping off the surfaces.

In some of the model factories I have seen, notably in the industrial plant at Beyer's chemical factory at Leverkusen, the walls of
all the shops are tiled, white and smooth, presenting not only a
beautiful appearance, but giving surfaces which are easily cleaned.

The character of the inner wall surfaces will, of course, depend

The Hammerbrodt Werk: A Socialist Co-operative Bakery in Vienna, Austria.

upon the character of the building, the material of construction
and the processes carried on in it.   Where the walls are made of
wood and are not plastered on the inside, it is best to have these
walls painted with an oil paint of light color.   Such walls, of course,
are very absorbent unless they are properly painted; and much
dust and dirt is apt to lodge in the cracks and crevices inevitable
in such walls.   It is better to have the inner walls plastered, and
then have the plaster either lime-washed, which must be done
frequently, at least every three months, or painted, which should
be done at least once a year.   Where the walls are of brick with
lime or cement mortar, it is better not to have any plaster surface
on the inside of the wall, but to have the bricks painted with an
oil paint, which makes sometimes a better covering than a plastered

wall, which is apt to crack and harbor dust, dirt, etc. Concrete walls or concrete and cement-covered walls may be treated in a similar way.

Floors of factories are of great hygienic importance. Floors are made of various materials, as follows: earth, wood, concrete cement, brick, asphalt cement and concrete. The sanitary requirements of a floor are that it should be (1) non-absorbent, (2) not too hard, (3) durable, (4) not a too good conductor of heat, and (5) readily cleaned.

Non-absorbent floors are especially necessary in factories where there is much moisture or where much water is apt to be spilt upon the floors. In such factories an ordinary wooden flooring is bad, as it gets foul and saturated, and is apt to keep the shoes and feet of the workers in a damp condition. A better form of wooden flooring consists of one made of narrow boards dovetailed, and nailed on an underwooden floor. It is still better to have such a wooden flooring set on an asphalt cement, which fills in the space between the boards and also preserves them and prevents them from becoming watersoaked. Some wooden floors, especially in places where there is little moisture, may be partially preserved by a coat of hot oil or plain oil paint. The color is also important, since a light-colored floor will show dirt and is liable to be kept cleaner than one of a dark color.

Besides the sanitary considerations, one must also take into consideration the waterproofing of a floor in case of fires, when it is profitable to have a floor which will not let through the large amount of water poured in a building at that time. From this point of view, the best form of wood flooring is that made of hard wooden blocks preserved by creosote and tar, and set in asphalt or asphalt cement.

Floors made either of brick or concrete with a cement top, are apt to be too cold, as they are good conductors of heat, and workers often complain that they make their feet cold. Their extreme hardness is also injurious to the workers, because constant standing in one spot on a very hard surface often causes flat feet and results in injuries to the health of the workers. Such floors are also easily broken up by the moving of heavy machinery into ruts, holes and crevices which are apt to contain dirt and become foul. The dust which is created by such floors is also injurious to health.

Floors made of brick, set in cement mortar, or of stone plates, or of various sizes of tiles set in cement, are often necessary in factories where large amounts of water are apt to be spilled on the floor. In such factories, the top layer of the floor must be laid on a six-inch thickness at least of concrete. It is best in such fac-

A Modern Facotry: Concrete and Hollow Tile.

Turner Construction Co.

tories to have the floor so graded as to let the water go down to a pitch and be drained either into a properly trapped, sewer-connected drain, or into outside scoopers. To prevent the workers from suffering from the coldness of such floors, it is advisable to use either rubber mats, thick linoleum or wooden planks raised upon blocks. This last method is often used in slaughter houses, and such other places where much water is apt to be on the floor.

An asphalt coating or asphalt cement top makes a good floor, since it is damp-proof and not so cold as an ordinary cement floor. A linoleum covering on a floor is good if the linoleum is of such structure as not to tear easily, and so become insecure for walking; and provided it is not too slippery.

In places where it is necessary to have a floor of extraordinary durability, special precautions are taken. A floor of an electro-plating establishment, which I saw in a foundry at Berlin, was constructed as follows:

(1) A coat of 10 cm. of cement.
(2) A coat of bitumen paper.
(3) 2 mm. of sheet lead.
(4) A coat of bitumen paper.
(5) 3 cm. of cement.
(6) 3 cm. of Trinidad asphalt.

In new factories, the junction of the floor with the wall, whether on the ground or near the ceiling, ought to be made concave, so as to prevent accumulation of rubbish and dirt in the corners. When cement floors are used, it is easy, even in old shops, to make such concave surfaces, which will pay for themselves within a short time in the greater cleanliness of the shop.

Internal Arrangements. The construction of the factory so as to provide for future expansion, the arrangement of the factory so that each process may follow the natural mode of production from the raw material to the finished product, the elimination of unnecessary transportation and unnecessary reversing of operations, are all matters within the province of the efficiency engineer and architect. The hygienist is only interested in the internal arrangements, in the division of the inside of the factory, in the partitions, etc., in so far as they relate to fire protection, safety and general sanitation, subjects which will be taken up under their proper headings.

Model Factories. The conception of a model factory, naturally, is not a fixed one, but varies according to the general economic development and technical knowledge of the times. Factories that were once considered model in every particular are so no longer, as sanitary science and knowledge of the intimate relations between work and health advance.

The legal requirements of any country set forth only the minimum standards of construction, light, ventilation and sanitation. Yet, even so, these minimum standards are an index to the development of standards of factory construction. There are probably in Germany, where the legal requirements are highest, more factories model in every particular than in any other country.

Many factories are considered model on the strength of some one feature, such as an unusually fine lunch-room, or wash-room; but are far from model in other respects. While such factories, by drawing attention to their one excellence, may deceive the general public, it is more difficult to mislead those who have had experience in factory inspection and industrial conditions. I have, as a rule, found that the number of real model plants, some of which have never been heard of, are considerable in number, and are to be found all over the states and countries. In this respect, it may be interesting to relate that after several weeks' disheartening inspection of industrial establishments in Western New York, I happened one afternoon to pass a plant in an isolated locality outside of the precincts of Buffalo. As it was late on Saturday afternoon, I hesitated before entering this plant; but the outside of the plant made a favorable impression upon me and I made the inspection then and there. One may imagine how greatly surprised I was to find in this " piano keys and piano-action factory " a real example of what is and should constitute a model factory, one in which industrial efficiency was supreme, which was provided with splendid appliances for ventilation, where the wood and sawdust from all machinery was drawn in and utilized for the furnace, where every machine in the place was perfectly guarded and safe, where all conditions as to light, sanitation, comfort and care were as perfect as could be found, and where it appeared that the economic relations between employers and employes were peaceful and of the best. And yet, in a description of model factories of New York State, it is hardly probable that the name of this plant would appear.

To be considered "*model*" a modern factory must set high standards in (1) industrial efficiency, (2) economic relations of employer and employes, (3), general sanitation and (4) welfare work.

Industrial efficiency is a characteristic of model factories, because only in such factories is there possible the thorough utilization of natural resources, the most scientific applications of inventions and discoveries, the maximum of production with the minimum of expenditure, the largest productivity of labor and other characteristics of industrial efficiency, which mark the success of an establishment and the prosperity of an industry.

The improvement in the economic relations between employers and employes is the second indispensable feature of model factories. Amicable relations between employers and employes, freedom of organization, collective bargaining, self-government of each organ-

Factory of The United Shoe Machinery Co., Beverly, Mass.

ization, participation in the administration, benefits and profits of the establishment, and more or less permanent peace between the two warring factions of labor and capital, are some of the main features of model establishments.

Closely allied to the above are progressive sanitary and working conditions in the industrial plant such as pleasant surroundings, absolute fire protection, prevention of industrial accidents and provisions for safety, adequate light, and ventilation, special provisions for sanitary care and comforts of the employes, and other improvements.

Lastly, characteristic of a model factory are the provisions for the welfare of the workers, such as care of the health of the employés, medical supervision and aid, care for housing within, as well as without the factory, proper nourishment within and outside of the factory, and last, but not least, certain economic provisions for sickness, invalidity, old age and death, and the reasonable assurance of the workers in the security of their employment.

Model factories are not the invention of the twentieth century. They were known from the beginning of the modern factory system and even before. We have already noted that there were a number of large industrial establishments in the sixteenth and seventeenth centuries, in which under one roof were employed many hundreds of workers. In some of these factories model conditions of work were provided. A type of factory at that time was that of Van Robais at Abbeville, France, where 1200 workers and working women were under one roof under regular military régime. They were lodged in the factory, which had four great doors guarded by porters wearing the King's livery; for it was a royal manufactory.

Here is a description of a large factory existing at an even earlier period, towards the end of the seventeenth century. This was the factory of Saint-Maur, which made cloth of gold, and where several hundred persons worked:

" At daybreak the workers arrived. They found at the doors tubs of water and towels; they washed their hands and then set to work. In their workroom there were servants who swept four times a week, and brought the weavers whatever they needed. During work all blasphemy or obscene language was forbidden." *

As one of the early model factories may be cited Robert Owen's factory at New Lanark. As soon as Robert Owen bought his factories from Dale in 1816, he reduced the hours of labor to twelve, with one and a quarter hours for meals, leaving the actual working time but ten and three-quarter hours, at that time a very short workday. There were between 1800 and 2000 workers in his place, of whom 500 were children from parish workhouses.

Owen started a village store for the workers and had the streets patrolled. He also started schools for the children. These schools were models, and in them many educational ideas, which are even now far from general, were applied. No child under ten years was admitted to the works. Owen also started a library, an institute and an amusement hall, where the children and young people

* P. Brizon, Histoire du Travail et des Travailleurs, p. 169.

could dance. Medical attendance was provided for all the workers
and a savings bank started.

Owen proved that he could be successful in spite of all these
model features, which were at that time considered very advanced.
The success of New Lanark seems to have been very largely due
to the character of Owen himself. His simplicity, benevolence and
enthusiasm had a wonderful effect upon the community, though
even he had many difficulties when he first started his reforms.*

During the first part of the nineteenth century, a number of
reformers were busy with ideals of model factories, some of which
were realized, while others have remained more or less in the air.

Factory of the Friedrich Bayer Co. at Elberfeld.

Among these may be mentioned Fourier's Plan of Association—
the phalanstery, which was a combination of industry, agriculture
and science. The profits of the association were to be divided
annually into three parts:—seven-twelfths to labor, three-twelfths
to capital and two-twelfths to skill. By subdivision of labor, industry was to be made attractive; also by occupations of short duration, for no group of workers was to spend more than from one
hour and a half to two hours a day at any one kind of work.
Work was to be also divided into three classes: that of necessity,
of usefulness, and of attractiveness. The first was to be more
highly paid than the other two.†

* Frank Podmore, Robert Owen.
† A. Brisbane, A Concise Summary of the Principles of Association, p. 51.

At present there are many factories, which are model in some or in all respects, all over the United States as well as in most of the European countries. Some of these factories are a household name.

There are a large number of model factories in Austria, but those which struck me as especially worthy of note are the tobacco factories belonging to the government, which have the monopoly of tobacco production and sale throughout Austria-Hungary. These tobacco factories are models of their kind, have the external appearance of palaces, schools and universities, have the best provisions for light, ventilation, removal of dust and safeguarding of machinery that I have ever seen in other factories, and they also possess a number of facilities, lunch rooms, hospitals, dispensaries for first aid, etc.

There are also many well-known model factories in the United States, to mention all of which would be impossible. In some of the illustrations given in this part, as well as in other parts of the book, mention is made of some of the model factories, although it must be understood that this does not mean that these are the only model factories in the country.

As progress is made in industrial conditions, and as the relation of sanitary science to industrial efficiency comes to be more generally understood, the conception of a model industrial establishment advances, and the state and municipal provisions constantly change and progress; so that what is to-day considered a voluntary provision by enlightened manufacturers becomes tomorrow the minimum provision required by the state, and progressive employers are constantly spurred on to further improve industrial conditions and to again be in the vanguard of progressive industrial efficiency and welfare.

CHAPTER III

FACTORY FIRES AND THEIR PREVENTION

I

DANGER AND EXTENT OF FACTORY FIRES

THE road to safety too often, in America at least, seems to lie through disaster. It took the Iroquois theater fire in Chicago to force elementary precautions for public safety in theaters. The Collingwood school disaster resulted in a tardy concern for fire dangers in school buildings, and 145 workers had to lose their lives in the Asch building fire before the practice of safety in factories and workshops received general attention; this, too, in spite of the warning of the Newark factory fire only four months previous, in which twenty-five women workers were killed.

This fire occurred in an old four-story brick building built in 1855. It was of the usual factory type of those days—non-fireproof —with each floor constituting one large open room almost a city block long. The fire broke out in the morning at about 9:15, and within twenty minutes the top floor work-room, in which about one hundred girls were employed in making muslin underwear, was a mass of flames. The fire started on the floor below with the manufacture of electric lighting lamps. Some gasoline was being used which somehow exploded. The single stairway of wood led through the center of the building and acted as a chimney for the fire. This stairway, up which the smoke and flames rushed, cut the top floor workroom into two parts. The room was crowded with machines, the workers had never had a fire drill. They turned to the fire-escapes, but these were small, difficult to use, led past the fire raging on the floor beneath and were therefore useless.

The steps leading from the workroom to the sill of the window opening on the fire-escape collapsed with the weight of the girls crowding up on them, and added to the confusion. The old-fashioned windows with heavy sashes had to be propped up with sticks. Some of the girls were pinned beneath their weight and could not get through. Before the fire engines could reach the building many girls had leaped to the street and many more had met their death by fire within the factory.

This factory was not fireproof. Many fire experts supposed that such a casualty could never happen in a modern fire-resisting building, but the words of Peter J. McKeon, writing in the *Survey* for January 7, 1911, seem prophetic of the terrible disaster that followed within three months:

"This Newark fire is a challenge to public opinion throughout the metropolitan industrial district centering in New York, especially with respect to the fire hazards in the loft buildings in Manhattan. The fireproof factory buildings have an advantage in their incombustible construction, but this advantage is offset by the fact that they are built of such height and area that they represent a special fire problem whose possibilities are yet to be demonstrated."

And then on March 25, 1911, the Asch building disaster occurred. In contrast to the old-fashioned Wolff factory, the Asch building was a ten-story modern fireproof building; yet within twenty minutes of the start of the fire on the eighth floor in the Triangle Waist Company, 145 girls had either met their death in the flames or been killed in leaping from the ninth-story windows. It is not necessary to go into the details of this tragedy. The chief loss of life was on the ninth floor where about 200 girls were working. The workers on the eighth floor where the fire started were able to get down the stairs in time; those on the tenth floor escaped over the roof. Here again, the workrooms were great open spaces without fire-walls for cutting off the fire or confining it to one part of the factory. The rooms were crowded with machines, with rows of girls sitting back to back in the aisles. The machines extended right up to the windows, without any aisles running east and west. Wooden partitions about the doors, which were kept locked, made exit impossible until the fire had gained headway. The one fire-escape was useless, as it led past the ninth floor, from which the smoke and flames were pouring. There was no fire drill in the factory, and many of the girls did not even know of the existence of a second stairway. When the fire was over, the building was found to be scarcely injured at all; but the fierceness with which the highly inflammable contents had burned, was quite sufficient to have brought about this terrible loss of life.

The third factory fire, which also had its lessons was at the Freeman Overall Works at Binghamton in August, 1913. In this factory, all the devices required by law were installed. It was four stories high and fire-resisting, if not thoroughly fireproof; but again it was the same story of the overcrowding of workers on the top floor, lack of fire-walls for confining the fire, fire-escapes that proved useless by reason of the fire on the floor below, and the confusion of a workroom full of machines, cutting tables and stock, which brought about the death of fifty-one young workers.

In the reports on this fire, the factory inspector and the fire marshal both declared that the legal requirements had been complied with by the employer in every particular. Since the Asch building fire he had made many improvements and changes in his workroom to bring it within the requirements of the changed law. A fire drill had been instituted, and the girls were used to marching out of the factory in good order.

It is disasters such as these that have forced attention to the terrible dangers to the workers from the fire hazard in factories. The increase in periodical literature and in hand-books and compilations of all kinds dealing with the industrial fire hazard shows the public feeling in regard to the gravity of this situation. And yet we have no records of the loss of life in factory fires. In fact, for the United States there is no record of the fire loss in terms of human life—only in terms of property. Records of the property loss are available for the country at large, for each of the states, and for most of the larger cities. The loss of life through fire can only be estimated.

In 1907, the United States Geological Survey made an inquiry into fire losses in the United States and Europe. A report was received from 2976 cities and villages with a population of 34,103,453. It was found that within that year 1449 persons lost their lives and 5654 were injured through fire. This probably represents only half the deaths and injuries that actually occurred in the whole of the United States, as many fire chiefs did not report deaths, deaths from fire being included in the reports of the other city officials.

It is only when some great fire disaster occurs that any record is made of the loss of life. In the Iroquois theater fire in 1903, 600 lives were lost; in the Boyertown Opera House fire in 1908, 200 lives were lost; in the fire in the Collingwood schoolhouse in

1898, 165 lives were lost; in the three factory fires that have been described, 228 lives were lost.   The loss of life in these three industrial fires occurring within three years, is greater than the loss of life in any other fire disaster in the United States with the exception of the Iroquois theater fire.

Let us turn from the human waste involved in fire to the property loss.   The United States Geological Survey mentioned above, records a fire loss for 1907 of $816,476,029.   But these figures do not represent the whole story.   In addition the postmasters in rural districts report a fire loss of $3,519,769, representing a total loss of $819,995,798, or an average per capita loss of $2.51 for every man, woman and child in those districts reporting.   On this basis, property loss from fire in the United States for 1907 amounted to $215,084,507.

" If the government should suddenly lay an annual tax of $2.51 on every man, woman and child in the United States on a promise of spending the money for some useful purpose, that promise would not avail against the storm of protests that would be aroused.   Nevertheless, a tax which in the aggregate amounts to that is being paid by the people of this country—it is the annual fire loss of the nation upon buildings and their contents alone." *

That these fire losses are not decreasing is shown by the following table, giving the aggregate property and insurance losses in the United States from 1899 to 1909 inclusive, as compiled by the National Board of Fire Underwriters:

Year.	Aggregate Property Loss.	Aggregate Insurance Loss.
1899	$153,597,830	$ 92,683,715
1900	160,929,805	95,403,650
1901	165 817,810	100,798,645
1902	161,078,040	94,460,525
1903	145,302,155	92,599,881
1904	229,198,050	127,690,424
1905	165,221,650	103,805,402
1906	518,611,800	230,842,759
1907	215,084,709	117,433,427
1908	217,885,850	135,547,162
1909	188,705,150	126,171,492

The total fire loss for the past thirty-five years amounts to $4,904,619,235.   The national debt of the United States at the

* Walter L. Fisher, Secretary of the Interior, " The Fire Waste," p. 1.

highest point ever reached on July 1, 1866, amounted to $2,733,-236,173.*

Let us now compare the loss of life and the property loss of the United States with the experience of European countries. In a recent report, United States Consul Joseph I. Brittain, stationed at Prague, Bohemia, states that there has not been a life lost in consequence of a fire during the past fifteen years in that city of over 500,000 population, and the loss of property from fires during the past three years has been less than $20,300 annually. It has been shown by the Committee on Statistics of the National Board of Fire Underwriters that the average per capita loss in six European countries for a period of five years was 33 cents, distributed as follows:

Country	Years.	Fire Loss Annual Average.	1901 Population.	Loss Per Capita.
Austria...................	1898–02	$ 7,601,389	26,150,597	$0.29
Denmark..................	1901	660,924	2,588,919	.26
France...................	1900–04	11,699,275	38,595,500	.30
Germany..................	1902	27,655,600	56,367,178	.49
Italy....................	1901–04	4,112,725	32,449,754	.12
Switzerland..............	1901–03	999,364	3,325,023	.30

Official fire losses in the States of Maine, Massachusetts, New Hampshire and Ohio for a period of five years, were as follows:

State.	Five Years.	Fire Loss Average.	Population.	Loss Per Capita.
Maine....................	1901–05	$2,240,158	694,647	$3.22
Massachusetts............	1901–05	6,285,891	2,844,068	2.21
New Hampshire...........	1901–05	1,174,061	411,588	2.85
Ohio....................	1901–05	7,502,561	4,157,545	1.80

The total per capita fire loss in the United States for the five years ending with 1907 was $3.02, or nearly ten times as much as the European average quoted above. Had the United States a per capita loss of $0.33 as given for European countries, instead

* J. K. Freitag, " Fire Prevention and Fire Protection," p. 4.

Courtesy New York State Factory Investigating Commission.

Finishing Room in a Knitting Mill, Showing Overcrowded Condition of Workroom.

of an actual per capita loss of $2.51 for the year 1907 (based on a population of 85,532,761), then the total fire loss in the United States in that year would have amounted to only $28,623,290, or a saving in fire waste alone of $186,461,419.

In the year 1907 there were about thirty-five fires in Great Britain with an average loss of over $50,000, and not one that exceeded $400,000. In January, 1908, fire destroyed $24,000,000 worth of property in the United States.

According to the best obtainable information, the annual fire toll of the nation amounted to $203,408,250 in 1913. That was the least it has been since 1909, when it was $188,705,150. And although the 1913 toll was $4,135,650 less than in 1912, that was only 44 per cent of the previous year's decrease.

Big individual fires and sweeping fires involving several buildings did more damage in 1913 than in 1912. The losses by forty such fires amounted to $25,807,000, exceeding the total by 23 fires in 1912, $4,107,000. The sole fire of near-real conflagration magnitude in 1913 was the Hot Springs, Ark., fire of September 5th, which caused a loss of $2,250,000. The 1912 Houston, Texas, conflagration loss was twice that amount. But there were fourteen big sweeping fires or minor conflagrations in 1913 with losses amounting to $11,280,000, while in 1912 seven such fires piled up a loss of $8,350,000. In 1913, twenty-six big individual fires burned up $14,527,000 worth of property values. In 1912, the aggregate loss by sixteen similar fires was $13,490,000.*

According to a partial list compiled by Safety Engineering there were 152 fires in factories in 1913.

There are no general statistics in the United States or abroad of industrial loss through fire either of lives or property; but it is safe to assume that when the general loss of life and property is so much greater in the United States than in Europe, that factory fires are very much more frequent and the loss of life and economic waste much greater than in other countries. Safety in factories depends upon the general progress in construction, in fire prevention and education in regard to fire dangers, just as industrial hygiene depends upon the general progress of hygiene in the community. The American industrial fire hazard is simply one aspect of our ignorant and wasteful attitude towards our national resources, both economic and human.

* Safety Engineering, January, 1914, p. 28.

II

INDUSTRIAL FIRES—CAUSES AND PREVENTION

The data presented above give some idea of the extent and dangers of fires in industrial establishments. The dangers of industrial fires are so obvious and are such a grave menace to the safety of a great mass of workers that fire prevention and protection is one of the most serious problems at present confronting those who are interested in the safety of our industries and in the welfare of our workers. Industrial fire prevention and protection are the prime need of the hour; and the best-trained experts are at present endeavoring to minimize this danger.

The study of prevention and protection must necessarily be based upon a study of the causes of industrial fires. An analysis of such causes is herewith presented, followed by a brief discussion:

I. CAUSES OF ORIGIN OF FIRES:
   - (1) Spontaneous Combustion.
   - (2) Lightning.
   - (3) Exposure.
   - (4) Incendiarism.
   - (5) Personal Neglect.
   - (6) Power.
   - (7) Heat.
   - (8) Light.
   - (9) Materials.
   - (10) Processes.

II. CAUSES OF THE SPREAD OF FIRES:
   - (1) Congestion of Areas and Overcrowding of Buildings.
   - (2) Lack of Horizontal Isolation.
   - (3) Lack of Vertical Isolation.

III. CAUSES OF LACK OF CONTROL OF FIRES:
   - (1) Ignorance of the Presence of Fire.
   - (2) Absence of Signals.
   - (3) Lack of Means for Extinguishing Small Fires.
   - (4) Inadequate Local Control.
   - (5) Inadequate Municipal Control.

IV. CAUSES OF LOSS OF LIFE IN FIRES:
(1) Height of Buildings and Overcrowding.
(2) Improper, Insufficient and Inadequate Means of Egress from each Floor.
(3) Improper, Insufficient and Inadequate Means of Egress from the Building.
(4). Panics.

Causes of Origin of Fires. An analysis of the known causes of the origin of fires makes it evident that these may be divided into four principal groups: (1) those fires which are due to natural causes, such as spontaneous combustion, lightning and exposure of buildings to outside fires; (2) those fires which are due to criminal and personal negligence, among which are incendiarism and personal carelessness with matches, cigars, etc.; (3) fires which are due to defective installations and appliances of power, heat, light and electricity; and (4) those fires which are due either to the nature of the material used in the industries or to their characteristic processes.

Spontaneous Combustion. By spontaneous combustion is meant self-ignition of a substance, when such substance becomes heated through certain physical, chemical or biological changes taking place in the substance itself. The ignition is generally caused by oxidation. Some German scientists claim that bacteria play an important rôle in this process of oxidation, and are often the cause of spontaneous combustion in certain materials. Spontaneous combustion occurs only in certain materials under certain favorable conditions. Wool and cotton rags, sawdust and porous organic matter when soaked with vegetable or animal oils are especially dangerous. Oils, such as linseed, cod liver, seal, goose and hog fat and certain rancid fats, certain varnishes and glues in which these oils are an ingredient, are liable to oxidation.* Hay, fodder and bran, especially in the presence of moisture, bituminous coal and newly-made wood charcoal will also ignite spontaneously under certain conditions.

In the statistics of the fires of Boston between 1891 and 1905, those due to spontaneous combustion amount to 2.83 per cent of all the fires. Freitag says, "It is possible, indeed probable, that many fires reported as of 'incendiary' or 'mysterious' origin result from spontaneous combustion." †

---

* "Cyclopedia of Fire Protection and Insurance," vol. iii., pp. 55, 56.
† J. K. Freitag, "Fire Prevention and Fire Protection," p. 838.

Courtesy Joint Board of Sanitary Control.

Inflammable Material Obstructing the Exit from a Fire-escape.

Spontaneous combustion may be prevented by taking the following precautions: (1) large quantities of materials subject to spontaneous combustion should never be kept in warehouses, storehouses, cellars or basements of industrial establishments, but should be stored in properly enclosed spaces with fireproof walls and fireproof doors; (2) proper aeration of materials that must be kept on hand; and (3) the provision of metal or fireproof receptacles as containers for small quantities of rags, waste, oils, glues, etc.

Lightning. Many fires are due to lightning. This is especially true of buildings in isolated localities and such buildings as have large towers, and chimneys. The prevention of fires due to lightning is a matter which has received considerable attention since Franklin used lightning conductors for grounding electricity. Buildings may be grounded; lightning conductors may be properly installed on chimneys, towers and other tall projections.

Exposure. Some fires are caused by the exposure of buildings to outside fires. This is especially the case in industrial centers in congested districts, where a fire in one building spreads to other buildings nearby under favorable conditions. The prevention of such fires, due to exposure, may be accomplished by taking the following precautions: (1) detached buildings; (2) less congestion of buildings on certain areas; (3) prompt control of the fire by local or municipal fire departments; and (4) by proper construction of roofs, walls and windows in order to prevent fire entering the building. This last means of prevention depends upon proper construction and the use of fireproof materials, which will be discussed later.

Incendiarism. According to a report of the New York City Fire Commissioner of 1912, incendiarism is the cause of the destruction of at least four million dollars worth of property in New York every year.* According to ex-Fire Chief Croker, fifteen per cent of all fires in New York are due to what he calls " pyromaniacs." † Both Croker and Johnson claim that a large number of persons are subject to a certain insane pleasure in starting fires in buildings (so-called " fire-bugs "), and numerous instances of such fires and of such individuals are cited by these authorities. The same reports claim that there is an actual fire-bug zone in which fires in buildings are constantly occurring and are expected by the department and considered normal. There are a number of buildings in which fires occur from two to seven times in a short

---

* Report on Incendiarism in New York City, Joseph Johnson, Fire Commissioner, 1912.
† " Fire Prevention," p. 293.

period. A portion of these fires are also due to incendiarism, and
the same experts claim that there is actually a so-called " Arson
Trust " existing in some of the large cities, which makes a business
of insuring property above its value and causing fires in order to
gain the insurance.   In the Boston statistics of fires referred to,*
incendiary fires were only four per cent, showing that the sensa-
tional figures of the New York Fire Commissioner may have been
somewhat exaggerated in his laudable desire to call the attention of
the Mayor to this menace of incendiarism.

The methods for the prevention of incendiarism are: (1) vigilance
on the part of municipal authorities; (2) exemplary punishment
of criminal incendiarism; (3) control of fire insurance companies
and regulation of insurance so as to prevent over-insurance of
buildings and contents; and (4) spread of education in regard to the
dangers of fires and the means of their prevention.

Personal Neglect. Among the causes of fires due to personal
neglect, which may sometimes be criminal by reason of the dangers
resulting, may be cited smoking in factories and the practice of
throwing away lighted matches, butts of cigars, cigarettes and contents of pipes. So-called " parlor matches " which have a large
surface covered with sulphur and wax, are dangerous when dropped
on the floor lighted or unlighted. When unlighted, they are easily
ignited by pressure and by gnawing of animals; when thrown away
unextinguished they may smoulder; and when in contact with inflammable material may easily start a dangerous fire. Children often
play with matches and a great many fires are caused by parents
neglecting to remove matches out of their reach.

The means of prevention of such fires may be summed up as
follows: (1) the prohibition of the use of matches in industrial
buildings and the penalizing of employes for bringing them into the
building; (2) the use of electric lighters; † (3) the absolute prohibition of smoking within a factory or industrial establishment; and
(4) the elimination of all inflammable waste, rags, papers, etc.,
from floors and spaces under machines.

Power. Fires due to power and its installation may be caused
by the following: (1) fuel; (2) furnaces; (3) boilers; (4) shafting;
(5) bearings; (6) pulleys. It has already been mentioned that
certain materials used for fuel or light, such as oils, gasoline, or
coal, may sometimes be the cause of fire either by spontaneous

---

* Freitag, " Fire Prevention and Fire Protection," p. 28.
† Where electric lighters are not used, wax tapers may be used with greater safety, one person being delegated to light the lights, heating irons or ironing rolls.

combustion or by accidental sparks, or by ashes left from the fuel. The prevention of such fires will be partly discussed in the section dealing with gasoline, etc. The proper storage and aeration of all fuels, provision of metal ash-cans and the removal of all ashes as soon as possible from the building, are necessary precautions.

The fires caused by furnaces may be due to the overheating of the furnace, the contact of the furnace with wood or other inflammable materials and by sparks from the furnace. Such fires may be prevented by the proper construction of furnaces, by regulating their heat, by removing them from the proximity of wooden and other inflammable structures, and, if possible, by installing all furnaces outside of the building or in specially constructed fireproof sections.

The same rules apply to fires due to boilers. The prevention of fires and other dangers due to defects in boilers and their installation, is a science by itself, and comes within the province of special technically trained boiler inspectors. Rules are made by fire experts and fire underwriters for the care of boilers, their materials, their installation and their frequent testing.

Some fires are due to shafting and bearings which cause fires by friction especially if in close proximity to inflammable materials. The same may also be said of pulleys, especially wooden pulleys and loose pulleys, which are often causes of fires. The only means of preventing such fires is by proper inspection and oiling of bearings and shaftings as well as by proper use of the pulleys; and the prohibition of wooden pulleys.

Heat. Many fires are caused by the improper installation of heating appliances. Cast-iron stoves and their flues often cause fires when overheated and when in proximity to inflammable material. It is best not to use these primitive appliances in industrial establishments. Where stoves are used they should be provided with fire pots so as not to overheat the metal part of the stove; they should also be enclosed with metal shields at least four feet high. All flues should be at a distance from wooden ceilings or from places where a hot flue may cause ignition. Steam boilers as well as steam pipes may be a source of fires by their overheating in proximity to wood and other inflammable material. Boilers should be properly cared for in separate fireproof enclosures, while pipes should be wherever possible coated with asbestos and well protected, especially in their transit through floors and ceilings, by proper metal flanges, etc. Fireplaces and chimneys, which often cause fires by their defective construction, should be solidly

built of fireproof materials; lined with approved flue lining of hard
burnt clay with well-made joints.   They should also be frequently
inspected to prevent defective conditions which lead to fires.

Courtesy Joint Board of Sanitary Control.

Rear Fire-escape Balconies (Center Building) without Connecting Ladders.

Light.   A large number of fires are caused by lighting appliances.
The old method of lighting rooms by candles and oil lamps is a
thing of the past in large industrial communities.   Whenever
oil, gasoline or acetylene are used for fuel, power or light, they

should be kept in proper receptacles or tanks outside, about thirty feet from the building, and, if possible, underground; and the provisions made by fire underwriters and municipal authorities in regard to proper receptacles should be strictly observed.

Illumination. Coal or water gas is a frequent cause of fire, either because of leakage from defective pipes or because of defective meters or improper installation of the pipes and fixtures. Whenever gas is installed in an industrial building, a shut-off valve should be provided outside of the building, so that in case of fire the flow of gas into the building may be cut off, and thus the danger of explosion prevented. The gas meters should be placed upon a fireproof wall and if possible enclosed within fireproof material and frequently tested. Gas pipes should be made air-tight and frequently tested; no leakage should be allowed in cellars or lower parts of buildings. Gas brackets, when they are fixed, should be at a distance from wood and inflammable material and no swinging gas brackets should be allowed. The gas jets, especially when of the bat-wing variety, should also be carefully protected, and enclosed in globes when in proximity to inflammable materials.

Care must also be taken with incandescent lamps and mantles. No lanterns or lamps of the portable variety should be used unless they are what is known as safety lights or electric flash-lights.

Electric power and electric light and wiring are at present tested by the fire underwriters and municipal departments before and after installation and usually during stated periods in order to prevent fires caused by exposed and crossed wires, short circuiting, improper fuses, etc.

Arc-lights as well as incandescent lights should be protected in case of accidents or in case of breakage or when in proximity to inflammable materials.

Materials. A number of materials used in manufacture must be kept in proper receptacles, while there are others for which special precautions must be taken. Among the inflammable materials are wool, cotton and other animal and vegetable fibrous materials. The clippings, cuttings and rubbish from such materials must be put in proper receptacles, metal if possible, and tightly covered. In establishments where fats, oils, glues, varnishes, alcohol, drugs, chemicals, rubber, celluloid, explosives or other highly inflammable materials are stored and worked with, special precautions must be taken in their storage and in the processes of manufacture.

State or municipal departments demand a separate building for the storage of highly explosive or highly inflammable materials. There are also detailed provisions made by the fire underwriters as to storage of drugs, chemicals and other such inflammable material. The buildings in which such materials are stored are usually rated as extra hazardous, and are not only a danger to persons within the buildings but also a menace to the neighborhood.

Processes. There are certain processes of manufacture which by their nature often cause fires. These processes consist in blasting, firing, burning, heating, drying, varnishing, japanning, etc., all of which possess elements of danger either by the nature of the processes themselves or because of accidental or criminal negligence of the persons in charge of these processes. Definite rules are provided for certain of these processes, while the general rules for the prevention of fires consist in the proper installation and care of the appliances, and in constant vigilance and supervision on the part of those who operate and control them.

III

SPREAD OF FIRES

Causes and Prevention. The three main causes of the spread of fires, are (1) the congestion of area built upon and the crowding of buildings upon certain areas; (2) lack of horizontal isolation and (3) lack of vertical isolation in our building construction.

Density of Area and Crowding of Buildings. The crowding of buildings upon a circumscribed area and the height of such buildings play a most important part in the rapid spread of fires, and are the cause of great destruction of buildings, property, and often life. Of the 45,000 industrial establishments in the great state of New York, there are no less than thirty odd thousand establishments in Greater New York alone, and three-quarters of these are on Manhattan Island. The majority of establishments on Manhattan Island are concentrated within a small, so-called " loft zone " of about twenty-five blocks in length, and about two or three blocks in width. In a dense area like this, it is quite possible for a small fire, which in a less congested locality would burn itself out within a short period, to spread and become a conflagration, and destroy a whole section of the city.

Courtesy Joint Board of Sanitary Control.

Drop Ladder Missing at the Rear of a Shop Building.

The remedies proposed for this evil may be summed up as follows: (1) limitation of the height of buildings, (2) limitation of the number of industrial buildings according to certain zones, (3) building industrial establishments in outlying localities away from the tenement-house quarters of cities and towns, (4) better means of transportation so as to induce industrial establishments to locate outside of cities, (5) stricter building codes in order to make the building of industrial plants within the city limits as safe as possible with the present technical knowledge, and (6) regulation of building construction and supervision by competent municipal authorities, (7) confining extra hazardous industries to fire-proof buildings along the water front or within specified zones.

Lack of Horizontal and Vertical Isolation. Elemental forces once freed are difficult to control unless insurmountable barriers are put in their way. The stopping of a raging fire is like the damming of a flood; it may be stopped only by a solid obstruction which cannot be overcome. In ship construction, the principle of water-tight compartments has long been a recognized form of construction for preventing the loss of the whole structure. In building construction, the only means to prevent the spread of a conflagration is by so building that the fire comes to a natural barrier, which stops its further progress and gives an opportunity for its control.

Hence, in our cities the buildings are separated from each other by what are called " fire walls;" that is, walls made of such material and of such thickness and so constructed that they are able to withstand a siege of fire and prevent its rapid spread beyond the bounds of the building. Each building therefore constitutes a unit, and the fire walls between individual buildings are the first step in vertical building isolation.

The second step in vertical isolation, which has not as yet become a standard in construction, is the division of the building into vertical units, so that each part of the building, and each room, should by itself constitute a unit in which the fire may be confined. The following of this principle in building construction would mean that each room or each vertical partition in a building should be so constructed as to hold the fire and let it consume the contents of that unit without going beyond it, giving time for those in charge to control and extinguish the fire.

As to horizontal isolation, this becomes necessary when story is piled upon story, and the height of buildings reaches into the sky. In buildings of many stories a number of building units are superimposed one on top of the other, and give food to the flames, which sometimes spread more rapidly in a vertical direction than in a horizontal one. Thus, a fire on one floor, especially in the lower part of the building, will, if unchecked, spread through the building and consume the whole structure.

Isolation which would make not only each building but each story and each room a unit, consists in separating the lower floors from the others by floors and ceilings constructed of fire-resisting materials. Especially necessary is the proper isolation of the cellar floor, where many fires originate, from the first story.

Vertical isolation may be accomplished by proper division of buildings by walls, by partitions, doors and windows. The horizontal isolation of buildings, however, is not sufficiently controlled by the proper construction of floors. Our buildings are so constructed that openings are necessary, to serve as means of communication from floor to floor and from story to story. In all many-storied buildings we must have stairways, elevators, hoistways, openings needed for plumbing pipes, for heating pipes, for power transmission, etc., all of which serve as a possible means of communication of fire from floor to floor.

The prevention, therefore, of spread of fires by horizontal and vertical isolation practically means the proper construction with proper materials of the following: walls, partitions, doors, windows, floors, elevators, shafts, stairways, etc.

Materials of Construction. All building materials must be judged as far as fire prevention is concerned by their fireproof or fire-resisting qualities. Here, perhaps, it is best to state that there is a misconception in the usage of the word fireproof.

There is no material which is fireproof in the sense of being absolutely unaffected by fire. The National Fire Prevention Congress at London in 1903, rightly decided that the term " fireproof " now indiscriminately applied to building materials, is misleading; and the congress considered that the term " fire-resisting " more correctly described the varying qualities of materials and systems of construction intended to resist the effect of fire for shorter or for longer periods, at high or low temperature, as the case may be; and they advocated the general adoption of this term in place of the word fireproof.*

The fire-resisting qualities of a material are relative, and the final destruction of any material by fire is due either to chemical

* Quoted by Freitag, " Fire Protection and Fire Prevention," p. 207.

and molecular changes or to mechanical rupture of the structure due to excessive heat. Wood offers the least resistance to fire, and wooden frame factories are easily destroyed by fire. Such construction is at present prohibited in most industrial centers. Frame constructed factories are still found in a number of cities, mostly outside of the so-called fire limits. Most of the establishments housed in frame shacks are those which are considered temporary; especially the chemical trades, and such trades where isolation is an advantage. Wood, however, when properly used in "mill construction" is capable of considerable fire-resistance, due to the manner and mass in which it is used.

The following is Atkinson's definition of "mill construction:"

(1) "Mill construction consists in so disposing the timber and plank in heavy and solid masses as to expose the least number of corners or ignitable projections to fire, to the end also that when fire occurs it may be most readily reached by water from sprinklers or hose.

(2) "It consists in separating every floor from every other floor by incombustible stops—by automatic hatchways, by encasing stairways either in brick or other incombustible partitions so that a fire shall be retarded in passing from floor to floor to the utmost that is consistent with the use of wood or any material in construction that is not absolutely fireproof.

(3) "It consists in guarding the ceilings over all specially hazardous stock or processes with fire-retardant material, such as plastering laid on wire-lath, or expanded metal or upon wooden dovetailed-lath, following the lines of the ceiling and of the timbers without any interspaces between the plastering and the wood; or else in protecting ceilings over hazardous places with asbestos air-cell board, sheet metal, Sackett wall board or other fire-retardant."

(4) "It consists not only in so constructing the mill, workshop, or warehouse that fire shall pass as slowly as possible from one part of the building to another, but also in providing all suitable safeguards against fire." *

Iron, whether cast or wrought, or steel, is often used in factory construction, but when it is used, it should be protected by sufficient thickness of brick, terra cotta or concrete.

Stone is sometimes used, but its use must be limited, as it is subject to disintegration by heat.

Terra cotta, which is a burnt-clay material, has not much fire-resisting quality, although when properly manufactured and of a certain thickness it is often used as a protective material for iron

* Quoted by Freitag, p. 75.

and as an ornamental covering for façades of buildings. The best authorities, however, do not consider terra cotta as a first-class fire-resisting material.

Brick is perhaps one of the best materials for the construction of factories because of the fire-resisting qualities of well-made brick. The fire-resisting qualities of brick have been proved in a great many fires, and nothing has as yet been found better for the solid construction of a fire wall or as a protective covering for metal than good, well-made brick.

Concrete, which is a mixture of cement, sand and aggregate, usually made of broken stones, cinders or some other material, is considered a good fire-resisting material, provided the aggregate is not made of soft-coal cinders and provided the concrete is properly made. Concrete is subject to dehydration when exposed to temperatures over 600° F., and therefore if used in thin layers is apt to crumble away and disintegrate under a high degree of heat, and leave the columns, protected by it, exposed to the heat. Broken stones, broken brick and blast furnace slag make the best aggregate for concrete. For the protection of columns, etc., it must be used in a thickness of at least four inches.

Mortar and plaster made either of common lime, cement or plaster of Paris, when mixed in the right proportions and used on a metal lathing or wire mesh may serve as good fire-resisting materials for inside surfaces of walls, ceilings and similar places.

By reinforced concrete is meant a concrete mixture reinforced by steel, so combined that the steel will take up the tensional stresses and will assist in the resistance to shear. At present a large number of buildings are being constructed of reinforced concrete, and have proved to be fire-resisting to a high degree.

Of the other fire-resisting materials only a few need be mentioned. Many of these consist of some composition made largely of a form of concrete on a cement base or one that has a proportion of asbestos in it. Asbestos is a mineral which has very high fire-resisting qualities. It is used either by itself or in mixture in places where it is desired to have a specially good fire-resisting covering; thus, on roofs, around steam pipes, etc.

Wire glass is a glass in which wire is embedded in the process of manufacture. It is a good fire-retardant material when not less than one-quarter inch thick, and is often used for windows and doors.

Other materials which are called fireproof, are, of course, not fireproof at all, but possess certain fire-retardant qualities, and are often used either for floors and trim or in places where extra fire hazards exists; and where materials must be used which are not easily subject to ignition.

Fireproof wood is made by heating blocks of wood, extracting the moisture and resin of the wood and then filling the pores under pressure with ammonium salts.

Finally, certain paints may be used for inside surfaces, which have fire-retardant qualities. Among these may be included plain whitewash, which is said by some authorities to " give excellent results, and is the equal, if not the superior, of many of the so-called fireproof paints." It is made and applied as follows:

Slack one-half bushel of unslacked lime with boiling water, keeping it covered during the process; strain it and add a peck of salt dissolved in warm water; three pounds of ground rice, put in boiling water and boiled to a thin paste; one-half pound powdered Spanish whiting and a pound of clear glue dissolved in hot water; mix these well together and let the mixture stand for several days. Keep the wash thus prepared in a kettle or portable furnace, and when used put on as hot as possible with painters' or whitewash brushes.

Construction. Important as are the materials of construction used for the various parts of a building, it is still more important to use those materials judiciously in order to bring out their advantages. The parts of the construction which are most important from the standpoint of fire prevention are the walls, floors, partitions, doors, windows, stairs, shafts, roofs, etc.

The modern requirement for walls outside of their bearing qualities and their ornamentation is that they should have sufficient fire-resisting qualities to act as fire walls either between separate buildings or within one building. Such walls are best made of good hard-burned brick laid in the best of cement and lime mortar with joints flushed full. The National Fire Protection Association demands that such walls must not be less than sixteen inches thick for the two upper stories, increasing in thickness four inches each three stories below or fraction thereof. If walls are over one hundred feet high, they shall be four inches thicker than the above or they shall be strengthened by piers or pilasters placed not over twenty feet apart. Thus, an eight-story building would have three twenty-four-inch, three twenty-inch, and two sixteen-inch walls.

Courtesy Joint Board of Sanitary Control.

A "Winder": One of the Most Dangerous Types of Stairways in Case of Fire.

If carried on steel frame, non-bearing walls for skeleton con-struction buildings must be made of brick not less than twelve inches thick in any portion; this, in addition to ornamental facings or any other materials.

A self-supporting or bearing wall must not be less than sixteen

Courtesy Joint Board of Sanitary Control.

Dangerous Interior Stairway. It Leads to the Top Floor of a Rear Building and has Wooden Treads.

inches thick for the two upper stories, with the same requirements as those of a brick bearing wall. All vertical metal supports must be insulated by not less than four inches of brick or of concrete or of terra cotta or of other insulated approved material. Brick is preferred for column covering, as it has been proved that terra cotta does not resist fires as well as brick. The insulation referred to should not include any ornamentations of plaster of Paris, etc. The upper face of the upper flanges and the lower face and edges of lower flanges must have not less than two inches of brick or concrete or other approved insulating material.

The protection of columns by single metal and plaster coverings, even by double metal plastering with air space, is not as good as a solid covering of brick or of concrete. Concrete when used should not be less than three to four inches in thickness, depending upon the size of the column.

The general construction of floors depends much upon the material of which they are constructed, the number of stories in the building and the type of construction. Metal floor beams must be well insulated by not less than two inches of terra cotta or concrete. The floor beams must be properly spaced so as to carry the superimposed weight; and the National Board of Fire Protection has detailed instructions as to the approved kind of brick, terra cotta, or other materials for arches and for floors in general.

The floor must be of non-inflammable material and a concrete of good quality must be used to fill the space between the flooring and the arches, and a cement top for the floors or a fire-resisting wood should be used for the floor surfaces.

Partitions are too often constructed of flimsy materials; such as thin pine boards. Such partitions are a menace to the safety of the workers in a factory, since they hamper escape and spread the fire throughout the whole building. If partitions are to be used for purposes of vertical isolation they must be made of fire-resisting materials. The best partitions are those made of brick, but these may be too heavy or expensive. Metal studs with metal lathing and plastering of four-inch thickness; terra cotta well burned and laid in lime and cement mortar; a concrete partition, or one of plaster boards properly made, neither resting on wooden floors nor using wooden studs, or framing and plaster of Paris, may serve as barriers to the spread of fires.

Doors. It is absurd to construct walls or partitions as efficient barriers against the spread of fire, and at the same time close the openings within these walls and partitions with non-fire-resisting materials, which allow the spread of fire through them. It is obvious that doors and windows in walls and partitions must be no less fire-resistant than the walls and partitions in which they are framed. The materials of which doors are made are various; some of them are wood, metal protected; others are wholly made of metal or of a composition, or are of hollow metal construction.

The method of construction must naturally depend upon various factors; but in order to resist fire, not only the material of doors but their frames and manner of hanging are vitally important. The National Board of Fire Underwriters has issued detailed and specific rules as to doors, and in all new buildings as well as in some older buildings, it is best to follow these specifications.

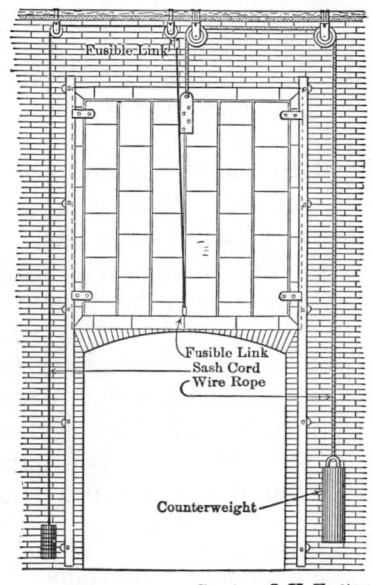

Courtesy J. K. Freitag.
"Fire Prevention and Fire Protection."
Automatic Vertical Fire Door.

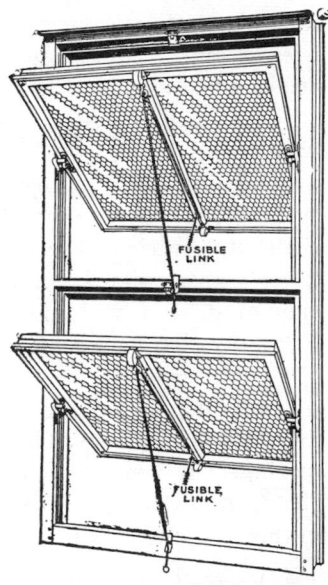

Courtesy J. K. Freitag.
"Fire Prevention and Fire Protection."
Automatically Closing Sheet-metal Window.

Some of the provisions which apply to doors also apply to windows: to the frame, sash, trim and to the manner of putting windows into position. Windows in all factories should be made of wire glass of at least one-quarter inch thickness. Iron or other metal shutters are also often used for preventing exposure to fires through windows; and certain rules are made for the sheet iron, corrugated iron or other forms of shutters where these are needed. There are also several devices by which windows may be protected against outside exposure to fires, such as automatic sprinklers.

Mention has been made of the necessity of horizontal isolation. Such isolation is accomplished by the floors, for which detailed specifications are given by municipal and state building codes. In every building, however, the difficulty of horizontal isolation is very great on account of the necessity of communication between stories, which is often impossible without piercing the floors which separate one story from another. Stairways, elevators, hoistways, courts and shafts are difficult to construct without open communication from the lower to the upper stories. Plumbing, heating, and other pipes, electric wiring and transmission of belts, etc., are perhaps a lesser evil. The present progress of mechanical science makes such connections easy to protect. In some buildings all pipes are carried within the supporting columns in special pipe receptacles, while in all buildings all pipe openings should be well protected not only by floor and ceiling metal plates, but by a covering of cement or other approved fire-resisting material. With the progress of the application of electricity to industry, the need of running power transmission belts, shafts, etc., through floors is practically eliminated, and such piercing of floors should not be permitted under any circumstances.

Courts between or within buildings which are covered at the top, and constitute one unobstructed opening from bottom to top are very dangerous. The same, of course, is true of the vertical openings, in which are located stairs, elevators and hoistways. The Committee of the National Fire Protection Association sums up this evil and its prevention succinctly, as follows:

" Vertical openings throughout buildings as far as stairs and elevators are concerned, rapidly communicate fire to all stories. With buildings of considerable height or combustible contents, this is likely to result in fire conditions beyond fire department control. All such floor openings should be enclosed in brick-wall shafts, crowned by thin glass skylight, and extended through roofs with fire doors with openings to stories. Any enclosed vertical openings are considered to be the most prominent features contributing to the fire cost and loss of life. Neglect to guard these openings is common throughout the country. Pains should be taken to rectify this condition in all existing buildings as well as in those hereafter erected, particularly of mercantile, manufacture or storage occupancy."

Perhaps the ideal mode of constructing a building with a number of stories superimposed one upon another, would be to have no communication whatever within the building between floor and floor, but to have all stairs outside of the building; and perhaps it is best to have a separate stairway leading from each floor to a separate place.   As we cannot get this ideal isolation, then we must insist that any openings found in the building, whether for light, or for stairways, or for elevators and hoistways, should be entirely separated from the building by an enclosure of fire-resisting walls and by fire-resisting doors.   The enclosure of these openings should be made of the same material used for fire walls, with a minimum wall thickness of at least six inches, and the best material is well-laid brick.   Shafts should extend above the roof and have a sky-light of thin glass protected by standard wire screens both above

Courtesy J. K. Freitag.

Stairway Adjacent to Elevator Well.

and below the glass.   There should also be a ventilator on top of the shaft.   Standard fire doors should be placed at the openings to each floor.   All shafts used for ventilating or for light should be enclosed in the same manner.

The proper construction of the stairs, of the strings, risers, treads and rails, the materials of which each part of the stair should be constructed, are all given in detail in the municipal, state and fire underwriters' rules and regulations.

It may be mentioned here that at present there is a tendency to construct stairways in separate towers not connected with the floors, and separated on each floor not only by fire-resisting doors but also by balconies, so that these towers are practically independent of each floor, and not only fireproof but also smokeproof. The cuts on pages 123 and 125 illustrate the present requirements of some codes.

Wherever stairways or similar means of escape are used, they should be extended to the roof of the building, which is often the best means of escape from fire, especially when adjacent buildings are of about the same height; so that those escaping may reach the zone of safety on the roofs of adjacent buildings. Such stairs leading to the roof should be provided with fire-resisting doors and automatic fastenings.

In regard to stairways, the treads are of importance, as certain materials, such as stone, are not permissible, because they crumble and disintegrate under the influence of heat. Stairways of plain iron easily become heated, and may burn the persons using them. Slate and marble treads and platforms are often used and are also not very fire-resisting. The present New York Building Code makes the following provision for stairways:

" In all buildings hereafter erected of more than seven stories in height, where treads and landings of iron stairs are of slate, marble or other stones, they shall each be supported directly underneath for their entire length and width, by an iron plate made solid or having openings not exceeding four inches in same, of adequate strength and securely fastened to the strings. In case such supporting plates be made solid, the treads may be of oak not less than $1\frac{5}{8}$ inches thick. In connection with stairways, it is also important to have proper railings on all sides of a stairway. Such railings must be made of iron or gas piping."

Of the width, etc., of stairways, we shall speak later

IV

THE CONTROL OF FIRES

Eternal vigilance is the price of safety. Fire is a treacherous enemy and is apt to appear at unexpected times and places. Constant watchfulness is absolutely indispensable on the part of the occupants of a factory building, if it is desired to discover fires as soon as they originate and at their places of origin; for only at such times may small fires be prevented from becoming conflagrations, and only by early and quick extinction of small fires may loss of property and perhaps loss of life be prevented.

Not only is it necessary to discover fires early, but it is also imperative for those who detect fire to be able to communicate the knowledge of its presence to the persons who can control and fight it. Watchmen who are constantly on duty should be employed by owners of factory buildings. Such watchmen are often employed in large establishments during the night, but for the safety of the workers therein, no large industrial establishment should be without a watchman during the day as well. In order to control these watchmen, certain devices have been invented. These devices consist of recording watches and clocks, either portable or stationary, which the watchman is supposed to operate at certain intervals, and which show the owner of the building that the watchman is doing his duty.

Another means of detecting fires is by the use of thermostats or interior alarms. These are devices so constructed that certain parts made of fusible solder are quickly affected by heat. When the heat reaches a certain degree, those parts melt and complete an electrical circuit which operates a transmitting mechanism, sending the alarm to other parts of the building or outside. Thermostats are used in places where fires may easily originate: in cellars, bins, closets, etc.

Fire-alarm systems may communicate in the interior of a building, or may be connected outside of the factory with the central fire-alarm station or with the fire department direct. Manual fire-alarm boxes are so constructed that when a lever is pulled or a button is pushed, the gongs ring throughout the building a stated number of times, indicating the number of the floor on which the alarm is given. Most of these fire-alarm boxes are glass covered, and it is necessary to break the glass before being able to reach the lever. Municipal fire departments as well as the underwriters have detailed rules in regard to the kind of automatic or manual alarm boxes to be used, the place where they are to be located, the conduits and wiring which connect the alarm box with the various alarm stations within the building, the enunciators on the main floor, the source of the power to be used, and all other details of construction. The fire-alarm system and each part of it must be frequently tested.

The New Jersey factory law requires factory buildings of more than two stories in height to be equipped with a system of fire alarms with large gongs located on each floor of the factory building, and within each separate room, where more than one factory is located on a single floor. This system is to be so installed as to permit the sounding of all alarm gongs within the building whenever the alarm is sounded in any part of it. The means of sounding these alarms must be placed within easy access of all operatives in the factory or the room, and must be plainly labeled. The system of fire alarms is not to be used for any other purpose than in case of fire or fire drill. The New York State law also demands fire-alarm systems to be installed in all factory buildings and stipulates that such fire alarms must be connected with the Fire Department.

Extinguishing of Fires. There should be in each factory some means by which a small fire may be readily and quickly extinguished before it becomes uncontrollable. The means of extinguishing fires within a building are the following: (1) by water buckets, so-called fire pails; (2) by mechanical extinguishers, such as sand, etc.; (3) by chemical extinguishers; (4) by standpipe and hose; and (5) by automatic sprinklers.

Water pails, which are so often the only means used in large as well as in small factories for extinguishing fires, are made of galvanized iron, round or flat bottom (must never be of wood), usually painted red, and lettered with the word " FIRE." They are filled with water and set on hooks, benches or shelves, and are used in case of small fires. An insufficient number of fire pails is usually found in factories; the water is not often changed, and frequently evaporates; and on inspection, one often discovers these pails either only one-third full or covered with a slimy film, and placed in corners and out-of-the-way places where their location is unknown and their use problematic in case of fire.

The requirements of the New York Fire Department are two pails for every one thousand square feet. They must be set in special places easily reached and seen, and must not be placed higher than $4\frac{1}{2}$ feet or lower than 2 feet from the floor. Fire pails must have a capacity of at least ten or twelve quarts. The fire pails should be so distributed that they will be near at hand in every part of the building. In certain sections where inflammable materials may accumulate, an extra number of these pails should be placed. They should also be placed near exits, and somebody should be charged with the duty of refilling them at least once every three or four days.

When fire pails are placed where the water is liable to freeze in cold weather, some anti-freezing mixture should be dissolved in the water. Chloride of lime is the best mixture for this purpose.

An improvement upon the common fire pail is the metal bucket tank, painted red, plainly labeled and containing six pails one in another, so that when each pail is taken out it is automatically filled with water. Bucket tanks are usually covered, the cover easily opened and the pails withdrawn without difficulty.

Where oils or other volatile liquids are stored, water is not a satisfactory extinguishing agent. For this purpose sawdust, sand, sodium bicarbonate, or carbon tetrachloride should be kept.

Chemical Fire Extinguishers. There are few extinguishers which may truly be called chemical. The use of certain chemical powders in tubes, etc., has not been found practicable, and there are as yet very few extinguishers in which a chemical powder or solution is used which can be depended upon to work properly. The name of chemical extinguisher is usually applied to a device consisting of a can filled with a weak solution of sodium bicarbonate, and containing in a glass a certain amount of sulphuric acid which, when liberated into the sodium bicarbonate solution contained in the tank, produces carbonic acid gas. The consequent pressure produced within the tank lets the water out through an opening in a hose under a certain pressure, thus extinguishing the fire chiefly by the water and only in small part through the fire extinguishing quality of carbonic acid gas.

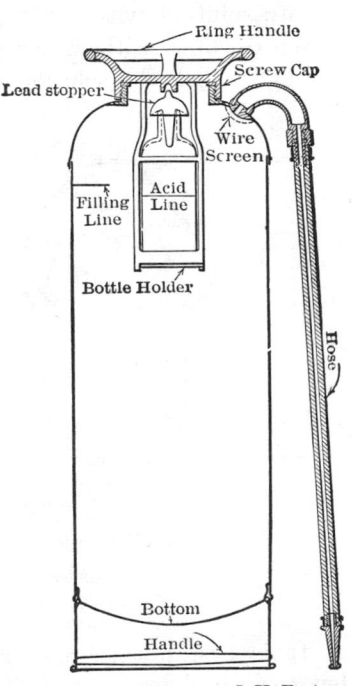

J. K. Fretag.

Chemical Fire Extinguisher.

For these so-called chemical extinguishers the requirements are the following: a tank, a glass container, a hose. The tank is usually made of copper and must be strong enough to withstand a pressure of 350 pounds per square inch, and the hose, which is usually made of the same strength, should be provided with a lead nozzle of about one-eighth to three-sixteenth-inch outlet without any shut-off stopcock. The tank, which is usually made to contain, when full, about thirty-five pounds, is filled with water, in which sodium bicarbonate is dissolved.   The solution is made by mixing $1\frac{1}{2}$ pounds of bicarbonate of soda in $2\frac{1}{2}$ gallons of water, stirring the mixture until the soda is dissolved.

The glass container in the common extinguishers consists of a bottle containing four fluid ounces of commercial sulphuric acid. There is usually a mark indicated in the bottle above which no acid should be put in. The acid bottle is fitted with a lead stopper, so that when the tank is turned over the stopper is released and the acid slowly drops out of the bottle, mixes with the sodium bicarbonate solution within the container, and goes through the wire screen opening with which the rubber and linen hose is coupled, through which the solution comes out with considerable force.

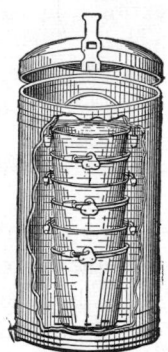

J. K. Freitag.   Courtesy J. K. Freitag.

"Sanitary" Fire Bucket.   Safety Fire Bucket Tank.

From J. K. Freitag's "Fire Prevention and Fire Protection."

It is best not to rely upon these chemical fire extinguishers, but to keep them in addition to the common fire pails. The extinguishers must also be frequently tested to see that the solution within them is not frozen or has not come out and also that the glass container has not lost its sulphuric acid contents. The placing of the extinguishers should be similar to that of the fire pails. In case of fire, these extinguishers are carried in their usual position, and only when reaching the fire should they be tipped upside-down.

The extinguishers are valuable especially in small fires, in hidden places under floors, in enclosed spaces, boxes, etc., or in fires which are overhead and are not so easily reached by ordinary fire pails. Care should be taken to have the extinguishers always in good order, and a special person should be charged with their care and also with their use in case of need.

Standpipe and Hose. By standpipe is usually meant a vertical iron pipe of sufficient capacity, connected with the ordinary city or town water pressure, or with a special water system, to be used in case of fires only. This pipe is always filled with water, and has couplings and valves on each floor to which a line of stout hose is attached, and through which a stream of water may be trained on the fire.

Specific requirements are made by municipal departments and by fire underwriters for the material of the pipe, the size, according to the character and height of the building, the character of the couplings and valves, the diameter of the same, the material, size and diameter of the hose which is used, the nozzles to which the hose is joined and the location not only of the pipe, but also of the hose, etc. Such auxiliary means of fighting fires are very important in industrial establishments, especially those of great height; and of course care must be taken that there is constant and abundant water under pressure either from the street or from tanks on the roof or top floor and that the couplings, valves, hose and nozzles are in proper condition, ready for use, and also that there are some persons within the buildings to care for this part of the auxiliary apparatus, and who are charged with the duty of using it in case of need.

Automatic Sprinklers. Perhaps the greatest beneficial invention of the last century in regard to fire protection and prevention consists of the sprinkler system. The principle of the sprinkler system of extinguishing fire is simple. It simply provides a sufficient amount of water under pressure carried through the building by a pipe and extending into the network of pipes under the ceilings of each room to be protected by the sprinkler system. At certain intervals, ten to twelve feet apart, there is an opening in the system of overhead pipes through which water may come out either directly in one stream or in a shower through larger or smaller openings, each opening covering a certain area.

The modern system of sprinkler is the so-called "automatic wet-pipe system." All the pipes are constantly filled with water under pressure, and the perforations or openings in the overhead network of pipes, instead of being unprotected, are closed by sprinkler heads, consisting of a device fitted with fusible metal which melts at a certain temperature, usually about 160 degrees F.

As soon, therefore, as there is a fire at a certain spot, the heat of which reaches the sprinkler head under the ceiling, the fusible metal melts, the head opens, and a stream of water under pressure, sufficient to extinguish the fire, is let loose. Of course, much depends upon the proper and careful installation of the whole system as well as upon the quality of the material used for each part of the system, and the pressure of water available.

In view of the very great importance which is attached by insurance companies, underwriters and municipal departments to the proper installation of an automatic fire sprinkler system,

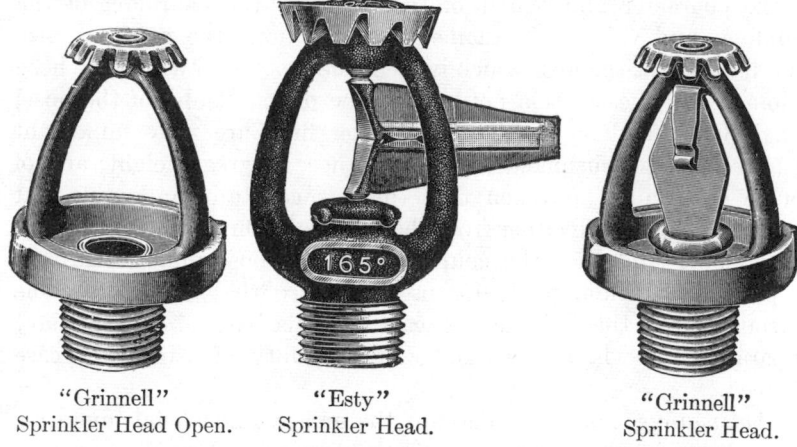

"Grinnell"   "Esty"   "Grinnell"
Sprinkler Head Open.   Sprinkler Head.   Sprinkler Head.

Courtesy J. K. Freitag, "Fire Prevention and Fire Protection."

and also in view of the great utility of this system, which has been proved over and over again, strict and minute specifications are made for the proper installation of such system in each building. Proper provision is made for a large supply of water under pressure, either from the city water system or from roof tanks, the material, size and location of the pipes, and of the risers (as those pipes are called which are carried vertically through the house), as well as the plan of the network of the pipes installed throughout the building under the ceilings, and especially the kind of sprinkler heads used. It is unnecessary to go into the details, which may be found in the printed requirements of the fire underwriters.

Control of Fires. Aside from the various devices and apparata used for extinguishing fires within the rooms and buildings in which they are liable to occur, there are in every municipality special fire

fighting institutions, which have charge of the prevention and extinguishing of fires within the precincts of the municipality. These
institutions usually consist of highly trained specialists and experts
in handling fires, have usually a uniformed force under strict
discipline and always on duty, and are assisted by mechanical
appliances and apparata for extinguishing fires, for reaching fires
and for controlling fires.

In a number of large industrial establishments, local fire fighting
corps have been organized, and are of very great service and value.
Such organizations are usually miniature copies of the larger
municipal fire fighting institutions and possess, as a rule, most of
the fire fighting appliances used by larger fire departments. The
number of large industrial establishments which have organized
their own fire departments is not as yet very large, but it is increasing rapidly, and it is the hope of those interested in fire protection
that each large industrial establishment, especially those located
outside of city limits and not within easy reach of municipal fire
departments, will install and organize such a system,

V

LOSS OF LIFE IN INDUSTRIAL FIRES

Mention has been made in the first section of this chapter of the
fact that no data is available as to the number of lives lost in
industrial fires, except when fires are accompanied by great loss of life
under spectacular conditions. In addition to the actual loss of life
there are undoubtedly a large number of persons who suffer various
injuries, and others who are disabled by the mental and nervous
shock concomitant with those fires.

Analyzing the causes of loss of life in fires occurring in industrial
establishments, we come to the conclusion that they may all be
grouped under four divisions: (1) causes due to the inflammable
contents, overcrowding and the heights of factories and workshops;
(2) to the improper facilities for egress from each floor of the factory;
(3) lack of proper means of egress from the building; and (4) panics.

The first group has already been partly discussed. Reference
has been made to the inflammable contents of a building, especially
those buildings in industrial centers where clothing, textiles and other
milars inflammable materials are being worked at, and to the

custom of keeping these materials in wooden boxes on wooden
shelves, etc.   Reference has also been made to the fact that a
great many buildings, especially tenant factories, are of such great
height that a fire occurring in such buildings causes panics and

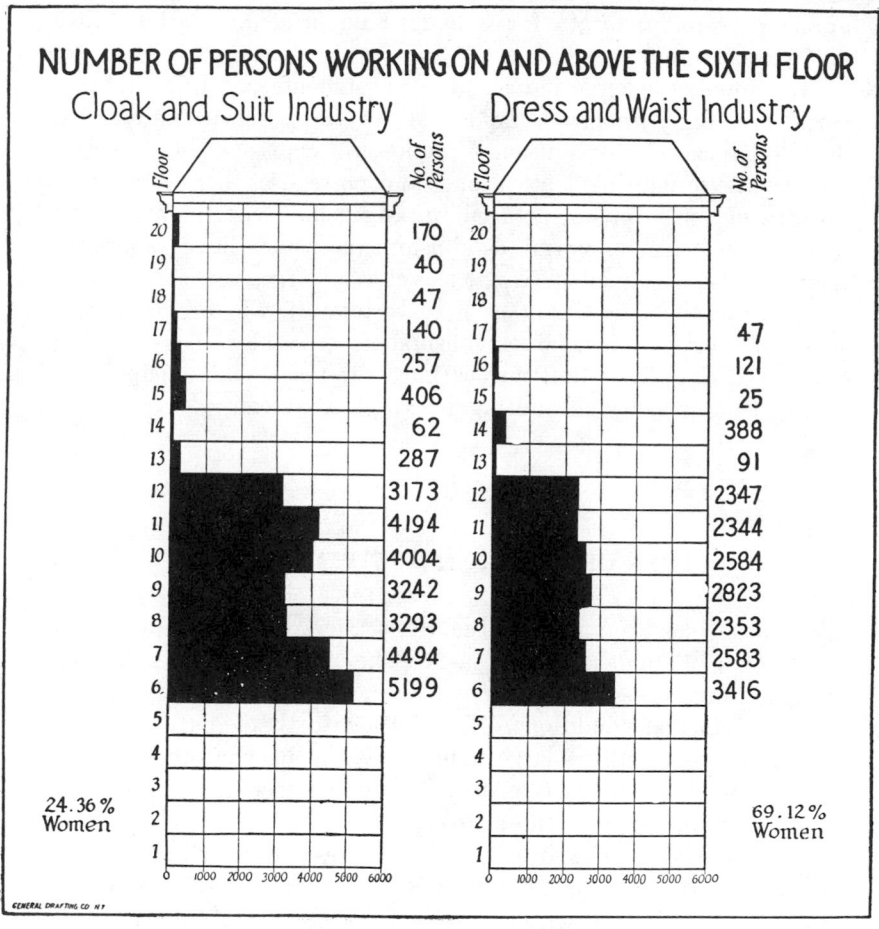

Joint Board of Sanitary Control.

unnecessary loss of life.   Moreover, the difficulty of fighting fires
occurring in lofts above the fifth story, has justified a great many
fire experts in declaring that a fire above a certain height is impossible to control.

There are certain industries in large cities like New York and
Chicago, which are concentrated in loft buildings in certain zones

of the city, and in which a large part of the working population is
employed above the fifth floor. In an investigation of the cloak
and suit industry, and the dress and waist industry made in 1913,
it was found that a large number of workers, among them a very
large percentage of women, are working above the fifth floor, and
some of them as high as the twentieth floor. The graphic chart
on page 108 shows the number of employes in the two industries
mentioned working on each of the floors above the fifth.

An additional hazard in extremely high buildings is the overcrowding of employes on each floor, an overcrowding which is
noticeable in the so-called seasonal trades. Loft buildings are
usually constructed without any reference to the purposes for
which they are to be used. The builder simply constructs a loft
building from eight to twenty stories in a four-walled enclosed
space. The occupant of a single loft or several floors begins by
dividing the space into compartments, according to his own needs.
The division and separation is not done by the original builder or
by the municipal authorities, but is accomplished by the occupant
of the loft. The partitions are of flimsy construction and of the
most inflammable material. The so-called fireproof loft is thus
changed into a far from fireproof partitioned factory. The floors
are all of wood and are very often oil soaked from the machine
drippings or from the processes carried on. The incoming and
outgoing goods are packed in pine-wood boxes, the goods are stored
on wooden shelves, and paper boxes are strewn all over the floor.

There was no limitation in any of the states (until the New York
State law of 1913) placed on the number of persons allowed
to be employed on one floor, except a provision for 250 to 400 cubic
feet of space for each occupant. Outside of this limitation, which
has very little scientific foundation, it has been found that the
number of persons employed on one floor is frequently entirely
disproportionate to the floor space.

The remedies for these evils which are such a prolific cause of
the loss of life in factory fires have been referred to previously,
and consist of the following: As to waste in buildings—metal-
covered boxes for storing all inflammable materials should be substituted for the customary wooden boxes. All clippings, rubbish,
and accumulated waste material should be removed two or three
times a day from each floor and at least once a day from the building.
As to overcrowding and extreme height of buildings—this is a most
difficult problem and one with which a great many states and muni-

cipal authorities are grappling.   Various schemes have been proposed, such as (1) decentralization of industries; (2) removing industries from the centers of the cities to outlying precincts; (3) inducing employers to locate their establishments in smaller buildings in communities in outlying precincts; (4) regulating the construction of buildings and prohibiting the construction of buildings above a certain story according to various industrial zones in the city; (5) limiting of occupancy of a floor of a building by provisions for the proportionate employment of persons according to floor space, and according to width and means of exit.   The New York State Law of 1913 is one of the first attempts to provide for the regulation of occupancy of factory buildings, and the provisions of this law are given in the appendix.   Briefly, they consist in proportioning the number of

Economy Metal Furniture Co.

Metal Boxes for Clippings and Waste.   They open at the side and may be kept under the work tables.

persons allowed to work on a floor according to the width of the stairway as well as to the means of extinguishing fires in a building, allowing fourteen persons for every eighteen inches width of stairway, and increasing the permissible number of occupants if the building is provided with a fire wall or automatic sprinklers.

Egress Facilities from Floor.   Loss of life is caused by improper and inadequate means of egress from each floor.   In case of fire, where there are a large number of persons working on a floor, all must go through the exits in as short a time as possible.   These exits are the windows and doors.   If then these doors and windows are insufficient or improperly constructed, and if the aisles and passageways throughout the factory are so filled with obstructions that the workers are unable to reach those means of exit quickly, it is but natural for a panic and loss of life to ensue.

The proper construction of doors, their number, width, method of closing, etc., are of course of the utmost importance. As a matter of fact, at present we find on inspection a number of factories with large floor space having but one or two door openings, sometimes located fifty to one hundred feet from the place of work— doors which are sometimes so narrow that two persons can scarcely pass through side by side. Add to these evils the fact that a large number of doors in industrial establishments are made to open inwardly, so that if the door is closed the persons rushing to the exits form a wedge which obstructs the passage and leads inevitably to loss of life.

In an investigation of the cloak and suit industry in 1912, out of 1800 factories investigated, 1379 were found in which doors

Courtesy Joint Board of Sanitary Control.

Tenant Factory with Window to Fire-escape Barred and only Measuring 17×36 Inches.

opened *inwardly;* and while this number has been greatly reduced within the last two or three years, 43.8 per cent of the factories in this industry and 31.98 per cent in the dress and waist industry still have doors opening inwardly. Not only do these doors prove an obstruction to egress, but a large number of them are locked from the inside with such locks that it takes time to have them opened. The number of prosecutions by the labor department against owners of shops in which inspectors find doors locked is considerable.

The windows in a great many industrial establishments are easily destroyed by exposure to fires. Those windows which lead to fire escapes are usually of the sash variety, and it is often difficult to raise them either because of their natural weight or because of some defect in their construction. Moreover, the height of the sill under these windows renders escape through them very difficult, especially for women and minors, because of the necessary climbing. Sometimes these windows, as in the illustration on page 111, are so small that it is difficult for a person to crawl through them.

In a great many of the factories the aisles between machines and between rows of operatives are so narrow and so obstructed by boxes, chairs, dummy figures and other things, that in case of excitement it is difficult for persons to pass through them and therefore, instead of being a means of egress they become an obstruction.

The number of doors should correspond to the number of exits from the floors and their width and number should correspond to the number of persons on the floor. The doors should always be made to open outward with proper automatic stops, so that it is not necessary to hold them. It is needless to add that doors should never be locked.

All windows opening on fire-escapes and serving as means of exit should be glazed with wire glass and have metal frames and sash. They should be so counterbalanced as to open easily and be large enough to permit rapid exit. The sills should not be more than eighteen inches above the floor. Doors to fire-escapes are much better and safer than windows and the difference in cost is so little that the use of windows is not to be tolerated, except in changing conditions in existing buildings. The doors opening on fire-escape balconies should open outward and be so arranged as not to obstruct the stairs.

In the arrangement of machines and grouping of workers on the floor, owners should always bear in mind the possibility of a fire and provide for rapid escape through the passages leading to the exits. These passageways should always be kept open, free from obstructions, and the workers should be instructed how to use them.

Egress from Building. The means of escape from a building are (1) the roof, (2) an adjoining building, and (3) the street. The roof becomes a zone of safety only when there is easy access to it from the floor by proper stairways of sufficient width, etc., when the opening to the roof is protected by a fire door, and most important of all, when access may be had to the roofs of adjoining buildings. Where buildings join others of a similar height, the roof is a most valuable means of escape because of the possibility of reaching safety by way of the roofs of unaffected houses.

The best means of reaching a zone of safety is by entering an adjoining building. This may be accomplished either by the above-mentioned escape to the roof of an adjoining building by balconies or bridges which join two buildings together, or by doorways in the fire walls between the two buildings. If it were possible for every

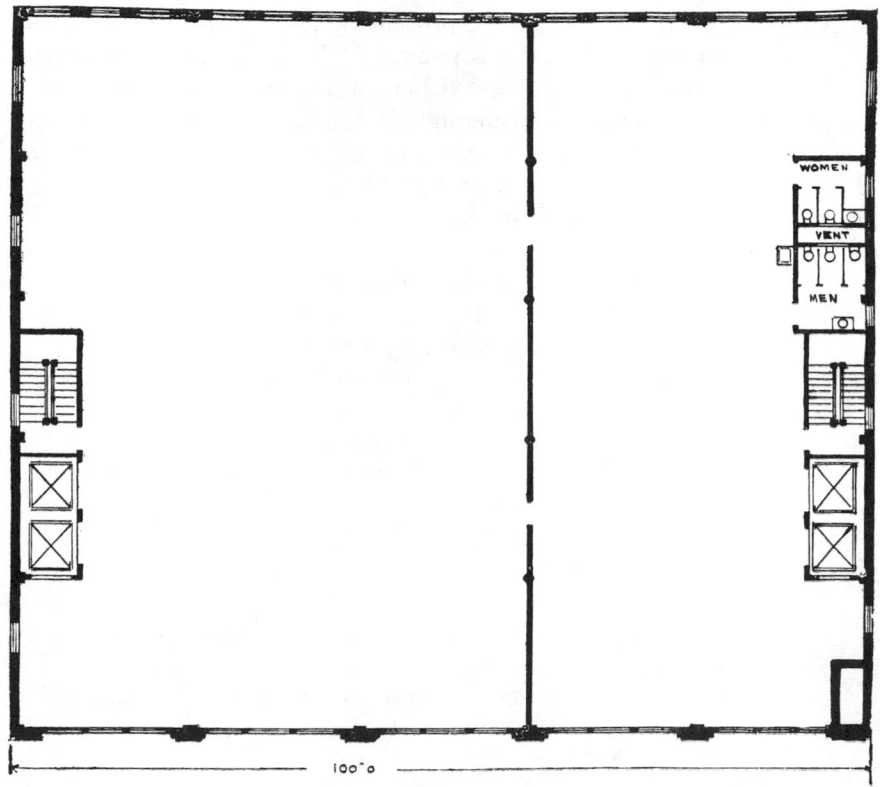

N. Y. State Factory Commission.

A Bisectional Building.

Floor plan of typical loft building, showing fire wall with doorways. The fire wall restricts the fire to one-half the building, allowing the occupants to escape horizontally from the fire as if they were on the ground floor.

building, whether adjacent to or at some distance from another building, to be joined on each floor by a bridge or balcony through which persons could pass from one building to the same floor of the adjoining building, this would be the ideal method of egress in case of need. This has been done in a number of establishments. Of course, care must be taken to construct these bridges and balconies properly, of a sufficient carrying capacity and size to allow the quick passage of all within a floor to the floor of the adjoining building.

A more direct means of egress is through openings in the fire wall between two buildings or through a fire wall which is specially constructed within the building itself. The provision of fire walls with fire doors as a means of preventing loss of property by fires in industrial establishments is not new. In Germany, particularly in Berlin, this provision has existed for nearly seventy-five years, and, as will be seen in the chapter on legislation, the German laws are very strict in respect to this provision. Lately, the possibility of utilizing the fire wall as a means of preventing loss of life during industrial fires has been brought forward and strenuously advocated in this country.

The illustration on page 113 shows the method of providing a fire wall within a building. The advantages of the division of large areas by fire walls are summarized by Freitag as follows:

First, to localize or confine internal fire, so that it need not spread beyond the unit area in which it originates, thus effectively limiting the fire damage and consequent financial loss.

Second, to minimize the damage resulting from severe exposure or conflagration conditions, by breaking up large undivided floor areas into efficiently surrounded units.

Third, to aid fire department work in the extinguishment of fire.

Buildings which are provided with fire walls are usually given a lower rating by the fire insurance companies.

The following quotation from the report of the National Fire Protection Association upon the Baltimore conflagration is of interest:

" Large unbroken floor areas assist the spread of fire and serve to augment its severity. Buildings of considerable area and having large quantities of combustible contents should be subdivided by substantial brick fire walls sufficient to form a positive barrier to the spread of fire.

" The large areas now so common, and particularly in those buildings having unenclosed vertical openings, undoubtedly furnish conditions which render even the most approved methods of fire-resisting construction now in use of doubtful value.

" It was noticeable, even in office buildings, that the damage was generally greatest, where there were large offices without any subdividing partitions."

The building code of the National Board of Fire Underwriters makes detailed provisions as to the size of areas to be limited by fire walls; while the German law requires such a wall for every forty meters of space.   There is, however, some objection on the part of builders and factory owners to the construction of fire walls within buildings, on account of the interference of these walls with light and ventilation.   Especially is objection made to the construction of these walls in old or already existing buildings, in which it is claimed that the cost of construction is too great.   Of course, the problems of light and ventilation may be overcome; while the matter of expense should, of course, have no serious consideration in view of the possible loss of life in industrial fires.

Stairs.   The necessity for a stairwell isolated by fire-resisting walls, so that the stairwell and the stairway within should be in a perfect zone of safety in case of fire, has been referred to above. Unfortunately, neither the stairwell nor the stairway is safe as constructed at present.   It is rare to find a well-constructed fire-resisting separation between the building and the stairwell, which is often, instead of a means of escape, a menace to safety, by becoming full of smoke and spreading the fire from floor to floor.   We also find a large number of factories with only one stairway.   As a cardinal principle of construction, every factory several stories high should be provided with two inside stairways, so that in case one stairway is cut off by fire the other may be used as a means of egress.   This, indeed, is provided in many of the foreign state regulations and in some of the building codes in the United States.

Of importance also are the materials of construction, treads, risers, landings, rails.   Of the utmost importance, of course, is the width of the stairway.   A large number of stairways in factories do not allow the passage of more than two persons, and the stairways are apt to become jammed when a number of persons try to use them, acting impulsively under excitement, and all endeavoring to pass the stairway at one time.   As Mr. H. F J. Porter says:

" The stairway is simply a tube with which each floor is connected; and when these floors try to empty their contents simultaneously into it, this tube will accommodate only a definite number from each; and should any more try to crowd in, they jam it, and the flow downward is arrested. The reason for this jam is that the irregularly-shaped bodies of the people interlock and the friction of their clothing aids the wedging action, so that there is an actual arch formed across the stairs, and the greater the pressure behind it, the tighter it holds."

Mr. Porter continues:

" The average loft building with a height of story between floor and ceiling of from ten to twelve feet, has a stairwell which, if it is the minimum width of three feet allowed by the building code, will accommodate one person per foot of height per floor, and if it is four feet wide, just double that number. It will not be safe, then, to house more than ten to twelve persons in one case and twenty to twenty-four in the other, unless more stairwells are installed or unless a separate stairwell is installed for each floor."*

The number of persons using a stairway at one time is naturally limited, and if there is a large number of persons on one floor all trying to go out at the same time, the result will be either the breaking down of the stairway, the forcing open of its rails, or the jamming of the whole structure; thus creating a worse condition than if there were no stairway at all. Moreover, when a stairway in a many-storied building is to be used by persons located on every story of the building, and there is a sudden downward rush from all the floors, the situation is a still greater menace, and the possibilities are horrible to contemplate.

The question of the number of persons who may be safely allowed on a floor has not yet been determined. Some persons claim that a 36-inch wide stairway will admit two persons abreast, and the capacity of the stair will be about 24 persons per story; while a 4-foot stairway will accommodate three persons abreast and the maximum number of persons allowed should be 45. It is therefore:

" the surplus people above the capacity of the stairways, who in fire casualties have been the ones who have either jumped to death or been burned up, and it is this surplus over the usual stair capacity which must be provided for either by (1) added stair capacity, (2) adequate outside escape, or (3) bi-sectional fire wall."†

It is evident, therefore, that the stairway as constructed at present, is an inadequate means of emptying the building, and that buildings of many stories, each containing a greater number of people than the figures given, are practicably unemptiable. Even with a fire drill such buildings cannot be emptied promptly in case of fire.

The increase of escape facilities by the fire wall has already been

---

* Report to the State Factory Investigating Commission," vol. i, 1912, p. 158.
† J. K. Freitag, " Fire Prevention and Protection," p. 510.

spoken of. The increase in capacity of stairways is, of course, possible by increasing the number and width of stairways, but it is hardly possible with the present means of construction and

Courtesy H. F. J. Porter.   Report of N. Y. State Factory Investigating Commission.

Stairway Congestion.

A stairway, 12 ft. high between floor and ceiling, 3 ft. wide, will accommodate 12 people per floor. If the width is increased to 44 inches, the capacity is doubled, viz., 24 people per floor.

If there are more people per floor than these numbers, they will collide on the landings, and congestion will occur so that the downward movement practically ceases. All the occupants of each floor beyond the capacity of the stairways in case of fire, jump down or burn up. The fire wall offers a middle road to safety by a horizontal escape.

types of buildings, to put more than two stairways in a building 50 feet wide by 100 feet deep, or to make the stairways wider than four feet. Indeed, the present mode of construction usually limit the stairways to 40 inches.   A somewhat increased capacity may be obtained by stairways of the straight run type, so that there are no winders or zigzag turns, and the flow of the persons downward is not halted by the turns of each stairway.

Of great importance also is the outlet of the stairway to the street on the ground floor. Very often the stairways end in a cul-de-sac, from which it is difficult to find the proper outlet to the street or in a dark vaulted passage, which is sometimes narrower than the stairway and impedes the rapid egress of persons coming down. All stairways should end on the ground floor with free, light and unobstructed passageway to the street.

I have already referred to the necessity of enclosing stairways by fire-resisting solid walls separating the stairways from the other parts of the building, and leaving, as the only means of communication between each story and the stairway, a self-closing fire door of proper construction, so as to prevent the spread of the fire from one floor to another, or from the stairway into the floor. The newer types of stairways are constructed in so-called "fire-proof towers," where solid fire-resisting walls wholly enclose the stairway and open by single or double self-closing fire doors to each floor. Some of these towers are made smoke-proof by being separated from each story not only by doors but by an open or covered balcony, which still further enhances their safety.   Fire or smoke-proof towers do not give the enclosed stairways any greater capacity; they only protect from smoke and flames the people who can enter them.

Fire-Escapes.   The inadequacy of stairways as a means of egress from buildings has led to attempts to provide emergency exits outside of the building.   It is probable that the first emergency fire-escape outside of a building was simply a plain rope, which was perhaps afterwards improved by being formed into a rope ladder.   Indeed, there are still on the market some types of rope ladder fire-escapes, which are occasionally recommended by their vendors, either as a sole means of fire-escape or as an auxiliary emergency exit.   In time, a straight iron ladder consisting of two stringers with bar rungs was substituted for this rope ladder.   This again has given place to the more commonly found type of fire-escape, which consists of two parts: (1) the platform enclosed by rails and called a balcony, which is placed securely outside the window or door openings of each floor and serves as a means for temporary shelter and safety zone for a limited number of persons

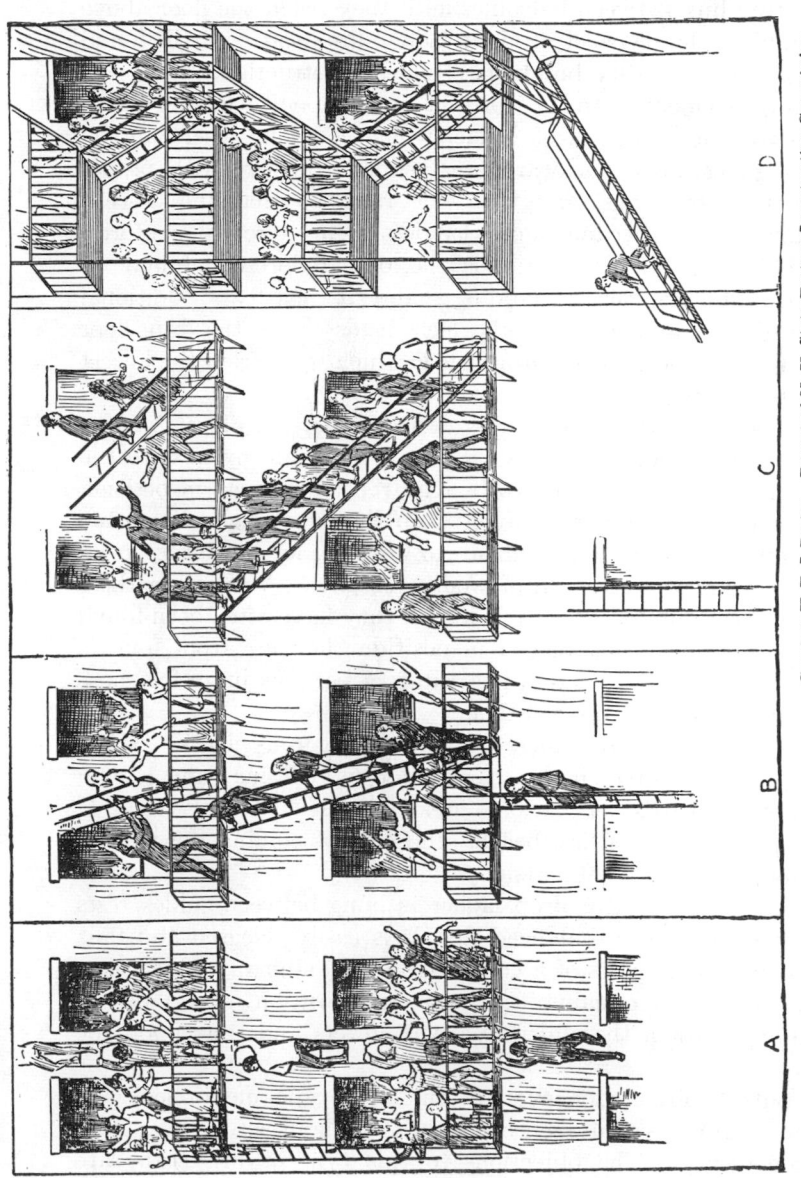

Courtesy H. F. J. Porter, Report of N. Y. State Factory Investigating Commission.

A Comparison of the Capacity of Different Types of Fire-escapes.

A. A straight ladder fire escape, capacity 2 per floor.
B. Inclined ladder fire escape, capacity 4 per floor.
C. Straight stairway, 22 ins. wide, capacity 12 per floor.
D. Mezzanine platform stairs, 44 ins. wide, with cantilever steps to ground, capacity 24 per floor.

When more than these numbers try to crowd in, they form a jam and stop the flow downward altogether.

in case of emergency; and (2) straight iron ladders which serve as a connecting link between balconies until they reach the floor above the ground. This type of straight ladder fire-escape is still found in a great many factory buildings of older construction.

An improvement upon this form of fire-escape was made by substituting for the straight iron ladder which could be used only by a person going down backward, an inclined stairway with proper steps, instead of rungs, and with side rails, so that the descent from each balcony became somewhat less of an acrobatic performance. This type of fire-escape is the one at present found on practically all the newer buildings, and it has two additional fixtures; the goose-neck ladder which leads from the top floor balcony to the roof, and the drop ladder which leads from the lowest balcony to the ground.

There are several types of this drop ladder; the oldest variety is a plain iron ladder hung on some part of the balcony next to the lowest balcony, and supposed to be removed and placed in position by the persons descending. Such drop ladders weigh from 150 to 200 pounds and are most difficult to lift even for a robust person, and are beyond the strength of women or girls. Very often these drop ladders are placed out of reach; and they have often been found too short, so that when placed in position they are from four to ten feet above the ground and necessitate a perilous jump for those who are lucky enough to reach them.

Some of these drop ladders lead into dangerous places. Many fire-escapes are located in the rear or side of buildings and end in closed courts, yards, or locked areas, which become veritable roasting pens in case of fire, because the persons coming down have no means of escape to the outside.

An improved form of drop ladder is hung between guides, rests upon a hook and is so balanced that it is easily released and falls into position; or consists of a counter-balanced stairway which is so constructed that it remains in a horizontal position until a person steps upon it, when the stairway slowly lowers and rests upon the ground.

An outside fire-escape even of the best type mentioned is a misnomer. It gives a false sense of security without actually assisting in an emergency. The objections to this type of fire-escape are tersely summarized in the brief submitted by Rudolph P. Miller, Superintendent of Buildings of New York City, to the New York State Factory Commission.

"All outside fire-escapes are open to the following objections: Inmates are not accustomed to their use and do not generally seek

Standard Double Run Fire-escape.

them except as a last resort. They do not allow of a quick and ready means of escape, as persons are unaccustomed to them and will move along slowly, thus delaying those who are following.

In wintry weather they are liable to be obstructed by snow and ice, and become unsafe. Very often they are rendered useless because of smoke and flames issuing from the windows at which they are placed. The means of getting from the lowest balcony is generally the least satisfactory of the entire equipment, and greatly delays quick egress. Fire-escapes are liable to be blocked by being used as storage platforms, and no amount of inspection can entirely prevent this in crowded districts. Numerous instances may be found in the public press in which inmates seeking fire-escapes have failed to know what to do and have waited for the fire department to come and take them down. On account of the contracted dimensions of these fire-escapes large persons have sometimes found difficulty in making proper use of them. The fire department has generally advocated their use, but it will be found that this advocacy is based on a desire to have a means of getting into the building; but if desirable for this purpose, then they should be provided as such and not offered to the inmates as a satisfactory means of egress." *

Whenever fire-escapes are constructed for emergency exits, the same precautions as to freedom from obstructions should be observed as in the case of windows, doors and passageways. The tendency at present is to condemn the ordinary outside open fire-escape even of the better type, and to construct regular stair fire-escapes and so-called tower fire-escapes, sometimes called " Philadelphia Tower Fire-Escapes." Such a fire-escape is really a stairway which is enclosed by brick or other fire-resisting walls and entirely isolated from the building and from the floors of the buildings, except that the exterior balcony of each floor forms a means of communication and is open to the air between the tower and the interior of the building. Such towers are not only fire-resisting but also smoke-proof and form the best emergency exit possible. Of course, the proper construction of such fire-escapes is important, and the balconies or enclosed vestibules must be solidly constructed, and of sufficient capacity for a number of persons to use them from each floor. The accompanying illustrations show the form of these fire-escapes.

A new fire-escape which is recommended by some is the so-called " Kirker Bender Slide Fire-Escape " which is constructed on the principle of shooting-the-chutes. It consists of a central standpipe or tube with an enclosed helical slide built around it with entrance doors provided on every floor and at the roof. Balconies connect windows or doors from each floor with this tube fire-escape. The

* Report of New York State Factory Commission, 1913, vol. i., p. 73.

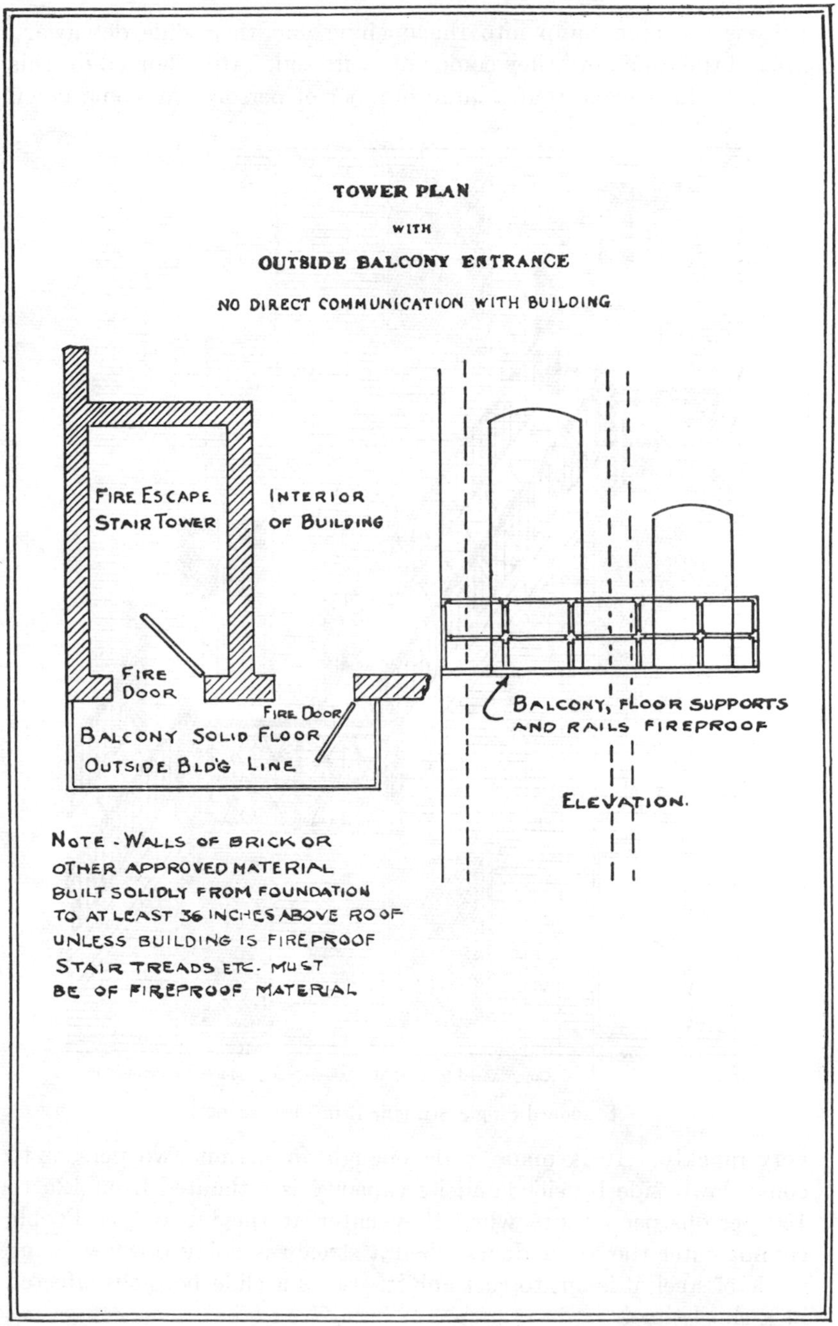
TOWER PLAN
WITH
OUTSIDE BALCONY ENTRANCE
NO DIRECT COMMUNICATION WITH BUILDING
FIRE ESCAPE STAIR TOWER
INTERIOR OF BUILDING
FIRE DOOR
FIRE DOOR
BALCONY SOLID FLOOR OUTSIDE BLD'G LINE
BALCONY, FLOOR SUPPORTS AND RAILS FIREPROOF
ELEVATION.
NOTE - WALLS OF BRICK OR OTHER APPROVED MATERIAL BUILT SOLIDLY FROM FOUNDATION TO AT LEAST 36 INCHES ABOVE ROOF UNLESS BUILDING IS FIREPROOF
STAIR TREADS ETC. MUST BE OF FIREPROOF MATERIAL

N. Y. State Factory Commission.

persons escaping jump into the opening and then slide downward around the tube until they come out at its end. It is claimed for this means of fire-escape that a large number of persons can come down

Standard Single Straight Run Fire-escape.

very quickly. It is made wide enough to permit two persons to come down side by side; and its capacity is estimated from 125 to 150 persons per minute when they enter at the top only. People cannot enter the lower doors when a stream is going down. Being made of steel, it is apt to rust and its use as a slide becomes affected in a short time.

Panics. One of the great dangers in factory fires to which a large loss of life may be attributed, is the panic which is apt to spread among a mass of workers, especially women and girls, when the dreaded cry of fire is sounded in a factory or workshop. More lives may be lost through a senseless panic by the

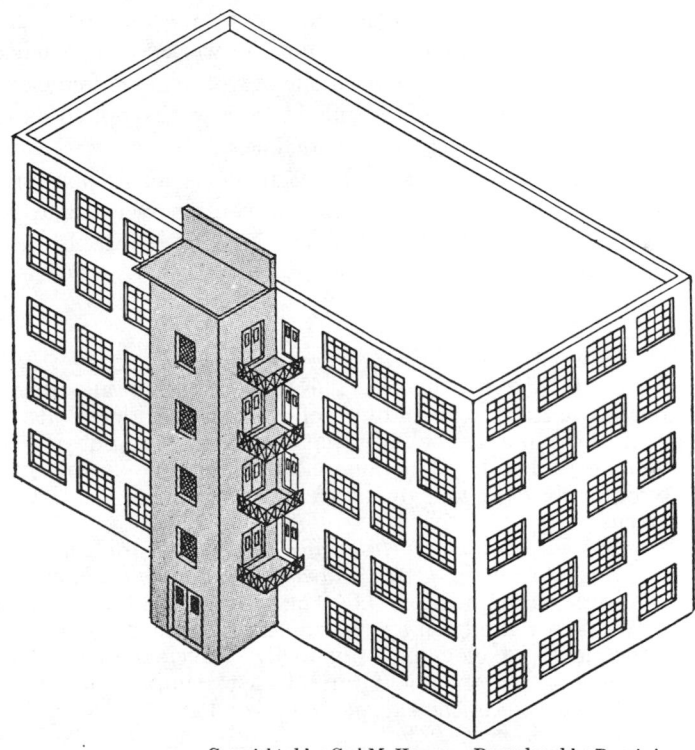

Philadelphia Tower Fire-escape.

people treading each other down and jamming in tight places than by the fire itself.

The prevention of panics is, of course, largely a matter of education. When workers are properly imbued with the idea of the possibilities of escape from a floor or from a building, when they know the dangers as well as the means of escape, when each worker knows the exits from the floor and from the building, when he is instructed, educated and trained to leave his place of work in a quiet, orderly manner at all times, and especially during unexpected alarms, when certain persons are appointed each of whom has charge of a number of employes and leads and directs them to certain exits, and when the whole working force is properly organized, trained and drilled, then if the exit facilities are adequate there will be no loss of life. Employers and those persons to whose care the safety and the lives of a large number of persons are entrusted, should be bound to take all these necessary precautions, to institute educational methods among the workers, to teach each one his proper place and his proper mode of exit in case of emergency, and to install and maintain fire drills in each workshop, so as to be prepared in times of safety for emergencies.

Perhaps the severest arraignment made against our present system of ignoring methods of fire prevention was made by an editor of the New York *World*, Don C. Seitz, in an address to the Safety and Sanitation Conference in New York City. He said:

" The study of human values can only be made in the light of mankind's regard for itself. This has been, in all times, all ages and all countries, the lightest of human considerations. My observations lead me to believe that mankind has not improved the treatment of itself. The human sacrifice is required just as much to-day as it ever was in the Temple of Baal or on the altars of the Aztecs.

" *The world has ample knowledge of its perils, natural and created, but it remedies only on the heels of disaster and safeguards only after sacrifice.* Notorious conditions of danger are tolerated until blood is shed. We then remedy in spots and await the next calamity. It required the death of eleven of my fellow travelers in the Fourth Avenue Tunnel to create the Grand Central improvements. *We have not yet had holocausts enough like the Asch Building disaster to produce real fire protection.*"

It is true that not all floors of factory buildings nor all factory buildings may easily be emptied with or without fire drills. It is true that a great many buildings cannot be emptied within a short time, and it is also true that it is perhaps futile to endeavor to empty one floor when the workers upon other floors are not drilled and do not know how to act at the same time in order to empty the whole building at once. It therefore follows that a fire drill in order to be a real protection to the workers can only be properly installed and maintained in an emptiable factory building,—in one where there are no obstructions to the exits and where the exits are of a sufficient number and capacity to empty the building in as short a time as possible. Nevertheless, taking all these facts into consideration, there should be no factory building, and no individual workshop, no matter how small or what part of a building it occupies,

Courtesy Nemo Corset Co.

Emergency Exit in Fire-wall Leading to Fire-escape.

in which some sort of fire drill is not installed and maintained. The introduction and maintenance of fire drills in factory buildings should at once be the subject not only of legislation, but of strict and rigid enforcement. A number of state legislatures have already passed fire drill laws, and a large number of factory owners have already endeavored to comply with these laws to the best of their ability.

Ex-Chief Croker, in his book on fire prevention, says:

" I am willing to assert that ninety-nine of every one hundred lives that have been lost through fire in the last ten years, could have been saved if proper methods of drill and of training and proper precautions in matters of building and means of escape had been the rule instead of the rare exception."

The principles of the fire drill are simple. They are: (1) that each employe should be instructed in the number of exits which lead from the floor to the stairways or fire-escapes: (2) that a group of employes should be organized under a chief, whose duty it is to see that they act according to instructions and go to the exits which are assigned to each group; (3) that the workers of each floor should be divided according to the number of exits from the floor, and each group assigned to a regular exit, and to an alternate exit which it is to use in case the regular exit is cut off; (4) that a brigade should be organized by the employer or those in charge of the fire drills, to (a) extinguish small fires by means of the fire pails or extinguishers, (b) to notify by telephone or personally reach the nearest fire station, (c) to man and work a hose from standpipe when available, (d) to provide sufficient guards stationed at each exit to prevent crowding and jamming of the outgoing stream of workers, and (e) to stop the machinery as soon as the alarm is sounded.

The suggestions prepared by the National Fire Protection Association for the organization and execution of fire drills in factories, etc., giving the details of this work, will be found in the Appendix.

CHAPTER IV

FACTORY ACCIDENTS AND SAFETY

I

EXTENT AND DANGERS

EVERY year thousands of workers are killed, tens of thousands are maimed and disabled, and hundreds of thousands are injured more or less severely. In every country innumerable lives are sacrificed on the altar of the modern system of production. Every industry and every industrial establishment exacts its toll of human life. So great are the risks of the trades that in comparison with the fatalities yearly occurring among the wage-earners, the number of victims in all the ruthless wars of the past fades into insignificance.

It is impossible to state exactly or even to estimate the numbers who are injured in the course of their work. It is only in the last decade that some attempt has been made in the United States to count the injured and to report the accidents occurring in industry. Hoffman estimates the number of industrial accidents in the United States for one year at 200,000 in manufacturing industries alone, and the fatalities among occupied males in 1908 at between thirty and thirty-five thousand.*

The number of industrial accidents in factories for 1912 for six of the large industrial states, with a total population of 3,087,593, was, according to the latest factory inspectors' reports, 66,946, of which 810 were fatal. In New York State alone, with a working population of little over one million, there were in 1912 no less than 51,084 accidents.

Nor are the reports from European countries more cheerful. In 1911 there were in Great Britain 156,232 accidents in the factories and workshops, of which 1260 were fatal. Belgium, with a factory population of 665,190, reports for the same year 87,261 accidents;

---

* Frederick Hoffman, Industrial Accidents, Bulletin of Bureau of Labor, No. 78, p. 418.

France reports for its 507,557 factories 474,396 accidents in 1911.*
Germany had over 600,000 industrial accidents in the same year.

Industrial accident data are at present gained from the reports
of factory inspectors and from the reports of the insurance and
workmen's compensation commissions. Such data have been
gathered for a number of years in some of the European countries,
notably in Germany. In the United States there are only twenty-
one states where accident statistics are gathered, and these statistics
are neither uniform nor complete.

Narrow Aisles between Machines with Unguarded Belts and Pulleys.

Not only is the occurrence of industrial accidents universal, but
there seems to be evidence that industrial accidents are on the
increase and that the number of victims is growing in many industries from year to year.

In New York State the number of industrial accidents has
increased from 19,431 in 1907 to 51,804 in 1912.† The increase
in the number of industrial accidents in British industries led in
1910 to the creation of a special commission, the appointment of
which was the result of the following resolution: " That this House

* Including commercial houses, state depts. and banks, also domestic service.
† New York State Commission on Employer's Liability, 2d Report, p. 8, and Annual Report, Commissioner of Labor, New York State, 1912, p. 67.

is of the opinion that the increase in fatal and non-fatal accidents in places under the Factory and Workshops Acts is of such character as to demand immediate attention."* The report of this commission showed that the number of accidents in Great Britain had risen from 100,695 in 1905 to 124,325 in 1907, and since that time to 156,332 in 1912. The committee reported that it was impossible to get absolute proof of the increase of risk in industry; that some of the seeming increase of accidents was due to better reporting; that minor accidents increased at a greater rate than serious accidents; that the increase of accidents was largely due to the expansion of industry; that much of the increase of accidents was undoubtedly due to certain special causes such as increased speed and pressure at work, fatigue, increased use of machinery, etc.

German statistics show that from 1901 to 1911 there was a decrease in accidents causing death, and partial or total permanent disability; but that there was a marked increase in accidents causing temporary disablement, lasting more than thirteen weeks. The increase of accidents is particularly due to the following causes: stricter control in regard to reporting accidents; employment of untrained and inexperienced workmen; more frequent prosecutions of claims by injured persons because of their better knowledge of the law; better knowledge of what is an industrial accident; increase of the cases in which the officials of the insurance system admitted a causal connection between existing malady or weakness and its aggravation by an accident; frequent granting of a transitory or accustoming pension, in cases where strictly speaking there was no longer a loss of earning power; and, finally, the frequency of changes in the personnel of the laboring forces of the plants. It was also conceded that accidents increased because of the more intense methods of the industry and by the extension of the use of machinery.†

Austrian accident statistics also show that those accidents which cause disablement from which the workman recovers seem to have increased, while serious accidents causing permanent disablement show a tendency to decrease.‡

Gruesome as is the evidence presented by international industrial accident statistics, it does not fully illustrate the extent of the risks and dangers of modern industry, nor does it permit one to

* Report, Departmental Committee on Accidents, 1911, p. 1.
† Henry J. Harris, Increase in Industrial Accidents, Quarterly Statistics for March, 1912, pp. 12 and 13.
‡ Ibid., p. 17.

GERMAN INDUSTRIAL ACCIDENT STATISTICS. 1901-1911.

(Amtliche Nachrichten des Reichsversicherungsamts, Jan. 1913, p. 14-15.)

Year.	Number of Full-time Workers.	Number of Accidents.	Number of Accidents Resulting in				Number of Accidents Per 1000 Full-time Workers Resulting in				
			Death.	Permanent Disability.		Temporary Disability Longer than 13 Weeks.	Total.	Death.	Permanent Disability.		Temporary Disability Longer Than 13 Weeks.
				Complete.	Partial				Complete.	Partial.	
1902	6,742,829	61,068	5099	834	28555	26580	9.06	.76	.12	4.34	3.94
1903	7,084,093	64,616	5256	899	29427	29034	9.12	.74	.13	4.15	4.10
1904	7,426,538	69,220	5544	898	30633	31945	9.32	.75	.12	4.15	4.30
1905	7,735,162	72,630	5770	852	31236	34772	9.39	.75	.11	4.04	4.49
1906	8,122,025	75,589	6033	843	31945	36768	9.31	.74	.11	3.93	4.53
1907	8,531,632	79,907	6751	820	32269	40067	9.37	.79	.10	3.78	4.70
1908	8,540,601	79,339	6678	764	31179	40718	9.29	.78	.09	3.65	4.77
1909	8,613,555	75,684	6196	654	27756	41078	8.79	.72	.08	3.22	4.77
1910	8,964,228	73,431	5843	627	25483	41478	8.19	.65	.07	2.84	4.63
1911	9,342,805	74,662	6398	573	24568	43123	7.99	.68	.06	2.63	4.62

easily comprehend the terrible sacrifice of human life under the modern factory system. It is only when we translate the figures into the more comprehensible economic terms that we are appalled by the great loss of life caused by industry.

" A conservative estimate of the economic loss in this country through industrial accidents places it above a quarter of a billion dollars each year. This is more than two million workmen could earn in a twelvemonth at four dollars a day apiece. With the universal adoption of a well-developed policy it is easy to believe that fifty per cent of them might be avoided. This would be a saving in the United States each year of about 20,000 lives, the prevention each year of a full million of bodily injuries of varying degree, and a money saving of $125,000,000 annually."*

According to Hoffman, " the thirty to thirty-five thousand fatal accidents and not less than two million non-fatal accidents not only involve a vast amount of human suffering and sorrow, but materially curtail the longevity among those exposed to the needless risk of industrial casualties."†

The social loss involved in 526 fatal work accidents occurring in 1908 in Allegheny County, Pennsylvania, computed by averaging the net economic gain from the life of a male wage earner from his fifteenth to his sixty-fifth year (method of Hoffman) was found to result in a minimum economic loss to the community of $3,828,090. The loss through total, partial or temporary disability computed in a similar way amounted to $1,320,636; while the hospital charges were estimated at $80,000. Thus, the loss to society from one year's work accidents in Allegheny County amounted to $5,228,736.‡

A similar estimate of financial loss was made in New York State in the course of an investigation conducted by the Employer's Liability Commission in 1909. The loss in wages within one year through temporary disability in 1297 work accidents in New York State amounted to more than $93,000.§

On the same subject Mr. Carl M. Hansen, Secretary of the Department of Accident Prevention of the Workmen's Compensation Service Bureau, said in his address to the National Association of Cotton Manufacturers in Atlantic City:

* J. Kirby, Jr., President National Association of Manufacturers: Address before the First Cooperative Safety Congress, 1912.
† United States Bulletin Bureau of Labor, No. 78.
‡ Eastman: Work Accidents and the Law, p. 317.
§ Report of the New York State Commission on Employer's Liability, First Report, p. 215.

" How largely the matter of industrial accidents enters into the cause of our social ills, I am not prepared to state definitely, but with a record of from 40,000 to 45,000 killed wage-earners annually and with an additional 200,000 working days lost on account of non-fatal accidents among the rest of our working population, I make bold to opine that it constitutes one of the largest causes of poverty and consequent dependency. Translated into actual dollars and cents, taking the minimum of 40,000 killed at a value as producing members of society of $5000 each, and $2 as an average wage of the non-fatally injured, we have the economic loss sustained to the nation as a whole on account of industrial accidents represented by the very munificent sum of $600,000,000 annually. This does not include all the indirect losses accruing in the form of restricted opportunities suffered by the dependents left by those killed and crippled wage-earners. What that amounts to, no man can calculate or estimate. I believe, though, we may safely put down our industrial accidents as one of the great causes of our social ills and as one of our greatest national wastes."*

We are therefore presented with the grave problem of the large number of fatal casualties in the modern factory, the great number of other accidents resulting in serious injury to the worker, often in total and permanent disability, and the ensuing misery and economic loss to the workers and to the community.

Is there a solution to this problem? Are all the accidents incident to industrial life inevitable and unavoidable, or may all of them, or a part of them, or any of them, be avoided and prevented?

This great problem and the methods of its solution have engaged the earnest attention of all those who are interested in industrial progress. The problem has been studied in all its aspects and serious efforts have been made in other countries to prevent the waste of human resources in modern industry and to make factories safer.

For nearly half a century these efforts have been made by European governments and corporate interests. The first attempts at accident prevention were made as far back as in the early part of the nineteenth century, when the number of accidents, especially those due to explosion of steam boilers, had attracted public attention. As a result, a boiler inspection service was instituted either by the governments or by private associations, to reduce the great number of fatalities. In 1867 one of the first associations, that of Mulhausen, was organized in Alsace, under the name of the " Association pour Prévenir les Accidents des Fabriques." Since that time numerous associations have been formed for the same purpose;

* Safety Engineering, October, 1913, p. 250.

such as the "Association des Industriels de France contre les Accidents du Travail," "Association Parisienne des Propriétaires d'Appareils à Vapeur," and many other similar associations in most of the European countries.

Courtesy Aetna Life Insurance Co.

Live Roll Gears Unprotected.

The greatest impetus to accident prevention and organization was given by the Accident Insurance Law of Germany, which was introduced in 1884, and gradually expanded until it embraced practically every industrial center and every worker in the country. During 1885 and 1886 no less than sixty-two trade associations of owners and manufacturers were organized in Germany. These associations did excellent work in the study and prevention of industrial accidents. Not only did they make thorough and comprehensive studies of accident risks and causes, but they also adopted in practically every industry a rigid set of rules and regulations, which they enforced themselves by means of the insurance rates imposed upon each member of the association and by their inspectors, who assist the state industrial inspectors.

The governments of the European countries have stood in the vanguard of accident prevention and have not only urged employers and corporations to go on with their accident prevention work, but have made the safeguarding of industry a function of a large factory inspection force. Special rules have been issued for each industry and group of industries, and valiant work has been done by the departments in charge of this branch of state work. In many European cities and industrial centers, collections of safety devices and museums of safety have been established, so that those who are interested may see and adopt the most modern protective devices.

It is only within the last five years that serious attempts at lessening the dangers of industrial accidents have been made in this country. From 1909 to 1913 no less than twenty-five legislative commissions were appointed in as many different states to investigate accident prevention and compensation for industrial accidents; while in three other states, commissions have been voluntarily appointed by their governors.

The increase of interest in the subject is illustrated by the number of articles in current magazines on the subject of accidents in industry and employers' liability. In 1909 there appeared in the current magazines only five articles; in 1912 there were not less than fifty-two popular articles on these subjects.

At present twenty-two states have adopted more or less comprehensive workmen's compensation laws. It is to be hoped that while we in these United States have been tardy in grappling with this great modern industrial problem, once we have taken the first step in its solution, we shall speedily overtake the most advanced nations.

Large corporate interests, and large employers of labor have lately taken a great interest in the subject. As examples may be cited the great work accomplished within the last few years by the United States Steel Corporation, the International Harvester

Company, and others too numerous to mention, who have joined
in the work of accident prevention. The American Association
for Labor Legislation has done splendid work in preliminary
agitation and the lately organized National Council for Industrial
Safety and a number of safety congresses bear witness to the great
interest taken in the subject.

What has been the result of all the agitation for accident prevention, of all the social cooperation and state endeavors to bring
about a lessening of the hazards of industry?   How much nearer are
we to the solution of the problem stated before?   One thing is clear

Courtesy Aetna Life Insurance Co.

Unguarded Opening to Elevator Hoistway.

and certain. It has been demonstrated that a very large number
of industrial accidents *may* and can be prevented and thus are unnecessary and inexcusable.

The Pennsylvania Railroad Company has decreased the number of serious accidents among its 33,242 shop employes by over
63 per cent through the installation of safety devices and instruction of workmen in exercising due caution.   The United States
Steel Corporation states that it has reduced serious and fatal
accidents in its various plants since 1906 by 42.3 per cent,* and
similar claims are being made weekly and daily by a large number

* J. Kirby, Jr., Address First Cooperative Safety Congress in Milwaukee, 1911.

of corporations which have within the last five years taken up the slogan of " safety first " and have done great work in accident prevention.

The solution of the problem, therefore, must come from industry itself. Industry as such, is primarily responsible for many of the risks and dangers incident to it; and it is incumbent upon those who are at the head of each industry to render it as safe as possible, to install and introduce all possible safety appliances and to maintain a campaign of education so as to reduce the number of industrial accidents to a minimum, and thus by prevention, inspection and education make industry less hazardous. Finally, since the progress of science has not advanced so far as to remove all the dangers of trades and to prevent all the risks of occupations, the industry and the employer should be made to bear the cost of the loss of life and the economic loss to the worker from injuries due to industrial accidents, by proper compensation and insurance for all accidents and injuries.

II

THE PERSONAL FACTOR IN ACCIDENT CAUSATION AND PREVENTION

The definition of an industrial accident has aroused a great deal of legal controversy, and the word has been variously defined by judges and courts at different times and places. In Great Britain an accident means " any unlooked for mishap or occurrence and includes not merely something external to the workman, as the bursting of a boiler or a mine explosion, but something internal as well, as rupture, straining of a muscle, etc. When an injury is caused gradually this is not an accident. Disease contracted while at work is not an injury by accident. Certain industrial diseases, however, are deemed to be accidents. Nervous shock through seeing an accident may be an accident."[*] Another definition of accident is the following: " An accident is anything which happens to an employe in the course of his or her work and causes immediate or remote physical pain or disease, whether incident to such employment or not, not caused by the wilful carelessness of such an employe and not a necessary accompaniment of the work engaged in."[†]

[*] Encyclopedia of Industrialism, p. 143.
[†] Barnett: External Injuries of Workmen, p. 57.

N. Y. State Factory Commission.

Open Caustic Pot in Foreground without Rail or Guard.

The German definition of the word accident as stated by the insurance office, is the following: "a sudden occurrence during work which injures the health and interferes with the earning ability of the worker."

The subject of prevention of industrial accidents must necessarily be based upon a thorough study of the causation of accidents, in order to determine the means by which they may be avoided.

The English classification of the causes of accidents takes into consideration the following main points: (1) accidents caused by machinery moved by mechanical power; (2) by machinery not moved by mechanical power; (3) struck by falling body; (4) persons falling; (5) struck by tools in use; (6) accidents caused by fire and other accidents.

The German Insurance Office gives fourteen groups of causes of accidents, as follows: (1) motors, transmission and machinery; (2) elevators and hoistways; (3) steam boilers, steam pipes and boiling apparatus; (4) explosives; (5) fire, dangerous materials, gases and fumes; (6) falling of objects; (7) fall from ladders, stairs, in excavations, hatchways; (8) loading and unloading by hand, carrying and lifting; (9) conveyances; (10) steam railroad; (11) transportation; (12) shipping; (13) tools and simple utensils; and (14) miscellaneous.

Whatever the causes of accidents may be, it is evident that there are very few accidents indeed in which the personal factor does not play some rôle, direct or indirect, remote or near.

When we speak of the personal factor in the causation of accidents we do not speak in the legal sense or intend to indicate "personal responsibility" on the part of the person injured. The personal element in the causation of accidents is always present, whether it is due to the fault of the person injured or to other persons or to the fault of no one at all. If we therefore attempt to classify the causes of accidents which are directly or indirectly due to the personal factor in industry, the following will have to be discussed: (a) age, (b) sex, (c) ignorance, (d) physical unfitness, (e) carelessness, and (f) improper personal equipment.

Age is a very important factor as a cause of accidents. A child or minor is not able to take proper care of itself, and it has been recognized by legislative enactments of practically all civilized countries that no child or minor under a certain age should be permitted to work in any place; and that minors under a certain age should not be allowed to work near dangerous machinery or processes.

The report of the departmental committee on accidents in Great Britain referred to above, clearly showed that the accident risk of young persons is considerably higher than that of adults.* The report adds that the higher rate for young persons is accounted for by the greater inexperience of boys and girls and the greater recklessness of the boys.† Statistics of accidents of practically every country are to the same effect, viz., that children under fourteen years are entirely unable to take care of themselves, and if allowed to work become ready victims of the slightest mishap in the factory; and that even older children under twenty-one years have not the same stability of character, and sense of self-preservation which may be expected from adults.

Statistics as well as practical experience have also proven that *women* as a class are more prone to industrial accidents than adult males, and that women especially do not take good care of themselves when working near dangerous machinery. It is also claimed that women are more apt to be injured because of recurring periodical weaknesses and pathological conditions, during which the female workers have not the same strength or ability to take care of themselves in emergencies. Labor legislation in many countries has taken cognizance of this fact and has prohibited women from working in specially hazardous occupations, restricted their work with certain machinery, and limited the participation of female adult workers in general industry.

Ignorance is a prolific cause of industrial accidents. By ignorance is meant ignorance of the trade, ignorance of the dangers of the trade, or ignorance of the language and manners of the place where the industry is located. It is obvious that in every industrial establishment it is only the one who is trained, who is skillful, who understands the trade, who knows the machinery which he handles and the tools with which he works, who can avoid the dangers and mishaps liable to occur while at work. It is also evident that it is not only unwise, but criminal on the part of employers, to entrust any work requiring skill or any dangerous part of the industry to those who are ignorant or unskillful, or who do not understand the tools or machinery which they are obliged to use.

In a country where so many industries depend on foreign labor,

* Report of the Departmental Commissittee on Accidents, p. 19.
† Ibid., p. 20.

many accidents happen through failure of the non-English speaking workmen to understand directions or to read the warning signals. In some industries the lives of " wops " or " hunkies " are held very cheap and their deaths are not even recorded. Out of 525 fatal accidents in Allegheny County, 132 were due to ignorance; 22 of the men killed were " green "; they had been in some cases only a few hours on the job; all had been on the job less than six months. Most of them were foreigners; thirteen of them were only boys from fourteen to eighteen years old.*

Unprotected Transmission Belt Less than Six Feet from the Ground.

The British report has the following to say about unskilled labor in industry:

" The unskilled worker is more liable to accident than the trained mechanic. Thus, in ship building, we heard that accidents were more frequent amongst the laborers than amongst the skilled men. In the cotton trade we were told that in the boom years the introduction of new and unskilled workers increased the accident risk . . . (It was testified before us that) the greater use made of unskilled labor during the introduction of automatic machinery in the brass trades was the cause of the increased accident risk; also that an increase in risk in engineering, ship building, iron

* Eastman: Work Accidents and the Law, p. 87.

smelting, general building and joinery is due to the decay of the apprenticeship system."*

The increase of accidents among workers in the chemical industries in New York State was proved by the New York State Factory Commission to be due to the large number of foreigners employed, especially in the western part of the State. The larger number of accidents among foreigners is certainly due not only to their lack of skill and ignorance of the trades, but also to their inability to understand the orders of the foremen or the notices and signs which are supposed to teach them the dangers of their calling.

The next most important factor in the causation of accidents due to the personal factor may be found in the *physical unfitness* of many of the workers, who have not the physical strength for the tasks allotted to them. The manufacturer who would not think for a moment of introducing into his factory an untested machine, the employer who will take all reasonable precautions to see that his tools and appliances are properly constructed and tested, will not hesitate to take into his employ a large number of workers of whose physical capacity and health he has no conception whatever, and who may be afflicted with diseases that make them a source of danger to the whole factory.

A person suffering from epilepsy is not a proper person to carry a box full of dynamite, and yet very few employers inquire whether their workers who are entrusted with such important tasks are subject to this disease. A worker who suffers from disease of the eyes may become a victim to certain accidents which are easily avoided by a worker having good eyesight. A person suffering from hernia is not to be entrusted with carrying heavy weights; while a worker having cardiac disease is not the proper person for too hard labor. It is only natural that when workers are accepted without preliminary examination and without a test as to their fitness, that accidents will happen which would not have occurred had a preliminary test been made to find out the physically unfit.

The accidents due to physical unfitness cannot be computed and do not appear in accident statistics, but there is no doubt whatever that many industrial accidents are directly due to the inferior health and the physical unfitness of the workers.

Whenever the causes of accidents are discussed with representa-

* Great Britain: Report of the Departmental Committee on Accidents, p. 19.

N. Y. State Factory Commission.

Unguarded Vats in Wire Factory. The Vats, almost Level with the Floor, Contain Sulphuric Acid and Scalding Hot Water.

tives of employers, great stress is usually laid upon the large number of accidents due to the *carelessness* of the workers. The subject of carelessness, heedlessness, bravado, recklessness, is harped upon over and over again by employer, superintendent and foreman in every factory an inspector visits; so that one is sometimes compelled to conclude that in the opinion of employers and their representatives, from 90 to 95 per cent of industrial accidents are due to nothing else than the personal carelessness, negligence and recklessness of the workers themselves.

That the carelessness of workers is very often a cause of accidents in factories cannot be denied. There is, however, no doubt in the minds of those who have studied the subject and those who are familiar with industry, that the importance of this factor has been greatly exaggerated. As one of those who has made a thorough study of the subject aptly says:

" For heedless workers no defense is made; for the inattentive, we maintain that the human powers of attention are in every case further limited by the conditions under which work is done—long hours, heat, noise and intensity of speed. For the reckless ones we maintain that natural inclination is in every case encouraged and inevitably increased by an occupation involving constant risk; recklessness is part of the trade. . . . These two kinds of carelessness cannot be fairly called the faults of the workers."*

In the steel industries or in the building of skyscrapers, the value of the worker is in his very recklessness and in his taking of chances which to an outsider seem foolhardy. In many of these industries the worker takes his life in his hands every minute, and it would be absurd to blame these workers, where such recklessness is a necessary corollary of their calling.

German statistics attribute about 20 per cent of accidents to want of skill and carelessness on the part of the workers. But even among these accidents many cases may be deducted in which the seeming carelessness was necessitated by the conditions under which the industry was carried on.

On this point the opinion of the English Departmental Committee on Accidents (p. 18) is of interest. The Committee was of the opinion that

" There is a large class of accidents sometimes said to be due to carelessness; but often arising from the inevitable fallibility of the human machine. Such are cases of workers allowing their hands

* Eastman: Work Accidents and the Law, p. 95.

to be drawn into rollers when feeding a machine or putting their hands under an automatic press. Such accidents are to be expected, especially when workers are constantly engaged at one monotonous operation and the ultimate deadening of the faculty of attention leads to the brain failing to cooperate with the hand or foot. Against all such accidents it is necessary to take every possible precaution. It is impossible, as some employers put it, to make factories fool proof but on the other hand it is important to expect and guard against accidents due to momentary inattention and heedlessness, slips of hand or foot or other consequences of human fallibility."

A great many accidents that occur in industrial establishments are due to the removal by the workers of guards installed on certain machines. Such removal is often made for the purpose of increasing speed, and leads to the nullifying of the safety devices installed by employers. While in most cases the workers themselves are at fault, one must take into consideration the fact that many of these safeguards are either improperly constructed or are so attached as to make the work more difficult, and the worker less able to earn his reasonable wages, especially when paid by the piece. The employer or his representatives are often at fault in these cases through devising appliances which are easily removable, or in failing by proper supervision and frequent inspection to see that the safeguards are maintained in their proper places.

Another serious cause of accidents is the *cleaning of machinery*. In an analysis of accidents by the British Departmental Committee on Accidents in Factories, it was found that 527 accidents occurred in one year while cleaning cotton spinning machinery alone. It is peculiar that one-sixth of the cases occurred on Saturday. It is also noticeable that in the total of all accidents to females in cotton spinning from Monday to Friday not less than 227 occurred on Friday, and that a gradual increase took place from 120 to 124 from Monday to Friday.*

Mr. Bellhouse of the factory department testified as follows:

" In considering the accidents as a whole, one is struck first of all by the large proportion that occur under this head. I have had the returns for this year carefully analyzed and it is found that more than 30 per cent of the machinery accidents were to be attributed to this cause, and that they cover a large proportion of the accidents."†

* Report of the Departmental Committee on Accidents, p. 34.
† Ibid., p. 35.

Women, minors and children are more apt to be injured while cleaning machinery in motion than male adults.   There is no doubt that cleaning machinery while in motion is one of the most prolific causes of factory accidents.

There is one more factor in the personal equation of accident

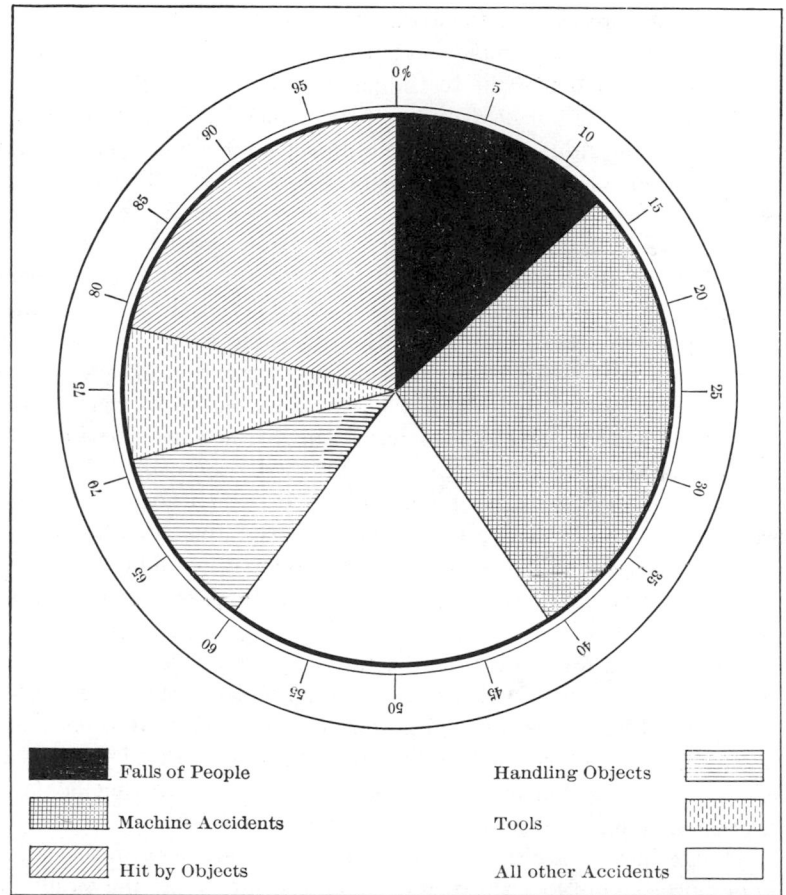

Comparative Chart of the Five Largest Groups of Accidents Reporte d during Eighteen Months (Industrial Commission of Wisconsin).

causation which is of importance, and which must be taken into consideration while discussing the causes of accidents.   This factor is the personal care which the employe takes of himself and his **clothes.**   Many accidents are caused by the hair of women being drawn into machinery, by loosely worn clothing which is apt to be caught in gears, etc.; and by the failure to wear proper glasses and goggles to protect the eyes in industries where they are liable to be injured by flying chips, etc. Many fatal and serious accidents are due to these causes, and no discussion of the prevention of industrial accidents would be of value which did not take into consideration the proper way for workers to care for their persons.

I shall here give a rapid review of the principles and methods of preventing accidents due to the personal factor.

In almost all civilized countries, the principle of prohibiting the participation in industry of children under a certain *age* has already been adopted as a cardinal principle of the law. The age limit differs in each country; in some states the age limit is as low as ten years, while in others it is as high as sixteen years. Prohibition is not only extended to general work in the factory but also to special industries, processes and appliances. Restriction is often graded according to the danger of the work. In some work, the age limit has been raised as high as twenty-one years; while in others the age limit ranges from fourteen to sixteen and eighteen years. The tendency of legislation is to a further raising of the age limit, although no ideal standard has yet been established. According to some, no person under the age of eighteen, and even under the age of twenty-one, should be at all employed in any industry; while others concede the reasonableness of the employment of minors between sixteen and twenty-one, but insist upon their restriction to certain kinds of work.

There is less unanimity on the subject of *women's* work. There are a few radicals who claim that there is no place for women in the factory. Advanced labor legislation has succeeded in prohibiting the night work of women, in prohibiting the work of women in certain specially hazardous industries and withdrawing a large number of dangerous processes from women workers.

That group of accidents due to *ignorance*, whether of the trade, dangerous elements of the trade, or of the language, may only be prevented by a system of education. Such a system of education must be thorough and comprehensive and should begin with childhood and be continued through all the stages of growth and development, and not be cut off even within the factory. Too little attention is paid at present in the public schools to industrial education. Very little attention is paid to vocational guidance and many persons enter trades for which they are entirely unfit.

Especially is there great need of apprentice schools and continuation schools, which have been established in some places to fit the graduate of the public school for his work in certain trades. It seems absurd to allow a child just out of school at the age of fourteen to select a trade for itself or to enter industrial establishments without preparation for the work it is to do. The period between fourteen and eighteen and perhaps twenty-one years should be spent partly within an industrial establishment and partly within an apprentice or continuation school. By such a method of industrial education it would be possible to train persons for industries to prepare them for the skillful trades, to make them realize the dangerous elements in each industry, and to prepare them for the handling of the tools, apparata and machinery of each trade.

Nor should education be discontinued on entering the factory. It should be continued within industrial establishments for young and old, in order to fit them for their work and to constantly improve their skill, and increase their knowledge and chances of promotion. This principle has been recognized by a great many employers in the establishment of the so-called " corporation schools," in which every endeavor is made by the employers to educate their employes, to increase their skill and enable them to avoid the dangers and risks incident to the trades.

Needless to add, no foreigner should be allowed to enter an establishment without receiving preliminary instruction in his own language in regard to the dangerous elements of the tools or machines he is to work with. In such cases the responsibility is placed squarely upon the employer and his representatives, and care must be taken by signs, by notices, by proper periods of instruction in the language understood by the worker to so train him that he understands all the elements of his work, and is able to take care of himself and to avoid those pitfalls and dangers which lurk on every step of the modern factory.

Accidents due to the *physical unfitness* of workers may be prevented by physical examinations and rigid medical tests of every applicant for work, a practice already established in the army, navy, railroad and public service work. A person entering the military service or the navy or becoming an employe of a railroad or other public service corporation must undergo a thorough medical examination. The federal government, the state, and the municipality will not accept a fireman, a policeman, a letter carrier or any other worker without a test of physical fitness. Why this system should not

be extended to all industries and should not be made a routine
practice in every industrial establishment in the country is difficult
to comprehend. We speak of efficiency and efficiency engineering,
and yet neglect one of the most vital points in efficiency, viz., the
physical fitness of the worker.

The practice should be extended even further. Not only should
there be a routine physical examination of every worker in every
establishment before employment, but there should be a periodical
examination, not less than once in three months, by competent
medical men, of every employe in the establishment, to determine
his physical condition and his fitness for his special work. The
medical supervisor in each factory is just as necessary a part of
industrial life as is the engineer or the superintendent of a factory.
Who can doubt that complete medical supervision of industrial life
will prevent a great many of the accidents of modern industry,
that it will remove a number of risks and dangers and alleviate
untold pain and misery? Medical supervision of industry is already
an established fact in certain dangerous trades in European countries. It is being at present introduced in many places in the United
States and is surely destined to extend until it will embrace our whole
industrial life.

There remain to be considered the industrial accidents due to
the so-called *carelessness* of workers themselves, to their neglect to
use the guards constructed for their safety, to the cleaning of
machinery during motion with or without the consent of the employers and to the lack of personal care. Some of these accidents,
such as those due to the removal of guards, may be prevented by
better construction of these guards, by introducing guards which
are not easily removable; while others, such as those occurring from
cleaning machinery in motion, may be prevented by rigid supervision and inspection, and centering the liability for accidents
upon the employers and their agents.

Many of the accidents due to this special factor could be prevented by rigid supervision and inspection, and by an attempt at
cooperation of employers with employes in the work of accident
prevention. The United States Steel Corporation and many owners
of large establishments have introduced systems of thorough supervision by the employers, by special inspectors, by safety committees, by the foremen and by the workers themselves. " Safety
first," at present the slogan of so many industrial establishments,
is sure to bring results and become a potent factor in accident

prevention. It is only by constant supervision that the number of accidents due to carelessness, to ignorance and to lack of personal care may be lessened. The education of workers and foremen within the establishment is a part of this method of supervision and is the basis of all accident prevention.

Improper dressing of the hair by women workers has been the cause of a great number of accidents, some of them of a very serious character. Girls with flowing hair bending under the machines have been scalped by having strands of their hair caught in gearing or shafts. In all occupations where such accidents may occur, the

Musée de Prevention des Accidents du
Travail et d'Hygiène Industrielle.   German Factory Uniforms.

Leather Leggins, Apron and Wooden Shoes worn by French Foundry Workers
for Protection against Metal Burns.

hair ought to be flatly dressed and tightly fitting caps should be worn. The sleeves of a coat or strings of aprons or part of a skirt are easily drawn into moving machinery, causing severe and sometimes fatal injuries to the worker. Special close fitting overalls should be worn by all workers having charge of machinery who pass near shafting and gearing.

Certain occupations require special dress: thus, boiler workers wear special overalls; also those who are working in foundries, in bleach chambers, in chemical works, etc. Wherever work is done near places where splashes of acid or burning liquids or sparks from burning matter may drop upon the clothes, the worker should wear a leather apron or other protective clothing. Workers in sand blasting chambers sometimes wear a closed helmet to protect them from the dust; such helmets are also worn in other specially dangerous occupations. Some of these helmets contain a supply of oxygen so as to allow the workers to breathe for a certain time without inhaling the air of the room in which they are working.

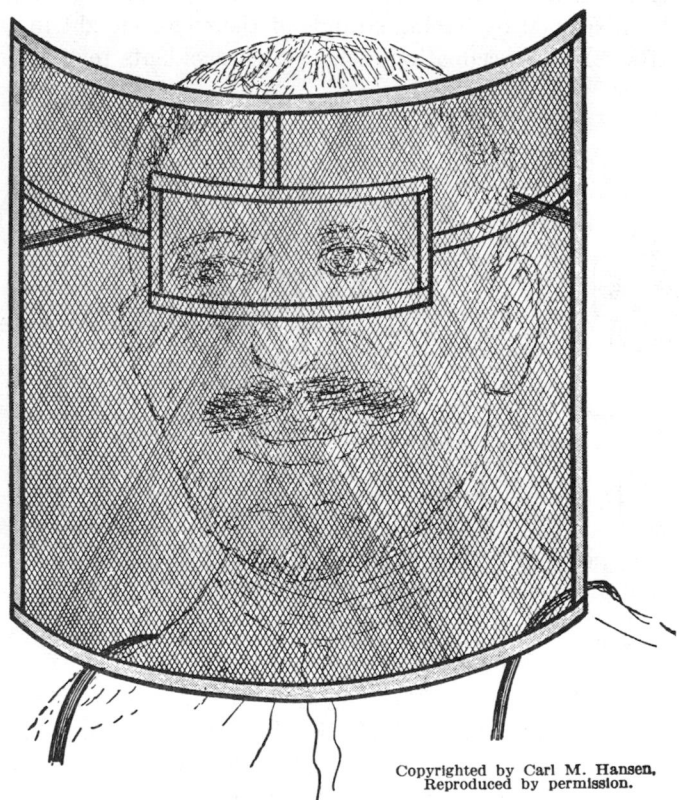

Face-Mask.

Sometimes it is important to have the feet protected. In foundries boots of a stout leather that will not burn easily and cover the foot well above the ankle should be worn. In certain chemical factories the shoes should be of a material that is not acted upon by the chemicals with which they may come in contact.

Workers on explosive materials must not have any metal tacks attached to their shoes. Workers in electrical workshops are usually protected by rubber gloves, etc.

Gloves are necessary in occupations where the workers must handle materials which are poisonous or liable to injure the skin of the hands. Complaint is made by employers and superintendents that the workers will not use the gloves and discard them as soon as they are out of sight of the foremen. In most of these cases the difficulty is due to the fact that the gloves are not furnished by the employer, but bought by the employes themselves; and as these gloves tear very easily, it is not to be wondered at that a worker will try to save gloves which cost him from fifty to seventy-five cents a pair, and need to be changed every week or oftener. In this respect it is important to add that all special clothing, caps, overalls, shoes, gloves, etc., needed for special work in factories, should be provided by the employers and should be maintained, laundered and kept in good condition by them; and the foremen or special inspectors should see to it that the clothing is in good condition and is being worn when necessary.

Eye Injuries and Eye Glasses. A large number of accidents resulting in injuries to the eyes of the workmen may be avoided by wearing protective glasses. The Wisconsin Industrial Commission cites a total of 366 eye accidents reported from September 1, 1911, to January 1, 1913.* In twenty-four cases the eyesight was lost completely; in seven cases eyesight was impaired permanently, and in the remaining 335 cases the injured persons were disabled for at least eight days or more. Approximately one out of every twenty-five accidents results in eye injury. In industries where a great deal of grinding and chipping is done, the percentage is much higher. The report continues as follows:

" The most significant thing about these accidents is the ease with which they may be prevented. Of the total reported in this state it is safe to say that 70 per cent might have been prevented by the use of eye glasses or goggles. The American Steel Foundry has adopted a type cf goggles for chippers shown in cut, and during the past three years has reduced eye injuries about 80 per cent."

There are many different kinds of protective eye goggles. In 1899 the Union of the German Trade Associations offered a prize for the best treatise on eye glasses and goggles for the protection

* Bulletin of Industrial Commission of Wisconsin, Vol. II, No. 7, March 28, 1913, p. 171.

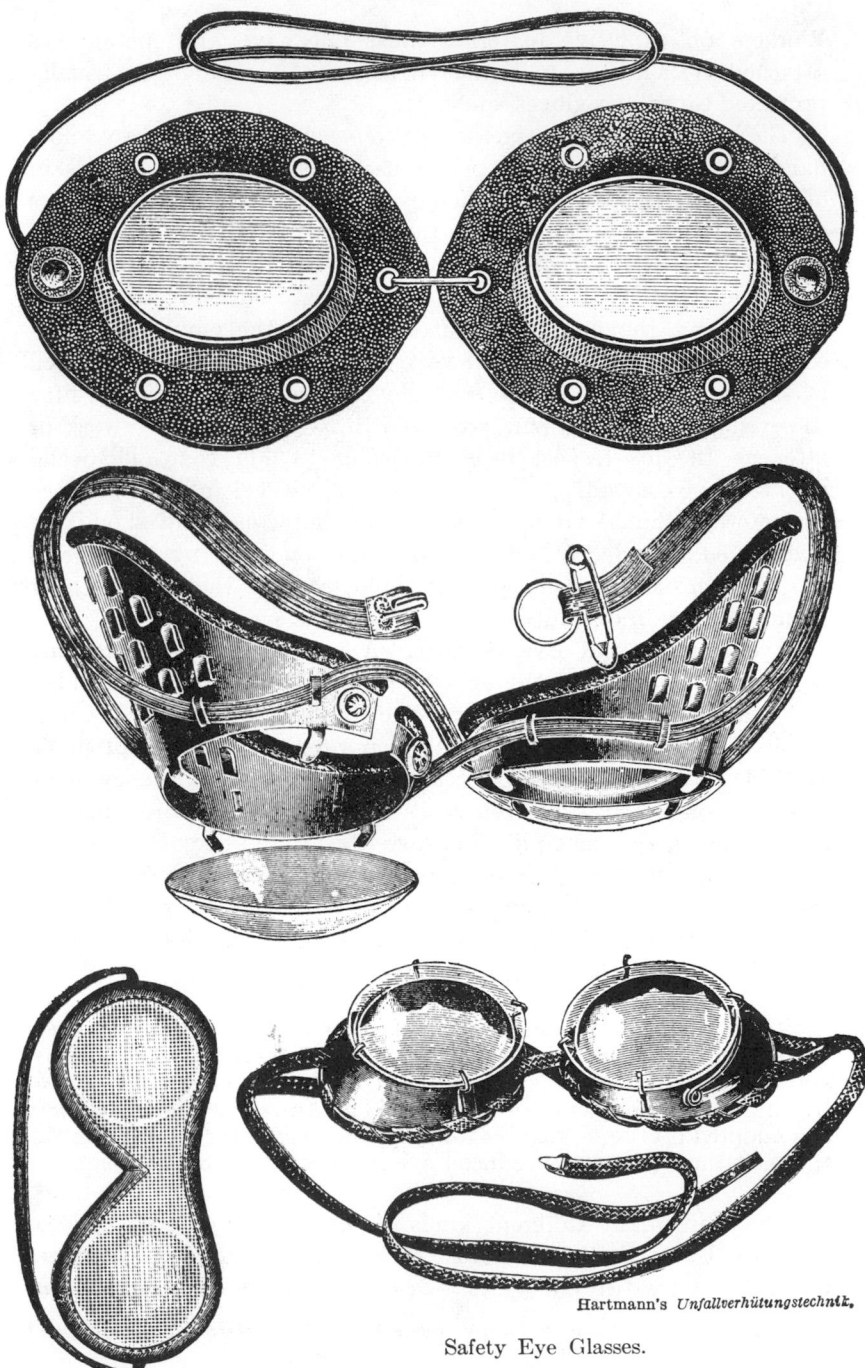

Hartmann's *Unfallverhütungstechnik.*

Safety Eye Glasses.

of workers, and Hartmann and Villaret won the prize for their treatise on the subject.

General Requirements for a Proper Protection of Eye Glasses for Workers

1. Glasses must be light and well framed.
2. They must be easily put on and comfortably fitted.

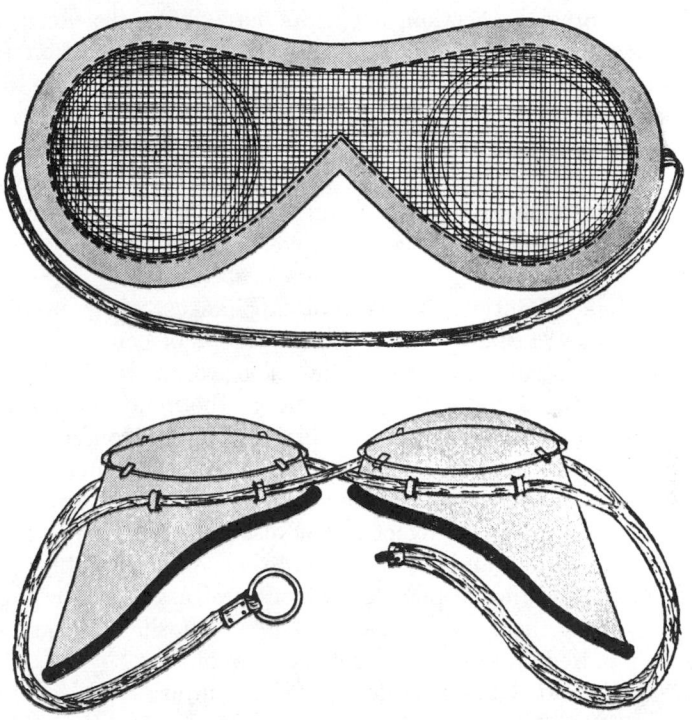

Copyrighted by Carl M. Hansen, Reproduced by permission.

Safety Goggles.

3. They should present as large a field of vision as possible.
4. The glasses must allow plenty of air circulation so that the eye should not be heated or dimmed by moisture.
5. The lenses in the goggles must be so fitted as to be easily exchanged.

In dusty or smoke-filled rooms eye goggles must be thickly screened and adhere to the face with some soft stuff such as leather, linen or cotton, and the lenses must be made so that they may be

easily cleaned. Workers in glaring light should wear glasses with
colored lenses to reduce the glare.

III

THE GENERAL CAUSES OF ACCIDENTS AND THEIR PREVENTION

In the previous section, accidents have been discussed which
are due to the personal factor in industry. In this section I shall
take up the general causes of industrial accidents, those mainly
due to defective materials, appliances, defects in the construction
of the factory, and certain economic and physical conditions, under
which industry is conducted. I shall also discuss the large group
of accidents which are due to falling objects, to falls from various
defective appliances, to fatigue, to overspeed and to long hours of
labor.

Defective Materials, Tools and Appliances. The number of
accidents due to this cause is large. It is, of course, impossible
to have all appliances, all tools, and all materials in a perfect condition at all times. But it is the fault of the management when a
tool or an appliance within a factory becomes a source of injury
to the workers. Handles made of iron or of other material, tools
of the same character, if cracked or partly broken, are liable to
cause great harm if the defect is not discovered in time. It is the
duty of the owner and his representatives to thoroughly test all
materials, tools and appliances which are used in his factory,
and to subject them to frequent tests, so that slight imperfections
may be repaired and more serious defects avoided.

Weights and Falling Objects. Many injuries are caused by
falling objects within the factory. In the statistics of industrial
accidents for the second quarter of 1913 of the New York State
Labor Department, 3890 cases belonged to this group.

The methods of preventing such accidents need not be gone
into in detail. When the factory is well constructed and properly
managed there is no reason for such accidents. Wherever temporary
repairs are made on the ceilings or upper parts of the walls or on
machinery, or other parts within the factory from which some
object is liable to fall, solid platforms should be constructed under
the places where the work is being done; or stout muslin covers
stretched underneath, and signs put out to warn the workers against

coming under places where they may be injured by falling objects; or the dangerous areas may be railed off.

Defective Floors, Stairs, Platforms, Ladders, Etc. In the same bulletin of the labor department it is stated that 1298 injuries occurred during the second quarter of 1913 as a result of falls from

Courtesy Aetna Life Insurance Co.

Triangular Ladder with Steel Points at Bottom.

Courtesy Aetna Life Insurance Co.

Safety Oiler's Ladder.

ladders, from scaffolds, from machinery, collapse of supports, falls from hoistways, stairs, falls by slipping, etc. In the British report for 1912 there were no less than 412 fatal cases and 18,728 non-fatal accidents due to persons falling. In the German statistics the accidents resulting from falls from ladders, stairs, etc., amounted to 1.43 per thousand.

Most of these accidents are due to defective or slippery floors, to stairs which are either not strong enough or have missing steps or rails, slippery or broken treads, insecure platforms, unrailed platforms, balconies, etc. A number are also caused by defective ladders or by ladders falling down because of improper support and insecure position. The Wisconsin Commission gives in its Bulletin No. 4, a very detailed report on the character of these accidents.* A total of 393 accidents due to slipping, stumbling, slipping on walks

Courtesy Aetna Life Insurance Co.

Dangerous Open Stairway on Outside of Building.

or passageways, etc., are given for a period of eighteen months from September 1, 1911, to March 1, 1913. For this period the report shows that 13.2 per cent of all accidents (of which there were 10,517) or *nearly one-half as many as occurred on all machines* were caused by the falls of workmen. Most of these accidents were of a very serious nature: 48 resulted in death, 425 in fractured bones, 30 in serious internal injuries. The actual loss in wages suffered by the injured amounted to almost $70,000.

* Bulletin of Industrial Commission of Wisconsin, Vol. II, No. 10, June 20, 1913.

The report continues:

" In many cases these accidents might have been prevented by better shop lighting and proper application of safety appliances. Better instruction of men and great care on the part of the workmen would have prevented most of the accidents."

Floors should always be in good condition. Floors must not be broken or chipped. Stone, concrete or cement floors must not have holes in them. Linoleum or other covering must be kept in good condition so as not to trip the worker through some imperfection. Stairs must be solidly built and provided with proper steps at regular intervals; such steps should be well constructed and their treads should not be slippery. In factories where there

Courtesy Aetna Life Insurance Co.

Stairway Equipped with Safety Tread.

is a great deal of moisture or where the materials worked with are such that they may cause moisture, the treads must be made of the type of so-called " safety-treads," which will hold the shoe and prevent it from slipping. All stairways should be provided with rails on both sides. If stairs are wide, a middle rail should be furnished. Platforms must always be guarded by rails or balconies and all openings, manholes in the floor, or any part of a factory should be properly guarded. All rails on stairways should be securely fitted and kept smooth and free from nails or splinters. Rubber mats or mats of other non-slippery substance should be nailed on the steps.

Falls from ladders cause many accidents of a serious nature, some of them fatal. Ladders are often not strong enough for the weight they have to support. Rungs are often missing or are weak and easily broken off. The Wisconsin report already mentioned shows that 141 accidents were due to falls from ladders, of which 68 were due to the ladders breaking. Proper inspection must be made of all ladders to assure the worker that these appliances are in good condition, and tests should be made to see whether they are able to stand the strain upon them.

Ladders should be equipped at the top with safety hooks to prevent them from slipping sideways. It is best not to use portable ladders at all, but to construct permanent stairways where frequent access must be had to elevated points. Safety hooks on the top are a means of preventing the ladders from slipping, but the legs should also be secured so that the step-ladder cannot spread, and should be provided with steel points or other means to prevent them from slipping.

Light and Ventilation. Many accidents are due to insufficient or improper lighting. According to John Calder,* " Insufficient lighting is the cause of numerous accidents, particularly serious and fatal falls." Mr. Calder has observed that the maximum of accidents occurs toward the close and the beginning of each year; that is, during November, December and January,—the months of minimum daylight. He says, " the influence of the duration and intensity of natural light in working hours in fatal and serious accidents is particularly noticeable in bridge building and ship building, engineering, steel and iron works, and other operations that have to be carried on within a large space, often entirely in the open air and not easily illuminated artificially to the exclusion of deep shadows." In the report of the New York State Factory Commission,† it was stated that in 24.5 per cent of all shops investigated light was defective. In the printing industry 48.4 per cent of the shops were poorly lighted; in the candy factories 49.2 per cent; and in laundries 36.7 per cent. The report on chemical trades draws attention to the large number (64.4 per cent) of the factories inspected where lighting was found inadequate. The report continues:

" In going through chemical establishments one often passes through dimly lighted passages where numbers of workers are engaged either in shoveling dangerous mixtures into wheel barrows, or packing toxic products into barrels, or working around vats, caldrons and tanks filled with dangerous liquids among clouds of

* Journal of American Society of Mechanical Engineers, Vol. XXXIII, Part I, p. 141.
† New York State Factory Investigating Commission, 1913, Vol. II, p. 428.

steam or chemical fumes. Any carelessness on the part of these workers resulting in a spurt of these liquids might mean a permanent injury. In one of the electrolytic plants at Niagara Falls a worker was observed in a dark corner passing under an iron trough clumsily supported on wooden blocks and filled with hot liquid caustic acid, every drop of which, coming in contact with the body, would produce a painful and permanent injury. The only light was an incandescent bulb held by the workers to illuminate the running of the caustic in the trough and the filling up of the iron drums with the liquid."*

The danger of insufficient light in a factory crowded with machinery in motion is obvious.

Lack of ventilation and bad air within the shop and factory often cause nausea, vertigo and insufficient oxygenation of the blood, and hence directly or indirectly may cause accidents.

Overcrowding, etc. There is no condition so conducive to the occurrence of accidents as lack of space and overcrowding in a factory of machinery, benches, boxes, and materials. Especially is overcrowding dangerous near moving machinery, shafts, gearing, etc., where the clothing or parts of the body of persons passing may be drawn in. Too narrow aisles between machinery in textile factories have been a frequent cause of accidents.

The remedy for this condition is simple and obvious. Roomier factories and the leaving of plenty of space around dangerous machinery pay in the reduction of accidents and in better general efficiency.

Accidents Due to Monotony of Work, to Fatigue, to Speeding and Prolonged Hours of Labor. A large number of accidents are known to be due to fatigue caused by overwork, by prolonged hours of labor, and by other conditions which weaken the body and dull the brain of the worker.

Monotony and overspeeding of machinery, long hours of labor, work during the night, work without sufficient rest, work in industries where the twelve-hour shift is employed, work in continuous industries which employ their workers during seven days of the week, —all these cause over-fatigue of the body, muscles and nerves of the workers, leading directly or indirectly to a great number of industrial accidents in our factories and workshops. Long hours are especially dangerous in those industries where women work. Testimony was presented by the investigators in canneries that some women were working excessive hours, and several cases were found where women were working as long as 115 to 117½ hours

* New York State Factory Investigating Commission, 1913, Vol. II, p. 465.

per week.* A photographic copy of a pay card of one of the women workers is reproduced on next page.

The report of the Pittsburgh Survey has shown that many accidents are due to the long hours or excessive speed with which the great steel industry is conducted. The seven-day week, the twelve-hour day, the twenty-four successive hours on duty of the men in the Pittsburgh Steel Mills have been found to be responsible for the enormous loss of life and limb within those mills. In the ceaseless drive and pressure of the factory something must give way. More often than not it is the worker. The long factory day results in fatigue for the worker, and fatigue brings death and injury in its train. The relationship between fatigue and accidents has been definitely established by investigations made in France, Germany, Italy and the United States. Briefly summarized, the results of all investigations show that the number of accidents increases with the number of hours worked, and the number of casualties occurring during the last hour of the forenoon and the last hour of the afternoon is almost double the number of those occurring during the first two hours of the day.

In the report of the Bureau of Labor on the Condition of Women and Child Wage-earners in the United States, an account is given of accidents occurring in metal manufacture, in cotton mills, and in general manufacture, in the states of Indiana and Wisconsin. According to a table of accidents given in the report, the hours between three and four in the afternoon show the heaviest accident rate; also the hours between ten and eleven and eleven and twelve. Of course, the accident rate is a complex product depending on a variety of factors, and deductions can not always be made from the figures. The Departmental Committee on Accidents of Great Britain also collected some figures, which indicate " that the most dangerous hours are from ten to eleven A.M. and three to four P.M.''; while another table seems to indicate that the most dangerous hour for women in both morning and afternoon is an hour later than the most dangerous hour for men.

As to speeding, the conclusion of the British Departmental Committee on Accidents was that:

" On the whole we are of the opinion that there is increased speed and pressure in a large number of industries, and that is probably operating to produce an appreciable increase in accident risk.''

* Second Report of the New York State Factory Commission, Vol. II, p. 820.

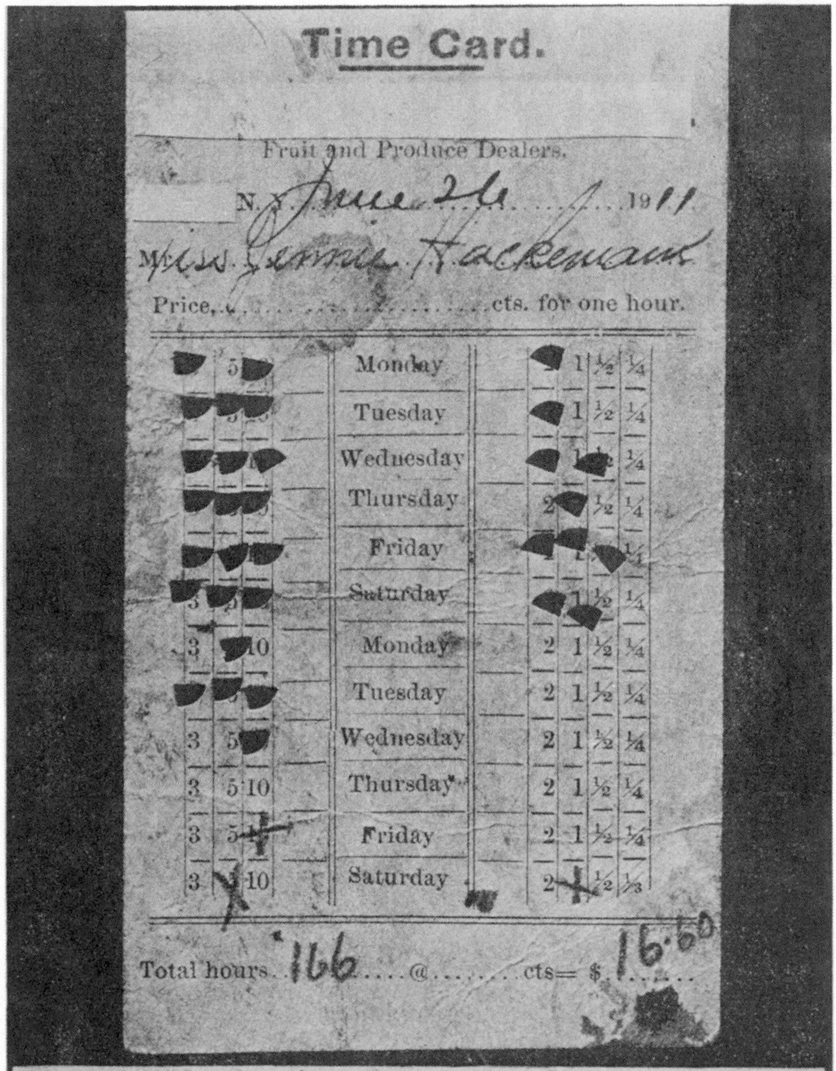

Time card showing hours worked for two weeks by a woman at a fruit cannery. The first week the hours are:

Monday-----15 hrs.   Thursday-----19 hrs.
Tuesday----20 "   Friday-------21-1/2"
Wednesday--21 "   Saturday-----21   "

Total for week 117 1/2 hours.
She got for this work 10 cents per hour.

The United States Government report, referred to previously, states that any increase of speed of operation, unless accompanied by some counteracting safeguard, may be expected to show a higher accident rate. That such increase of speed during part or all of the work period is the general practice, is the common opinion. The report continues:

" There will be some tendency to minimize the factor of fatigue in the above process, because it is not a matter of acute sensation. We can recognize and measure with some accuracy the gradual increase of the fatigued condition before sensation begins to advise us of its presence. It is a steadily progressive process. The margin of safety in modern industry is small. It is measured too frequently by fractions of an inch. Reduce the alertness and the exactness with which the body responds to the necessities of its labor, and by just so much have you increased the liability that the hand will be misplaced that fraction, which means mutilation."*

It is quite evident that if factory accidents are to be decreased, one of the first steps should be the reduction of working hours. Brief pauses during the middle of the forenoon and the middle of the afternoon would probably have some effect in reducing the number of accidents. Until the hours of labor in industrial establishments where the strain of industry is great are materially reduced, we cannot hope for any considerable reduction of accidents in industry.

In establishments where it is well known among the men that speed comes first and safety next, it is to be expected that the workers will take risks. When the accidents do occur their victims will be called foolhardy by the very men who would have praised their recklessness had the accidents not resulted.

" There can be no doubt that the unrelaxing tension and speed in the American steel mill makes for danger. To go slow would be to go backward in industry, and that is more than can be expected of America; but by shortening the hours of work the dangers of speed can be lessened. The minds and bodies of the men can be kept up to the pace of the mill. Greater intensity of work necessitates longer periods of relaxation. If the strain of the work cannot be lessened, duration must be. No steel company can maintain that it has done everything to prevent accidents until it has reduced the work hours of men in such responsible positions." †

* Report on Condition of Women and Child Wage-earners in the United States, Vol. XI, p. 101.
† Crystal Eastman: Work Accidents and the Law, p. 73, 74.

Efficiency engineers and practical manufacturers already know that a reasonable shortening of the daily hours of labor does not lead necessarily to a lessening of the output; but, on the contrary, often increases it. The human body, unlike the inanimate machine, has inherent power of self-recuperation, and the practice of working the body for all it is worth and then discarding it on the scrap heap, is wasteful and criminal.

Hours of labor should be adjusted to the physical fitness of the worker, to his bodily strength, to the industry in which he is employed, to the kind of work which he performs, and to the character of operations with which he is entrusted. Some of the larger states prohibit night work for women, and limit the weekly hours of work to fifty-four, and in some places to fifty hours. The eight-hour normal workday has been established in many industries, has been adopted by many enlightened employers, and is destined to become the general normal day's work. The three-shift system of eight hours each instead of the two shifts of twelve hours is being gradually introduced in the steel and other continuous industries, and will probably soon become a general practice in the United States.

It is to be regretted that we have not introduced in the United States the custom prevalent abroad of allowing the workers a quarter-hour pause during the forenoon and afternoon. I have often watched the workers in the large factories in France, Belgium and Germany, and have seen how they enjoyed the quarter-hour pauses at 10 A.M. and at 4 P.M., and how much more alert they seemed for work afterwards, and it seems to me it is a mistaken policy of the American manufacturers not to follow suit and introduce this procedure, which surely leads to greater efficiency and to the decrease of accidents.

As to the prevention of accidents due to monotony and certain monotonous processes, experiments have already been made by some manufacturers in changing the workers from one process to another; and much may be done by scientifically arranging the work so as to lessen the monotony and give the worker an interest that will keep his mind alert and thus prevent some of the accidents due to this cause.

There is one other consideration which as yet has received very little attention in this country except in one process, but which is destined to receive greater attention in the future. This is the adjustment of the hours of work to the danger of the trade, and the lessening of the hours of labor in specially dangerous trades. The only adjustment so far which has been made by legislation in this respect, is the considerable shortening of hours in caisson work, where the men labor in air with increased pressure. Doubtless, after proper study, a corresponding decrease will be made in other dangerous trades, so as to adjust and proportionate the hours of labor to the kind of work and the amount of danger in the processes and materials.

IV

THE PREVENTION OF ACCIDENTS DUE TO TRANSPORTATION WITHIN THE FACTORY

Much transportation is necessary within factories. Consignments of raw materials are constantly arriving which must be conveyed to the different parts of the establishment, and transported from one place to another, until finally the finished product is sent out from the factory. There are a great many opportunities for accidental injuries to workmen participating in the process of transportation. Indeed, a large proportion of accidents within the factory are due to this cause.

The methods of transportation within the factory differ with the character of the factory and the kind of materials and mechanical appliances used. A rough classification of all the methods of transportation within the factory would include the following groups: (a) hand carrying and lifting without tools; (b) use of tools; (c) hand-trucks, carts, wagons, etc.; (d) ropes, chains, and winches; (e) mechanical cranes for horizontal transportation, and (f) vertical lifts, hoistways and elevators.

Transportation accidents may be prevented by (1) providing mechanical appliances wherever possible so as to take off the burden of transportation from the workers themselves; (2) prohibiting minors, women, and adults who are not physically fit, from participating in factory transportation; and (3) an intelligent supervision of the process of transportation so as to give no worker too heavy a task.

A number of tools and appliances are used to facilitate the work of transportation. Certain materials which workers are unable to handle are carried on poles or by means of tongs or other appliances which may sometimes slip or get out of order and thus injure the worker. In carrying carboys filled with acids great care should be taken to prevent breaking of the carboys and the consequent possibility of injuring the workers with splashes of the acid, etc.

Hartmann's *Unfallverhütungstechnik*

Self-Acting Safety Catch.

Special means of carrying these carboys have been devised from time to time, and one of them is shown in the illustration on page 170.

Boxes, carts, barrels, rail wagons, etc., are often used in transportation. Where cars are operated on rails, brakes should be provided. When cars are large it is necessary to prevent persons crossing the rails while the cars are in motion. In such cases some means are needed for warning persons from coming into the path of the car.

Materials and objects are transported from one place to another by mechanical means, either by overhead steel cranes or mechanical conveyors. Conveyors are at present used in many factories for

Hartmann's *Unfallverhutungstechnik.*

Methods of Lifting Barrels and Sacks.   Overload Detector.

mechanical and automatic shifting of materials. They are the cause of a great many accidents. It is important that conveyors should not move at too great a speed, that they should be constructed so as not to injure the hands of the workers and should also be provided with handy stopping devices. Conveyors located near the floor should be well guarded and overcrowding of the factory should be avoided, as it may compel the workers to step on the conveyors and slip or fall.

Cranes are used in transporting and handling large objects and are very dangerous appliances when improperly constructed and operated without precaution and proper supervision. The installation of cranes must be made under the supervision of competent engineers and they should be tested before installation and at frequent intervals while in use. Cranes should be operated by skilled persons and provided with warning gongs and signals.

A simple and popular method of lifting certain objects within the factory is by the use of ropes, cables, or chains, which are put on pulleys and worked by winches operated by steam, compressed

Hartmann's *Unfallverhutungstechnik*. Friedrich Krupp, A. G., Essen

Workers in Asbestos Clothing Carrying Crucible of Molten Metal.

air or electricity. The important parts in such transporting appliances are (1) the catching device or that part which first gets hold of the objects to be lifted and carried, (2) the ropes, cables or chains by which the objects are lifted, and (3) the mechanical appliances by which the rope is lifted up and made to carry the object to the point desired.

There are a number of devices for the proper catching of objects and there are various forms of hooks, tongs, etc., so devised as not to slip. Some of these are shown in the illustrations on page 168. Where objects are sharp or angular it is best to wrap them up

with some rags, or blankets, or to insert pieces of wood, etc., in
different places so as to get a better hold upon the object. The
ropes and cables must be tested and should be able to carry the
necessary weights. They should also be so attached as to carry
the weight in its center of gravity. It is important in lifting an

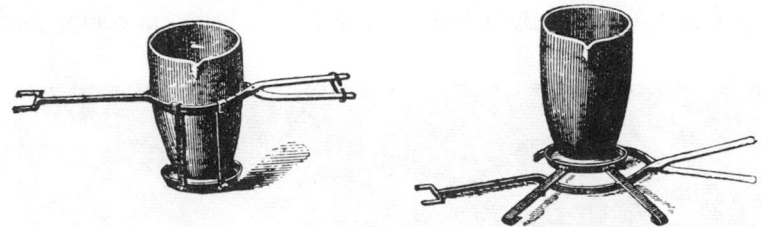

Museum of Safety, Charlottenburg, Berlin.

Tongs for Safe Carrying of Crucibles.

object to have someone to guide it so that it does not catch on
projections. All chains should be annealed at least once every six
months. Attention must also be given to the proper railing of
the floor openings through which the object is carried, so as to

Hartmann's *Unfallverhütunstechnik.*

Safety Wheel Barrows for Carrying Acids.

prevent persons from falling through them. Warning must also
be given to all persons standing near the place where the object
is descending. It is also important to fix the maximum load
which may be carried by the lifting apparatus and provide it with
a good brake arrangement.

The winches, tackle and mechanical apparatus for the winding of the ropes and chains must be properly constructed, all the gears guarded, and should be operated by a careful person. In a large industrial establishment of the Bayer Chemical Works I saw iron filings lifted by huge magnets carrying several tons at each ascension.

Hoistways and Elevators. Hoistways and elevators are the best methods of transporting weights and objects as well as persons in a vertical direction from one floor to another, but are a frequent cause of accidents in factories.

In an article on the " peril of vertical travel," Mr. Frazee says:

" The number of persons injured and killed throughout the United States by preventable elevator accidents is appalling, and

Museum of Safety, Charlottenburg, Berlin.

A Safe Method of Loading Barrels.

is increasing constantly, owing to the never-ceasing erection of buildings within which countless elevators are installed, adding greatly to those already in use throughout the United States. It was estimated in 1912 that there were in that year between 7000 and 8000 fatal accidents on elevators, and about 10,000 persons injured. From 1908 to 1912 in New York City alone, upwards of 400 persons were killed on passenger and freight elevators, and a greater number were injured."*

There is not much difference between the general construction of an elevator and a hoistway, except that the hoistway is, as a rule, not so well protected as an elevator and is used almost exclusively

* Safety Engineering for November, 1913.

for carrying freight, while an elevator is used for carrying persons as well as freight.

The following are the most important parts of elevators: (a) the shaft, (b) the cage, (c) the cables, ropes, and chains, (d) the motive

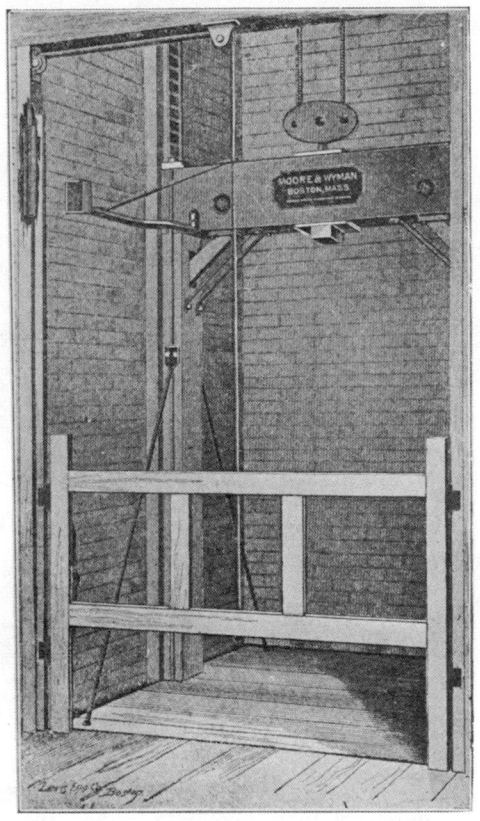

Courtesy Aetna Life Insurance Co.

Hatchway Safeguarded with Half Automatic Gate.

power, (e) the gearing, machinery, etc., (f) the safety devices, and (g) the operator.

Some elevators have no permanent shaft or airwell within the building, but are provided with adjustable trap doors which close when the elevator is out of the way, and automatically open as soon as the elevator reaches them.

The shaftwell is the most dangerous part of the elevator. It is open from the bottom to the top and is dangerous as a means of spreading fire and because of the possibility of persons falling into it. The shaftway should be surrounded entirely with a fireproof enclosure either of wire glass on metal lath and metal frame or of solid plaster not less than two inches thick, or of brick, concrete or tile of sufficient thickness to give rigidity. The enclosure must extend to the top and include the pent house where the sheaves or machinery above the shaftway are located. All projections in

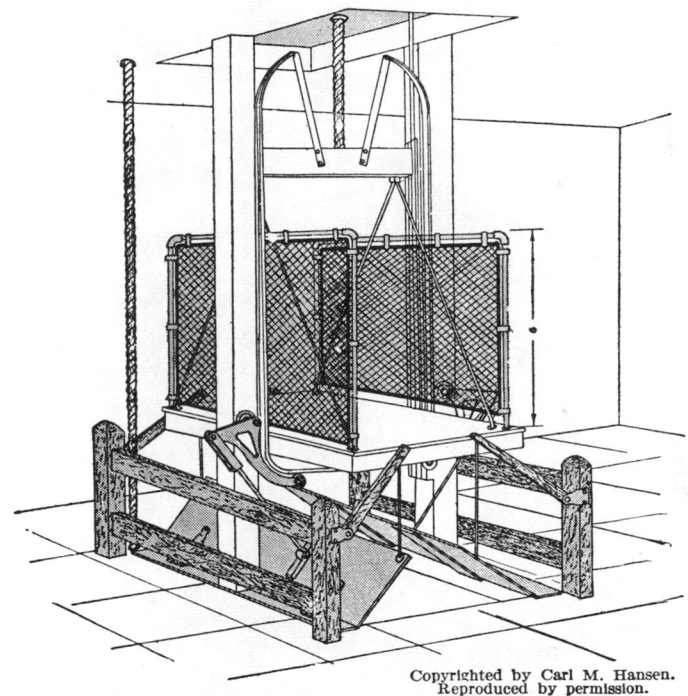

Copyrighted by Carl M. Hansen.
Reproduced by permission.

Elevator with Hatch Covers.

elevator shafts, such as floors, beams and sills, unless guarded against by the car enclosures, must be provided with smooth buffered guards fitted directly under them so as to push any such projection back of the car.

The doors from the floors to the shaft are the most important part of the elevator enclosure. These doors must fill the entire opening to the shaft and should be constructed of solid metal, wire glass, or grill work with openings not less than $1\frac{3}{4}$ inches square and $1\frac{3}{4}$ inches long by 1 inch wide. The doors must have sufficient strength to withstand a level pressure in the center of not less than 250 pounds. The use of semi-automatic gates, especially on freight elevators, is preferable. These gates can only be opened by the operator of the car, but close automatically when the car leaves the floor. Many of the new elevators are so constructed that

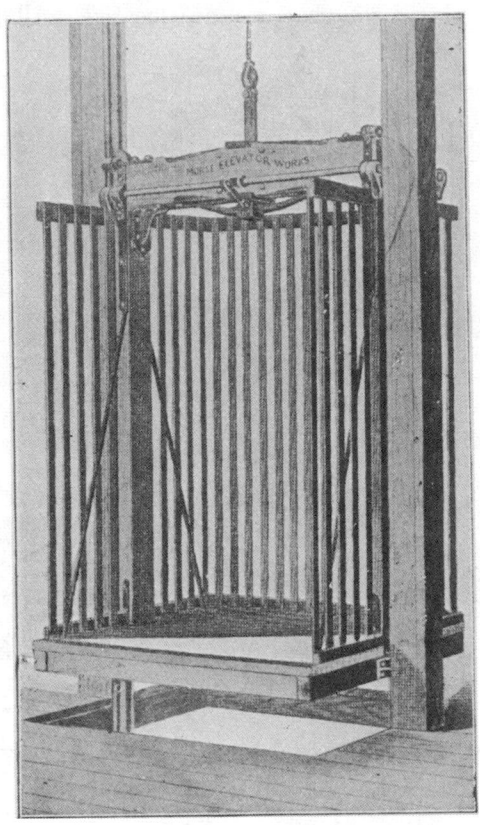

Courtesy Aetna Life Insurance Co.

Side Post Freight Platform Enclosed.

they cannot move either up or down until the door is locked. This is accomplished by mechanical devices or by electrical contact circuits. There are a number of mechanical devices for automatically locking doors; most of them are very good and tend to prevent numerous accidents.

The next important part of the elevator is the cage in which the freight or persons are being carried. The cage or car should be made entirely of metal or of grill work; and the platform of the car must, of course, have a certain factor of safety above and beyond its normal load. Cars should be entirely enclosed, as open platforms are dangerous even when railed off. The cars or cages should be provided with artificial light and have a light at the bottom of the cage near the door, so as to prevent persons from slipping or falling when the platform is not flush with the floor. Each car should also be provided with inside doors or gates which should always be closed while the car is in operation. The car or cage should be

Courtesy Aetna Life Insurance Co.

Full-Automatic Gate, Open-at-will Type.

roofed over and the roof made of solid material to prevent objects from falling into the car. Proper signals, gongs, etc., should be provided so that the operator of the car may communicate with persons outside of the elevator shaft when necessary.

The cables must never be single and must be strong enough to bear a much heavier load than usually necessary. Cables should be tested before installation and must be frequently inspected during operation. Most municipalities compel elevators to be provided with pit and overhead clearances so that there is a pit not less than two feet in depth below the lowest landing and an overhead clearance of not less than two feet above the highest landing. When elevators have a high speed, these pits and overhead clearances should be greater. Spring, rubber or oil buffers resting on substantial foundation in the pit should also be provided, and the car so constructed as to withstand the impact of the buffers. The cars should be provided with counterweights which are usually located in the elevator shaftway and should be properly guarded top and bottom.

The last, but not the least factor in elevator safety is the opera-

Semi-Automatic Gate for Elevator.

Gate raised by hand at landing and held open by a pawl, which an arm on the car engages with a weight lock connected with the gate by means of a rope. As the elevator moves away from the landing, the pawl is released and the gate drops back into position by its own weight.

tor. Many states prohibit persons under twenty-one years of age from operating elevators and hoistways. Elevator operators should be properly instructed and their knowledge and skill tested before being allowed to operate any elevator independently. They must know the rules as well as the technique of the operation of the machinery, and must always be careful to avoid accidents and possible loss of life. The following rules of the Wisconsin Commission give an idea of the requirements imposed upon elevator operators:

"Always keep in mind that a large number of serious accidents are caused by carelessness. In stopping a steam elevator, be careful to center the hand rope and if the elevator creeps after it is stopped, report at once to the foreman. The brake requires adjusting.

"Never allow anyone to scuffle or fool on your elevator. It is always dangerous.

"Never start an elevator until the door or gate at the landing is closed, and do not open the door at the landing until you have brought the elevator to a full stop. If an elevator, when it is stopped, does not hold the load properly, report at once to the foreman. The brake needs adjusting.

"All loose or tight ropes or any detected weakness or defect in the elevator should be at once reported to the engineer.

"The elevator should not be loaded more than its safe loading capacity.

"The speed of the elevator should be always adjusted and never be too great.

"The elevator should be started and stopped gradually. A sudden start or stop may throw the cables off the sheaves and subject the whole machinery to severe stress and serious accident."

Elevators and hoistways should be provided with safety devices, such as clutches, brakes, speed governors, etc., intended to prevent the falling of the car in case certain parts of the cables break and to prevent other accidents which may happen in the operation of the cars. The accompanying illustrations show some of the safety devices which are used in modern elevator construction. The constructors of elevators as well as insurance companies maintain at present a very high class of inspectorial service to guard against accidents by frequent inspection and testing. It is therefore unnecessary to go further into the technical details of elevator inspection.

V

THE PREVENTION OF ACCIDENTS DUE TO MOTIVE POWER AND TRANSMISSION APPARATUS

Machinery and Accidents. The modern factory system is chiefly characterized by machine production and the use of motive power. The motive power used in modern factories has changed. At first steam power was substituted for water power; now electricity takes the place of steam.

The rôle of mechanical production in the causation of industrial accidents is very great. While a number of accidents are due to other causes, there is no doubt that the increase of industrial accidents is largely due to the increasing use of machinery. According to the report of the British Departmental Committee on Accidents:

Courtesy Norton Co., Worcester, Mass.

Guard in Front of Fly Wheel.

"About 28 per cent of the total number of accidents are caused by machinery, and of the accidents which are reported by certifying surgeons, 80 per cent are caused by power driven machinery. The use of electric motors and gas engines has made it more easy to obtain power; new inventions have enabled machinery to perform operations, and even for simple operations automatic machines are constantly taking the place of hand work. The extent to which machinery is used is very much greater than it was. In steel mills there is more automatic machinery; in ship building, more automatic machines are used, etc. We have come to the conclusion, therefore, that the increased use of machinery considered as an isolated means is one of the causes operating to increase the accident risk."

According to German statistics, for every thousand insured persons in factories using power-driven machinery 33 are injured; while there are 16 per thousand injured in all industries.*

Courtesy Shredded Wheat Co.

Wire Mesh and Sheet Iron Guards Protecting Chain Drive on Ceiling Driving Wheat Elevator.

In Switzerland, the amount of horse-power increased from 44.1 for every hundred workers in 1882 to 119.1 per hundred workers in 1901. At the same time accidents increased from 32.01 per thousand workers in 1888 to 48.35 per thousand in 1901 and 1902, and to 62.5 per thousand in 1910.*

American statistics show the same proportionate increase of accidents accompanying the increased use of machinery. Of the total 18,806 accidents occurring in the factories in New York State in the second quarter of 1913, there were no less than 6317 accidents due to mechanical power, excluding those accidents due to electricity.

* Barten: Notwendigkeit, Erfolge und Ziele der technischen Unfallverhütung, p. 33.

Courtesy Shredded Wheat Co.

Double Guard: 1. Metal guard protecting Reynolds chain drive from motor
to countershaft. 2. Wire guard $\frac{3}{16}$-inch wire, 1-inch mesh, iron
frame, covering bevel gears and clutch.

The causes of accidental injuries to workers due to machinery may be divided into three groups: prime movers, transmission apparatus and machinery proper. This is a convenient method of classification and will be followed in the following sections.*

Reference has already been made to the fact that many accidents occurring in factories are preventable, provided certain methods of safeguarding are adopted. This is especially true of accidents due to machinery. In fact, there is no reason why such accidents

Courtesy Shredded Wheat Co.

Sheet Metal and Cast Iron Guards Covering Gear Chain and Worm Drives on Triscuit Oven.

should not be more easily prevented than others occurring in factories, for the ingenuity and skill that create intricate machines should also be capable of devising means of rendering them harmless to the workers.

The general principles of accident prevention may be briefly stated here before giving the special methods of safeguarding machinery. The present tendency to substitute electric power for steam is a great step toward the prevention of accidents, because

* In this and in the following sections no detailed mechanical appliances will be discussed except to illustrate the general principles and the special methods of accident prevention. I have also decided to exclude the discussion of accidents due to steam boilers and to electricity, as these are within the province of special inspectors, and discussion of the methods of prevention would require too many technical explanations and details.

of the abolition of large motors, engines, flywheels, etc., and because of the possibility of producing the electric current outside of the factory, thus avoiding the many accidents caused in the primary production of power, in the boiler houses, etc. Another advantage of electric power driven machinery is the possibility of installing

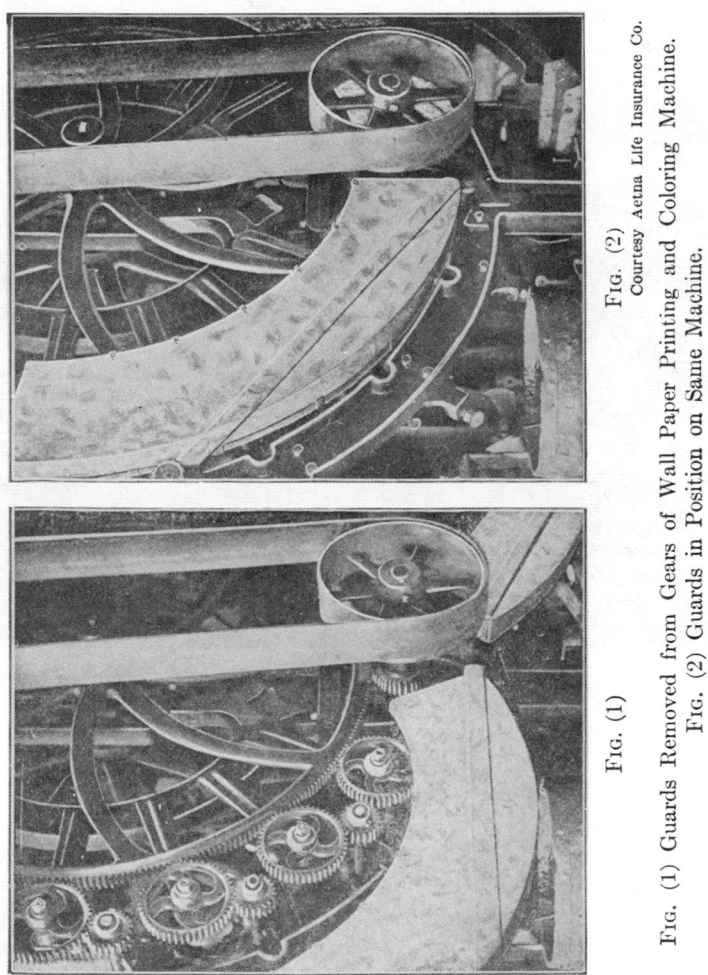

FIG. (2)

Courtesy Aetna Life Insurance Co.

FIG. (1)

FIG. (1) Guards Removed from Gears of Wall Paper Printing and Coloring Machine.
FIG. (2) Guards in Position on Same Machine.

small motors in each part of the factory and practically for every machine; putting the stopping and starting of each machine within reach of the worker and thus preventing a great many accidents

Guard on Bleach House Machine.

which are due to the difficulty of immediately stopping machinery in case of accident.

A most important method of preventing accidents due to machinery is the safeguarding of each machine by its maker—a method already adopted by the great trade associations of Germany, and which ought to be adopted in all states. There is no reason why each machine should not be provided with proper safeguards in the establishment where it is manufactured.

A method of accident prevention which is general to all industrial establishments is provision for the testing, supervision and inspection of the machinery and its parts before installation, as well as a periodical examination during maintenance. All factories where methods of efficiency have been adopted are at present making frequent inspections of the machinery, in order to discover defects and to repair them before they cause serious accidents.

The next basic principle of accident prevention is to man each machine with competent persons having the necessary knowledge and skill. Another important precaution is the placing of all especially dangerous large machines in separate buildings or parts of buildings, and only permitting those entrusted with their care to come near them.

The workers should be separated from the dangerous parts of machinery by fences, rails, barriers, bars or boards. Wherever such a separation is not practicable, the dangerous parts of the machinery should be covered with metal plates, wire mesh, etc.

Motors, Flywheels, Etc. The location of prime movers depends upon their type and upon the character of the power used. Large motors and engines are located in separate parts of buildings, usually the basements or cellars. When this is the case, the construction of the cellar or basement, or the separate building in which this part of the machinery is located must be solid and fire-resisting and effectively separated from all other parts of the industrial establishment. The parts of the building in which the prime movers are located should have ample light and adequate ventilation, especially where there is a large escape of steam which interferes with the proper light conditions and causes dripping upon floors and slipping and falling of persons. No overcrowding should be permitted in the engine room, and whenever engines, motors or parts of the machinery are located in pits, they should be fenced around and railed so as to prevent persons from falling into them. The engineer or the persons in charge of the motors should be able to stop them quickly, and signals audible in all parts of the establishment should be made for the starting and stopping of the motors. All engines should be equipped with automatic speed limit stops and with devices for stopping the machinery in each department or floor when necessary. When parts of the machines or engines are overhead, stationary iron ladders or stairways should be provided for reaching them. Governor balls, piston rods, etc., whenever exposed, should be properly guarded. Flywheels should be locked for repairs and cleaning.

Flywheels constitute the first stage by which power is transmitted from the motor to the other parts of the machinery. They should be railed off and fenced just as other parts of the motors, or safeguarded by being entirely covered with wire mesh. The danger of flywheels lies in their huge size, their rapid rotation and the draught they create, which is often strong enough to draw in the clothes of a worker passing near them. The accompanying illustrations show some of the methods of protecting workers against accidents from flywheels.

Wherever driving belts, ropes, etc., are passed through floors they are very dangerous. Such driving belts, ropes and chains, whether going through the floor or running horizontally, should be properly safeguarded by rails, fences, bars, metal wire mesh or solid covers to prevent the persons working or passing near from being drawn into them.

The danger of gears, cog wheels, sprocket wheels and other rotating, moving and turning parts of the machinery of transmission lies in their projections, in the speed which they usually attain and in the possibility of their drawing in the clothes and parts of the bodies of workers near them. The method of safeguarding such machinery is simple and consists in covering them with metal or wire mesh, as illustrated in the accompanying figures.

Perhaps there is no more dangerous part of the machinery than the rapidly moving shafts through which the power is transmitted from the motors. Their danger also consists in the possibility of persons being injured by being drawn into these shafts. The safeguarding of a shaft is necessary whether it is located near the floor or near the ceiling, or in any part of the building where it is in the proximity of the workers, either at all times or at certain times, when the machinery is being cleaned, etc. Many accidents have happened through failure to safeguard shafts which were above the ordinary height of persons.

The safeguarding of shafts consists in covering them with fixed or adjustable covers, either of metal or of some other material, as illustrated in the accompanying figures. It is important to safeguard the ends of shafts, as many accidents happen when the passageway between them is too narrow. Very often hinged plate covers are

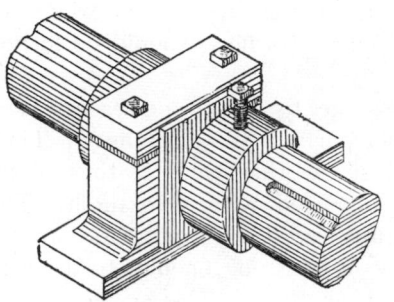

Courtesy Aetna Life Insurance Co.

Protruding Set Screw and Keyway.

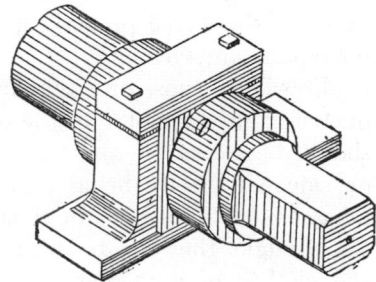

Courtesy Aetna Life Insurance Co·

Countersunk Set Screw and
Unprotected Shaft End.

used on top of the shafts, or hinged aprons extending down from the outside edges of the plate to cover the shaft. These aprons are usually made of wire screen on steel frames. Wherever shafts are near the floor and are not covered, they should be boxed or railed

Courtesy Aetna Life Insurance Co.

Safety Collars for Set Screws.

off. Wherever shafts are overhead, solid and suitable platforms for the use of cleaners and oilers should be provided. On a motor-driven line of shafting, a safety switch must be placed on top of the ladder, accessible to anyone working on this shafting. Wherever railing is used for safeguarding machinery, motors, flywheels, etc., it should be smooth 1½-inch angle iron or 1½-inch iron pipe, properly fastened and solidly constructed.

A dangerous part of transmission apparatus consists in the collars, couplings and screws with which shafts are fastened. Of the set-screws an authority says:

" Insignificant as it looks, the protruding set-screw in collars on shafting is the cause of more accidents than any other part of the machinery, and quite serious accidents leading to very bad injuries to workers. The danger of the set-screw is its rapid motion on the shafting and its catching and entangling loose sleeves, clothes or anything which comes in contact with it. It has often been the cause of a worker being caught and whirled around shafting and sometimes even fatally injured. There is absolutely no necessity for these dangerous protruding set-screws. Protruding set-screws should not be allowed to exist at all. They should either be countersunk so that they will not project beyond the surface of the collar, or they may be made in hollow form flush with the collar; and in both cases may be worked with some sort of a key. Sometimes when set screws are already constructed, they may be made safe by putting upon them a safety collar made of wood, in a hole of which the screw is placed. Safety collars are made in two parts and are screwed together on the shaft. The method of safeguarding a protruding screw by winding some leather or rubber or waste around it is not a good method, as the material may often be unwound or get loose. The best collars perhaps are those safety collars which are fixed on the shafting without the aid of any set-screws at all." *

Belts, Chains, Ropes, Pulleys, Etc. The transmission of power from the motors to machines, wheels, shafts, etc., is accomplished by gears, ropes, chains and belts. Chains and ropes are infrequently used and only on special transmission apparatus. Belts are made of stout leather of a width corresponding to the width of the part of the machinery to be used and of a thickness and strength calculated to withstand the necessary strain. The danger points in belts are the possibility of sudden tearing or breaking while in motion, or catching the clothes or part of the body of a person in their proximity. A large number of accidents in every factory are caused by belts.

Whenever belts are used they should be made of smooth leather without any projections, and great attention must be paid to their lacing and splicing, which are often faulty and cause many accidents.

While inspecting factories one frequently sees belts being tied together with wire, which may protrude and become a source of dangerous injury to workers. In whatever position the belts are,

Wooden Guards for Belting.

whether upright, horizontal, overhead or near the floor, they should be covered and safeguarded by either wire mesh or other covers. Exposed belts should be boxed in or railed off where they are not covered, and when they run near where persons are working.

Courtesy Aetna Life Insurance Co.

Driving Belt in Aisle Boxed In.

Courtesy Aetna Life Insurance Co.

Guarded Countershaft Used in Driving a Lathe.

A great many accidents due to belting are caused by hand shifting; and one of the cardinal principles of safety in a factory is the absolute prohibition of handling a belt without using proper shifters. Especially is it dangerous to attempt to shift an over-

Pipe Railing Around Rope Drive where It Passes through Concrete Floor.

Courtesy Aetna Life Insurance Co.

head belt which necessitates climbing over dangerous machinery. No belt should be carried directly on a shaft but should be placed on pulleys, of which there should be two—one a permanent pulley and the other a loose pulley, to which the belt may be shifted when it is not in use. Loose pulleys or idlers should be provided

on all machinery, and the shifting apparatus should be so arranged
that when the belt is moved to the loose pulley it will stay there and
not creep back on the tight pulley and thus start the machinery

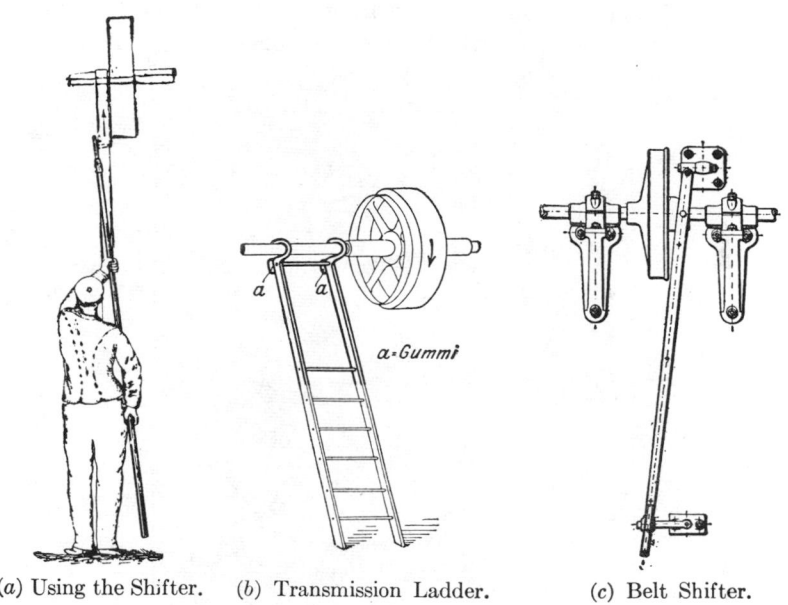

(a) Using the Shifter.   (b) Transmission Ladder.   (c) Belt Shifter.

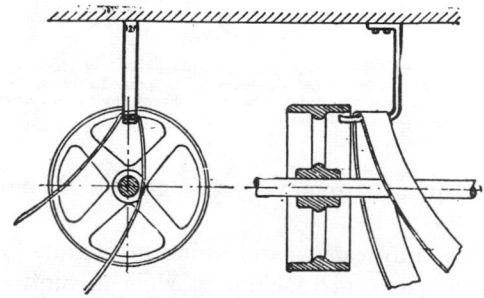

(d) Belt Hanger.

Hartmann's *Unfallverhütungstechnik.*

with which it is connected.   The loose pulley should be independently mounted; and pulleys should be made somewhat wider than
the width of the belt.   In German factories hangers, are provided

for the belts to be shifted upon, especially where shafts are near the ceiling.

A great many attached and unattached belt shifters have been devised for the purpose of shifting the belt from one pulley to another without danger to the worker. Some of the illustrations show the principles upon which these are constructed. Where belts

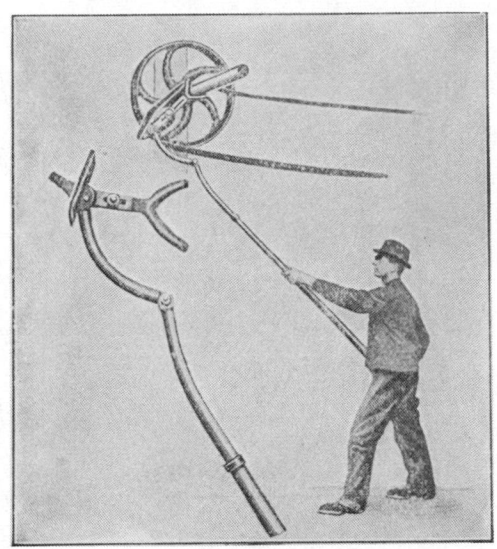

Courtesy Aetna Life Insurance Co.

Belt Placer.

This is a German device. It is hinged in two places and at the end is a fork which fits the shaft. At the first joint is a shoe on which the belt is placed to guide it on the pulley. The second joint, or the one nearest the handle, permits the placer to run around the pulley until the shoe is released between the belt and the pulley.

have to be frequently removed, the guards should be made on hinges or hooks.

The cleaning, lubricating and oiling of engines, motors, shafts, gears, and other parts of machinery while in motion may be prevented by the provision of self-oilers and self-lubricating devices, of which there are a number on the market.

VI

MACHINERY

Punch Press Showing Safety Guard in Operation. Clutch cannot be tripped
unless the guard descends past the shear plane.

It is difficult to make hard-and-fast rules for the safeguarding
of machinery of all kinds and types. In most industrial establish-

ments the machinery conforms to a limited number of types, such as: (1) hammers, presses and punches; (2) rolls and calenders; (3) grinders, mixers and centrifugal machines; (4) emery wheels, polishers and buffers; (5) saws.

Hammers, Presses and Punches.   There are many types of

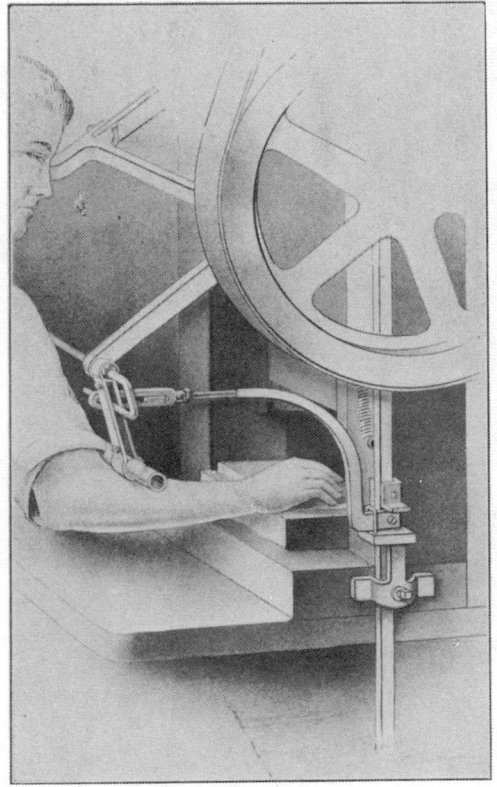

Corbin Cabinet Lock Co., New Britain, Conn.

Safety Guard on Press.

machines which have for their principle a downward movement of one part of the machine, for the purpose of hammering, pressing or punching various materials. Every industry has machines of this type. They are especially numerous in the metal, paper, textile, leather and similar trades. The construction, size and details of each machine differ according to the industry and kind of work.

Some of them are worked by hand, others by foot power; while others are automatic and mechanical. Some of these machines are fed by hand, others are fed automatically by self-feeders or revolving feeding arrangements and conveyors.

All of these types of machines are dangerous, in that the fingers and hands may be caught under the hammer, press or punch. This happens either because the operator stretches his hand too far while feeding the machine or tries to correct the position of the

Courtesy Benjamin Electric Mfg. Co.

Two-Hand Safety Device.

die or the material inserted, or attempts to clean the die; or, finally, because of slipping and falling under the press.

There are a number of methods by which machines of this type are safeguarded. The best method, of course, is that which provides for automatic feeding of presses, hammers, and punches either by conveyors or revolving feeders, thus obviating the necessity of hand feeding. This has been accomplished in beer bottling, cigarette making, box making, confectionery and other machines of this type, and has resulted in a great reduction of accidents. Insecure footing and consequent falling of persons upon the machine is prevented by properly constructed floors and by providing rubber or other non-slipping mats.

Foot treadles may be constructed so as not to be easily operated except at certain intervals, by the conscious pressure of the foot. Presses may be equipped with a speed clutch which prevents them

Courtesy Pullman Co.

Plate Glass Guard (indicated by arrow) to Prevent Chips from Punch Lacerating the Eyeball of the Operator.

from making more than one stroke with each depression of the treadle.   This clutch is so made that it is impossible for the operator to repeat the press.

For the purpose of preventing the hands of the operator from coming under the press, punch or hammer, there are several kinds of safeguards based upon different principles. One class of safeguards provides for intermediate instruments or tools, by which the objects fed into the machine are handled. Such tools vary from a simple piece of wood by which the object is shoved under the press, to variously constructed tongs, forks, or other appliances which

Courtesy Aetna Life Insurance Co.

Guarded Stamping Machine Used in Soap Factory.

The operator must put his hand over one of the two arms attached to the shaft to put the soap in position on the die. When the punch descends, the arms rise automatically and force the operator's hands out of the way.

prevent the hand from approaching the machine. Other safeguards are constructed upon the principle of the " two-hand system." This consists in making every movement of the press necessitate the handling of two levers simultaneously, which engages the hands of the operator while the press is in motion, and thus prevents them from getting under the machine. This is the best means of preventing accidents. The objection which is usually made against

this method of safeguarding is the fact that the operator is compelled
to adjust his die and material under the press first, and then take
charge of the hand levers. This takes some time and the operation
is consequently not so rapid.

Another system of safeguarding this type of machine is by
providing bars, plates or arms, each so constructed that with

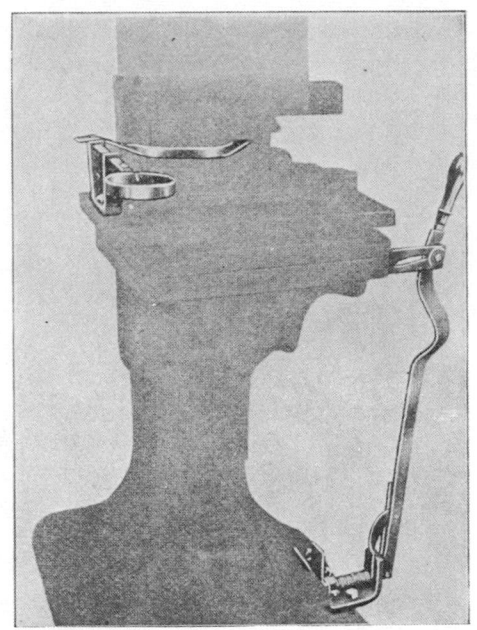

Courtesy Aetna Life Insurance Co.

Stamping Press Guard.

Operator's hands are pushed away by the guard.

every descending movement of the press or punch, they automatically force the operator's hands out of the way. This is a
device which may be easily constructed by any mechanic. Most
of the existing safeguards are constructed according to one or other
of the above named principles, and most of them are quite
effective, easily constructed, and should be installed in every
factory. (See illustrations for details of the safeguarding methods
described.)

Courtesy Eastman Kodak Co.

Corner Cutting Machine in Paper Box Department, Showing Adjustable Rods
Forming a Protective Stop for Operator's Hands and Fingers.

Rolls, Calenders, Etc. These machines are of various types, sizes and construction and are found in almost every industry. Their principal action is to catch an object and then by passing it between several close rolls, to flatten, roll, knead, mix, break up

Calender Rolls with Safety Clutch.
Power may be instantly shut off by operator pressing on lever indicated by arrow.

or press it. Sometimes these rolls are made in the form of knives with the same rolling action. Rolls and calenders are used in the metal industry for flattening and rolling bars and plates of metal, in all industries where certain masses are to be formed into flat or other shapes, in all industries where kneading, mixing and breaking up is done, such as flour mills, and confectionery factories; also in textile and clothing trades where ironing or pressing is done.

This type of machine is more dangerous than the press, punch and hammer previously described, for the reason that while in the former a hand or part of the body may be stamped upon and injured, in the rolls the whole body may be drawn in after the hand and arm, and fatal injury may result. Especially is this the case with heavy rolls such as are used in the metal industry.

The principles of safeguarding these machines and preventing

Courtesy Aetna Life Insurance Co.

Collar and Cuff Ironer Guarded.

Shows guarding of gearing and protective bar in front of the feed rolls.

accidents to workers operating them are not very different from those upon which are based the safeguards for presses and punches. The same precautions against insecure footing of the operator are to be taken; in fact, it is more important with these machines than with others. The devices alluded to before for the intermediate handling and feeding of the objects under the machine may be employed for this type of machine as well, although it is perhaps necessary to modify them in some respects. The feeding tools used should be thick enough to prevent their being caught between the rolls.

It is not as easy to provide self-feeders and automatic conveyors

Hartmann's *Unfallverhütungstechnik.*

Calender Hand Safety Guard.

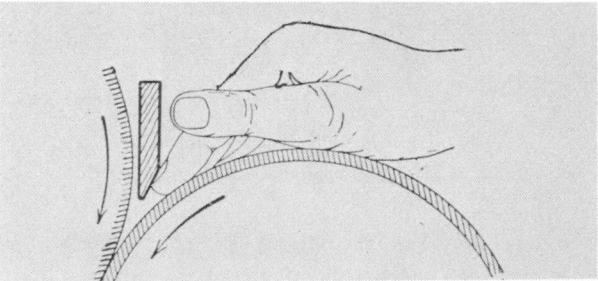

Hartmann's *Unfallverhütungstechnik.*

Metal safety bar to prevent fingers from getting into the rolls.

for rolls as for punches and presses; on the other hand, it is easier to provide some apparatus on which the object may be carried into the rolls without intermediate handling by the operator.

An important safeguard on this type of machine is an apparatus by which the action of the rolls may be stopped and reversed in case of accident and thus disengage the caught part. An auxiliary wooden roller is often constructed at the intake in front of the feed rolls. Bars or strips of wood may be placed in front of certain feed rolls, especially in laundry machinery, so as to prevent the hand from being drawn in. Most ironing machines may be easily guarded by such bars or rods.

Grinders, Mixers, Centrifugal Machines, Etc. This type of machine is used for grinding or mixing materials. These machines

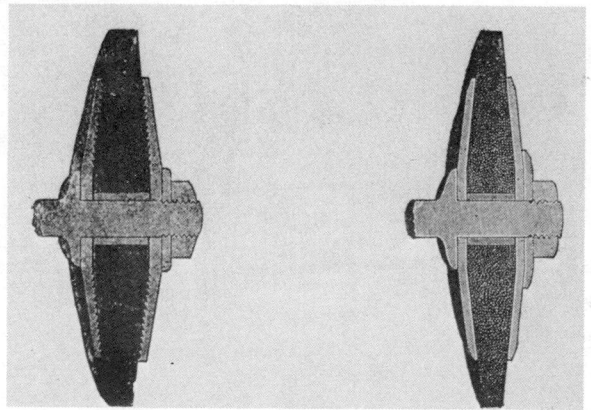

Courtesy Aetna Life Insurance Co.

Concave Safety Collars for Emery Wheel.

are worked either by hand or by power-driven motors. A number of them are constructed on the principle of centrifugal action.

The safeguarding of this type of machine consists first, in providing secure footing for the operator; second, in using proper material in the construction of the machines; third, in the provision of brakes or other devices to permit the immediate stoppage of the machines in case of an accident; and finally, in the provision of suitable guards and covers so as to prevent the drawing in of the hands of the operator. (See illustration on page 207.) The principal protection for this kind of machine is a mechanical or electrical device by which the cover is kept down as long as the machine is in action; and may only be raised and opened when the machine is at rest.

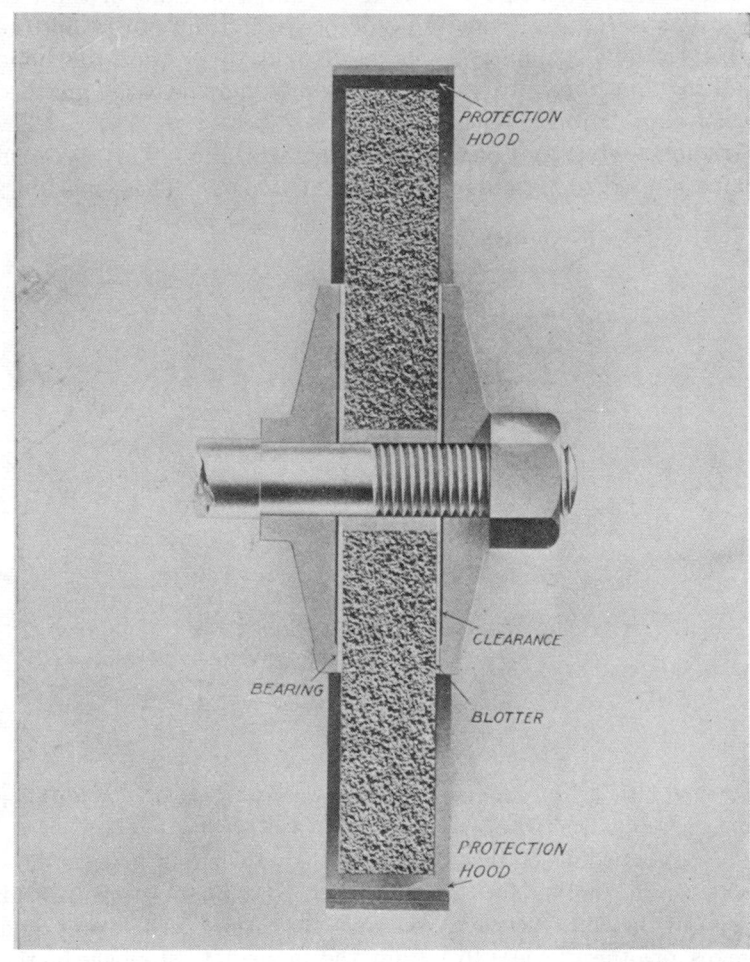

Courtesy Norton Co., Worcester, Mass.

Cross-section of Emery Wheel.

Courtesy Norton Co.

Closed Type of Protection Hood on Grinding Wheel Floor Stand. Hoods connected with a dust exhaust system.

Museum of Safety, Charlottenburg, Berlin.

Safeguard on Grinder; also Dust Remover.

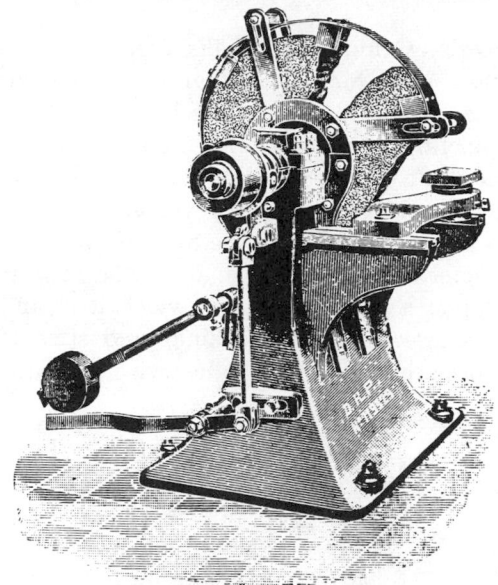

Museum of Safety, Charlottenburg, Berlin.

Showing How Guards Kept the Broken Grindstone from Injuring the Workers.

Museum of Safety, Charlottenburg, Berlin.

Safety Centrifuge.   (Cover cannot be opened as long as centrifuge is in motion.)

Emery Wheels, Grindstones, Polishers, Buffers, Etc. Emery and other wheels used for grinding and polishing are principally guarded by iron and steel covers which leave only a small space for the actual operation, and cover all the rest of the wheel, so that in case of bursting of the wheel, injury to the operator and to those in the proximity of the machine is prevented. Much of the safety of a grinding wheel depends upon the material of which it is made, upon the character of its mounting, upon the proper oiling of its bearings, and upon a moderate speed which it should not exceed.

Saws. There are many types, kinds and sizes of saws, most of which are used in the wood industry. The saws are named

Courtesy Aetna Life Insurance Co.

Splitter Adjusted to Large Saw.

according to their shape and functions: such as circular, band, rip, swing, equalizer, etc.

The dangerous part of all saws is the sharp cutting edge which may come in contact with the hand or part of the body of the operator. Accidents occur through the slipping of the hand which feeds the object to be sawed, through attempting to clean the saw while in motion, by the jumping back of the wood, by reaching the arm over the saw, by the under part of the saw coming in contact with part of the body, etc. Circular saws are more dangerous than others, although there is hardly a saw which is not dangerous.

The general methods of preventing accidents due to saws do not differ much from those adopted in operating other machinery. These methods may be summarized as follows: (1) secure footing for the operator to avoid slipping or falling on the saw; (2) a properly constructed working device to stop the running saw immediately either by throwing off the belt on a pulley or by other means; (3) proper care in feeding the wood to be sawed; (4) the use of a guide or push-stick in feeding so as to prevent the hand from reaching the saw; (5) the wearing by the operator of suitable clothes; (6) the stoppage of outdoor sawing in very cold weather,

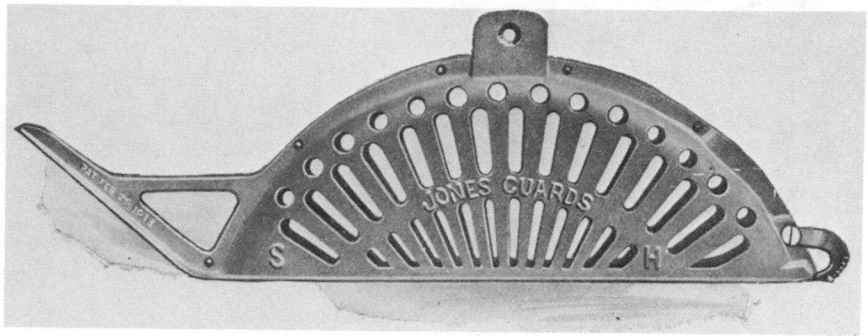

Courtesy Lockhart-Jones Co., Inc., Buffalo, N. Y.

Circular Saw Guard: Closed Front Hood.

as the hands then become numb and accidents are more liable to occur; (7) the appointing of a worker (called an " off-bearer ") to take care of the finished material behind circular saws. The off-bearers must not use their hands for withdrawing the sawed wood,

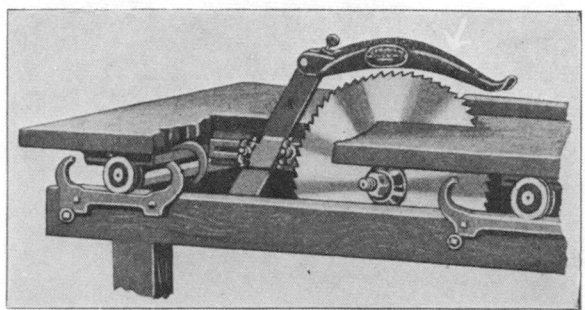

Courtesy Aetna Life Insurance Co.

Combination of Splitter with Light and Shallow Hood Protection for Top of Saw.

but should use hooks or other tools; (8) proper inspection and frequent periodical tests of the saws so as to insure their proper condition; (9) frequent oiling and setting to prevent the saw from wobbling; (10) keeping the saws well sharpened and their speed regulated.

One of the indispensable safeguards of circular saws is the splitter. A *splitter* is a metal disc or arc that is firmly attached

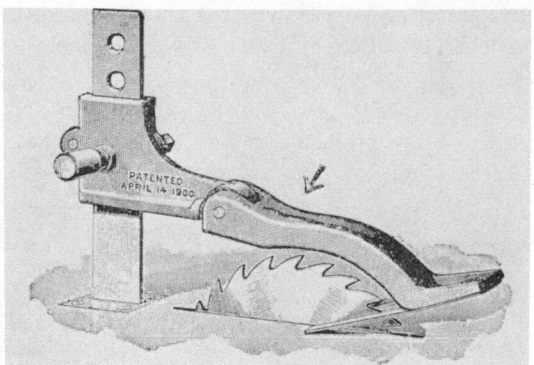

Splitter Guard for Circular Saw.

Hood is adjustable and hinged so as to be always close down over saw, except when raised by material coming in contact with the split finger arrangement in front.

behind a circular saw, and serves to spread the board or slab away from the log or plank from which it is being sawed, so that the saw

Circular Saw Guard.

Combination of splitter with a hood-like protection for top of the saw. Dog attached to splitter to aid in holding wood down.

runs freely and the wood is prevented from pinching. The use of a splitter does away with the necessity for the operator to reach over the saw, or an off-bearer to try to catch hold of the board,

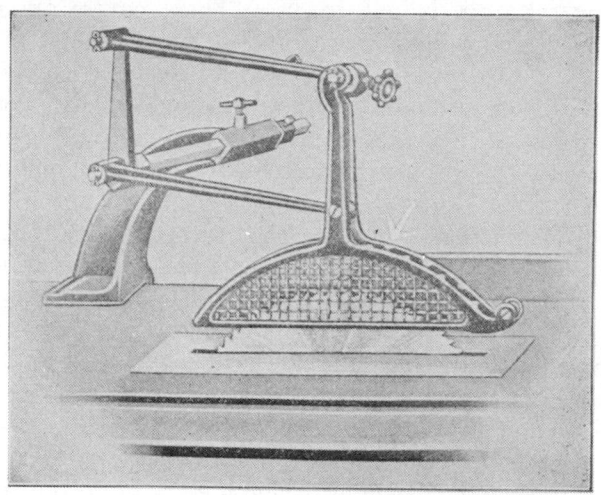

Courtesy Aetna Life Insurance Co.

Wire Hood Guard Supported by Bracket on Pedestal Curved to Permit Cross-cutting or Dadoing.

and also prevents pinching and jumping back of caught pieces. Splitters should be made of the best steel, smooth and securely fastened. They are usually made curved and should be properly adjusted to be in exact alignment with the saw and close behind it. German regulations of the Woodworking Trade Association give detailed and exact dimensions in millimeters for the location and position of the splitter, its size, height, etc.

A second very important part in the safeguarding of saws which is, as a rule, applicable to all kinds and types of saws, is a cover or hood, usually made of wood, or metal, or wire mesh, which covers all the parts of the saw whether above or below the table, which are not actually necessary for the operation of the saw, and should also cover the

Museum of Safety, Charlottenburg, Berlin.

Saw Provided with Iron Safety Cover and Feeder; Cover not Connected with Feeder; so Arranged as to Allow Uncovering of Saw only so much as is Absolutely Needed.

whole saw when it is not in use. These covers are made in different shapes and designs according to the character of the saw which they are to protect. They should always be properly fastened so that their use is not within the option of the worker and should always be in position. Of course, these covers must not interfere with the proper feeding of the wood. Some of these covers in circular saws may be attached to splitters or they may be hung from above. The accompanying illustrations show types of hoods and covers adaptable to various kinds of saws and are explained in the caption under each illustration.

Wherever it is possible to adopt feeding tables so as to obviate the necessity of a direct feeding by hand, it should be done; and this is possible in a great many cases and with a variety of saws. Other types of saws which are less dangerous than the circular saw also need to be protected. Some of the methods of protection are shown in the illustrations.

VII

GENERAL METHODS OF ACCIDENT PREVENTION IN SPECIAL INDUSTRIES

Besides the dangers from accidents in factories due to the causes previously discussed, there are in each and every industry some special danger points which are peculiar to that industry alone. The grouping of industries differs, but there are general groups such as the metal trade, wood industry, textile trade, and chemical industry, which are treated as industrial units in every country.

The rate and character of the accidents differ in each of these groups. The accident rate per thousand employes in England is 21.6 in the metal industry, and only 6 for the textile industry; while it is 21.7 in the wood industry, 8.26 in the chemical industry and 12.7 for all industries. This refers only to accidents caused by certain specified dangerous appliances and reported by the certifying surgeons. The general rate of accidents other than those reported by the certifying surgeons is much larger.

German statistics give only accidents involving disablement lasting longer than thirteen weeks; and, according to the German statistics, the wood industry shows the largest rate of accidents (12.28 per thousand employes), with a general rate of 9.44 per thousand in all industries, 3 per thousand in the textile industry, 7.73 per thousand in the metal industry, and 9.88 per thousand in the chemical industry. New York State statistics, as far as they can be obtained for 1910, show a rate per thousand of 25.2 in all industries and 142 per thousand in the chemical industry. The figures for New York State are disproportionately large because they include trivial as well as serious accidents.

Without going into details of the special processes in each of the

Courtesy Aetna Life Insurance Co.

Pinion and Gear of Tumbling Barrel Protected by Sheet Metal Guard.

several industries, certain general methods of accident prevention will be briefly discussed here.

The Metal Industry. The metal industry, in which metal is smelted and cast and metal articles manufactured, shows a large number of accidents, as is proved by various state reports. There are many danger points in this industry, some of which have already been discussed. The more serious accidents occurring in steel plants are due to transportation and to certain types of machines, which have been discussed above. During the process of smelting and casting, injuries may be caused by sparks, splashes of molten metal, slipping near red hot rails, etc. According to figures cited by the Wisconsin Industrial Commission, the records of that state show that in 1912 " 311 accidents were reported in which men were disabled for more than seven days because of serious burns from molten metal. In all, a total of 5,700 working days were lost by molders and molders' helpers due to this one cause. In one plant alone nearly 800 days were lost, which amounts to about one day during the year for every employe. Of the 311 accidents reported, 62 or 20 per cent occurred while metal was being poured into molds, 53 or 17 per cent while molten lead was being carried in hand ladles; 32 or 11 per cent because of stumbling in obstructed passageways; 30 or 10 per cent while ladles were being filled at the cupola. Metal explosions caused 19 accidents; 18 were caused by metal running out of molds; in 12 cases the ladle was defective and the hot metal broke through. Other accidents were due to various causes. Men carrying ladles bumped each other; on tipping the cupola sparks of metal burned men standing near; ladles fell from tongs, splashing the contents in all directions; ladle trucks jumped the tracks, tipping over and spilling the metal, etc. In 70 per cent of these accidents, the injured persons had one or both feet seriously burned; 43 cases resulted in injured eyes, one of which caused permanent impairment of sight; 19 cases resulted in burns to the legs and 26 in burns to other parts of the body." *

The above indicates some of the causes of accidents in metal shops resulting in burns. Besides burns, other injuries frequently occurring in metal shops are due to heavy metal objects falling on the feet and other parts of the body, and to gases and fumes engendered during the process of smelting and pouring, where no methods are employed to remove them from the foundry. A recent investigation of foundry workers demonstrated that they are subject to many diseases, especially of the respiratory organs, caused by the extreme temperature to which they are exposed, and to the general lack of sanitation in ordinary foundries.

The New York State Factory Commission, in its investigation in New York State, found that industrial insurance statistics show an excessive mortality rate from consumption among foundry workers, which becomes marked between the ages of twenty-five and thirty-four, a time when the workers are in the very prime of life. Among the recommendations of the Commission were the following: that all foundries should be properly lighted during working hours; that gangways should be so constructed and maintained as to make their use reasonably safe, and that such gangways should not be obstructed in any way; and that flasks,

* Bulletin Industrial Commission of Wisconsin, Vol. II, No. 8, p. 183.

molding machines, ladles, cranes and apparatus for transporting molten metal in foundries should be maintained in proper condition and repair. The Commission also recommended provisions for washing facilities, for toilet accommodations and recommended the prohibition of the employment of women in core rooms, where such rooms were not separated from the ovens by solid partitions. There are, of course, many excellently constructed and model foundries throughout the country.

The prevention of accidents from burns is accomplished by providing sufficient light, by having the employes properly clothed and supplied with stout congress shoes or special shoes manufactured for foundry workers; by protecting the eyes of the workers from glare, sparks and splashes with suitable goggles and glasses; by having the hand ladles equipped with hand shields; by the provision of tongs and better methods of handling and carrying molten metal in pots, etc.; by having all gangways in the foundry free from obstructions; and by a system of supervision and inspection that insures compliance with all the rules and regulations of the shop.

The Wood Industry. Accidents occurring in the wood industry are due to the use of sharp cutting knives, saws, etc., which often come in contact with the hands of the workers, injuring them more or less severely. We have already spoken of the dangers of saws and the methods of safeguarding them. Perhaps the next most dangerous machines in the wood industry are the " jointers " or " buzz planers." As the Bulletin of the Industrial Commission of Wisconsin says:

" Of all the hazards of the wood-working industry, none is so great as the old-fashioned square-head jointer or buzz planer. The annual harvest of fingers and hands in this state alone is appalling. Four out of every one hundred accidents in this industry occur on jointers. No other machine on which any number of accidents occurred—with the exception of cornshredders and feed cutters— has caused so many permanent disabilities in proportion to the number of accidents. Of the 77 accidents reported, 44, or 57 per cent, resulted in the loss of one or more fingers. In one case the operator had his entire hand removed. In all, a total of 71 fingers or parts of fingers, and one hand, were cut off by these machines. In four cases four fingers were cut off; in two cases, three fingers; in eleven cases, two fingers, and in twenty-seven cases, one finger.

" All but two of these accidents occurred on the square-headed jointer. In the two instances reported, in which the machines were equipped with safety cylinder heads, the injured person merely suffered a slight abrasion at the tips of his fingers. Germany has long since prohibited the use of this old type of ' head.' " *

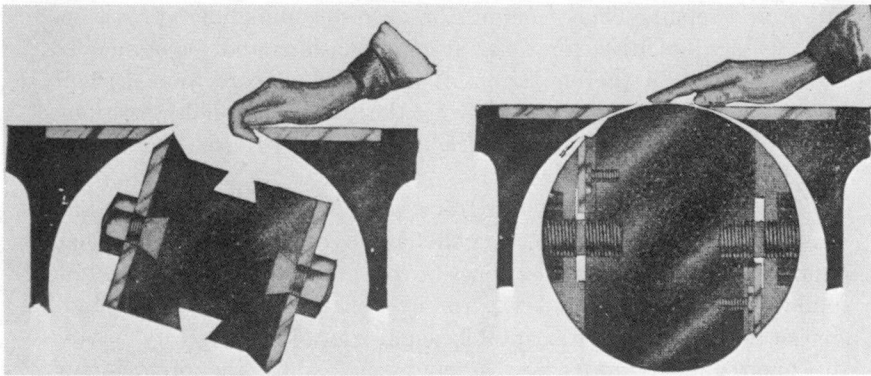

Old Style Square Buzz Planer

(Showing the position the hand is liable to get into, and the almost certain consequences.

Safety Cylinder for Buzz Planer.

Presents a regular surface and prevents the fingers from getting down below the table top and thereby being cut off or severely damaged.

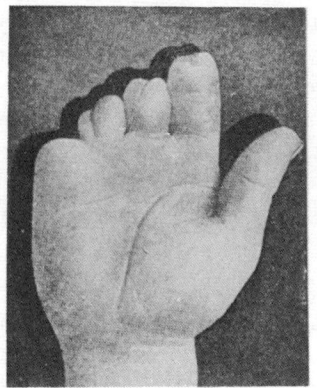

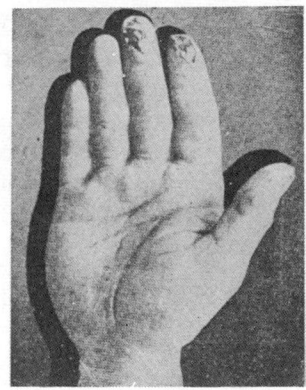

Done with Square Cylinder Planer.

Done with Circular Cylinder Planer.

The illustrations on this page show an old style square head, a safety circular cylinder and the character of the injuries caused by the square-head as compared with those caused by the circular cylinders. The danger of the old style square-head, as one authority says, lies in the fact that:

* Bulletin of Industrial Commission of Wisconsin, Vol. II, No. 4, February 20, 1913.

"Under ordinary circumstances the operator is dependent wholly upon his hands for control of his work. With them he pushes the stock over the knives and also keeps it firmly pressed to the tables so as to secure even cut. They are therefore brought frequently in close proximity to the danger point, the gap between the two tables in which the knife head is rapidly revolving. Any one of a number of causes is apt to throw a hand off the material and into the knives. A knot or change in grain may be struck, too heavy a cut may be taken, a piece of stock may be too small for such planing, or the operator may be doing his work carelessly.

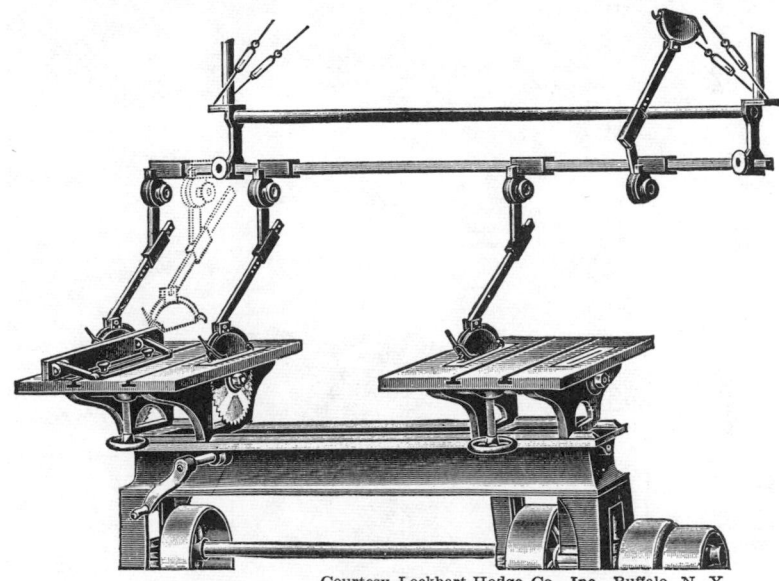

Courtesy Lockhart-Hodge Co., Inc., Buffalo, N. Y.

Double Cut-off Saw Guard.

Whatever the cause, the result is pretty sure to be a serious injury unless everything possible has been done to guard the machine. Some of the causes of accidents can be foreseen by the operator and avoided; but others are beyond his control and on both accounts the jointer requires as complete protection as can be given it." *

The safety cylinder is a most effective means for preventing accidents. The use of such a cylinder also prevents the kicking back of the material which is being planed. The guards which are

* Van Schaack: Wood-Working Safeguards, Aetna Life Insurance Company, p. 101.

being used on saws are illustrated in the accompanying figures. Some of these guards are adjusted vertically and horizontally and

Band Saw Guard.

can be swung to one side.   A number of these guards may be made by a mechanic within the shop, and most of them are effective in the prevention of accidents.   There are several other machines in use in the wood industry, such as shapers, sanders, lathes, planers, etc., all of which have serious danger points. They should be

Rip Saw Guard.

When there is no piece being sawed, guard hangs down completely covering saw. When board is started, guard rises up at (*A*) as shown in (1), rising against springs (*CC*) and turning on the joints (*DD*) and. (*EE*).

equipped with guards or the workers should wear some kind of protectors in order to prevent contact with the knives.

German Finger Guard.

Iron plate strips attached to strip extending along top of saw and oblique to the sawing direction. Strips lifted one by one by material fed and fall back into place after material has passed by.

The Chemical Industry. A report of the New York State factory commission for 1913 gives the following summary of the investigations conducted in the chemical industry under my direction:

"The workers in the chemical trades are subject to dangers peculiar to those industries. Chief among these are poisonous substances handled by the workers throughout the work-day; open and unfenced vats or pans containing acids or hot and corrosive

Hartmann's *Unfallverhütungstechnik.*

Safe Method of Filling Acid Bottles.

liquids; abnormal physical conditions such as great heat or cold, variable atmospheric pressure and humidity; dangerous processes, etc. Due to the dangers peculiar to the chemical trades, laws have been passed in the various European countries as well as in some of the states of the United States regulating the chemical industries."*

* Report of the Director, 2d Report of New York State Factory Investigating Commission, Vol. II, p. 611.

The number of fatal and permanent injuries per thousand workers in the chemical trades in New York State exceeds by far the number in England, Germany and France. A large number of the accidents can be eliminated by taking proper precautions; such as fencing of vats and pans, and carrying off dust and fumes.

The prevention of accidents due to burns caused by the action of acids and alkalies is possible if the workers wear appropriate overalls, shoes, gloves, caps and goggles, and exercise care in cart-

Belgian Labor Report, 1912.

(a) Safety Apparatus for Emptying Acid Bottles.

ing, lifting and carrying carboys, flasks, etc., and in handling dangerous materials.

Serious and painful accidents result from falling into vats, pans, and caldrons, filled with chemicals and hot and dangerous liquids. It is astonishing to note that in some large factories where otherwise humane conditions prevail, it is not thought necessary to safeguard vats filled with dangerous chemicals. Thus, I found in an otherwise well-managed establishment, pots filled with caustic potash, every spurt of which causes bad burns, entirely unprotected, with workmen standing on top of these slippery vats, ladling out the boiling contents without any precaution taken for their safety. Indeed, I was told that two men had fallen into these caustic pots, instantly losing their lives. The photograph on page 227 which I had taken while inspecting factories in which

Belgian Labor Report, 1912.

(*b*) Apparatus in Use.

(Note: Not entirely safe; does not prevent spurting of acids into face.)

these caustic pots were used, shows the dangerous conditions existing.

There are three methods by which vats, pans, and caldrons may be effectively safeguarded: (1) by raising them above the floor to a height sufficiently great so as to make it impossible for a person to fall into them; (2) by covering the vats with adjustable covers either of solid metal, wire mesh or other material; and (3) by railing or fencing them around so as to make it impossible for a person to fall into them.

The Textile Industry. The number of accidents occurring to workers in the textile trade is large and is due to the complexity

Annual Report of the Belgian Labor Office, 1912.

Soap Vat with Safety Grille: Grille lifted for the introduction of materials.

Annual Report of the Belgian Labor Office, 1912.

Same as above: Grille closed to prevent workman from falling in during the mixing.

of the machinery as well as to the character of the persons, many of them women or minors, who operate the machines. A great many of the accidents are due to general causes as well as to the machines, transmission apparatus and other processes in the establishment, the dangers of which have already been discussed.

Many of the accidents occurring in the textile industry may be prevented by proper precautions and by the installation of appro-

A Safeguarded Roving Machine.

priate safeguards. An interesting experiment was made by the English factory inspection department in calling special conferences of employers, operatives and inspectors to discuss the safeguards to be employed in special industries and to agree upon rules and regulations to be adopted. Several conferences have been held and reports issued covering conferences between employers, operatives and inspectors, regarding fencing of machinery and other safeguards

Courtesy New York State Factory Investigating Commission.

Spinning Machine in a Cordage Factory.   Fliers well guarded.

in the cotton spinning mills, in cotton weaving sheds and in woolen
and worsted mills.

As an example of the results of such conferences, I believe it will

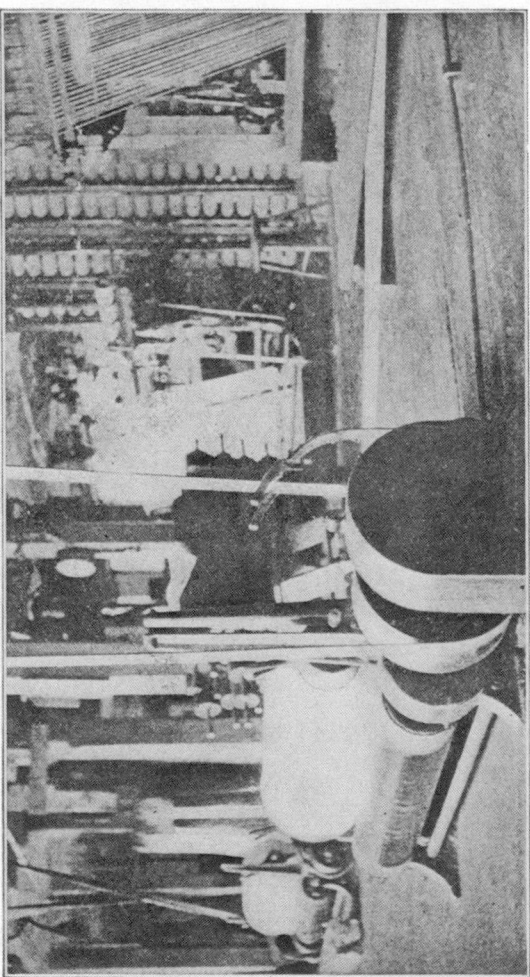

Courtesy Aetna Life Insurance Co.

Cotton Mill Balling Machine, Showing Guard in Place over Gears.

be of interest to insert here the rules and regulations agreed upon at
the conference on cotton weaving factories, since they deal with
dangers and conditions which exist in the United States as well.

Courtesy New York State Factory Commission.

Caustic Pots which Workers Sometimes fall into.

Courtesy Joseph Bancroft & Sons Co., Wilmington, Del.

Calender Pulley and Nip Guards.

NOTES OF AGREEMENT BETWEEN EMPLOYERS, OPERATIVES AND INSPECTORS CONCERNING SAFEGUARDS IN COTTON WEAVING FACTORIES.

Fencing and Safeguards.

I. **General Provisions:**

(*a*) On *new* machinery all projecting set-screws on continuously revolving parts shall either be countersunk or be otherwise efficiently protected. Projecting set-screws on *existing* machinery shall be replaced wherever practicable by grub-screws. Where projecting set-screws are placed inside box pulleys, they shall be deemed to be efficiently fenced.

(*b*) On new machinery the following wheels shall be plated:

(1) Balance wheels on looms; these to be without perforations except near the rim of the wheel.

(2) Flywheels on sectional warping machines, where the wheel is on the outside of machine.

(*c*) Ladders, other than step-ladders, shall be fitted with hooks or other non-skid device.

(*d*) Heavy overhead main driving belts or ropes shall be guarded underneath in all cases where there is liability of persons having to pass under them. It is agreed that there may be instances where the principle of this rule should be applied to counter-driving belts.

(*e*) Metal fasteners shall not be used for overhead driving unless the belt itself be securely fenced—provided that this rule shall not apply to metal fasteners consisting of a continuous wire stitching held together by a peg, other than a metal peg.

(*f*) Any woman or girl working about machinery shall have her hair put up, or otherwise confined in a net.

(*g*) A supply of sterilized dressings shall be kept available for first aid for any operative who receives a cut or wound.

(*h*) Floors, passages, and stairways are to be kept in good repair, and free from accumulations of dirt or size. Sand shall be provided for use on slippery floors.

II. **Fencing of Machinery and Other Safeguards:**

Winding Frames. Fencing shall be provided for:

(1) Traverse motion and mangle motion wheels, when on the outside of the frame; also when inside the frame, if the frame has an open end and the wheels are placed near that end.

(2) Where there is a double tin roller, the toothed wheels and the rope drive at the end of the rollers.

(3) Bevel wheels driving spindles of "Jumbo" cop winding frames.

Warping Machines. All bevel wheels, and also tooth and pinion wheels on winding-on machines shall be fenced.

Size Becks. The following shall be fenced:

(1) Bevel wheels working dashers, unless otherwise safe by position.

(2) Spur wheels at side of beck (if any).

(3) Cogs on boiling pan, and also the shaft connected with the same, if the shaft is on the floor level—unless these be otherwise safe by position.

Taping Machines:

(a) On new machines the distance between the periphery of the smaller and larger cylinders shall not be less than six inches.

(b) The following shall be fenced:

(1) Set-screws and bevel wheels on side shaft.

(2) Measuring motion wheels, unless safe by position.

(3) Bevel wheels and upright shaft for driving colored or top box (to be encased).

(4) Speed change wheels.

(5) Gears working cylinder at end of dry taping machines.

Looms:

(1) Shuttle guards to be provided in all cases. Rod guards shall be fixed as low as possible. A space of not less than five-eighths of an inch must be left between the temple and the guard, provided that this part of this rule shall not apply to velvet looms or to looms of 60-inch reed space and over. Laterally the guard shall extend to at least half the shuttle's length from the spindle stud bolt on overpick looms, or the trash plate on underpick looms.

(2) Except where the hammer head always extends over the breast beam, there shall be a space of not less than three-quarters of an inch between the hammer head and the beam.

(3) Duck-bills on all loose reed looms shall be protected both above and below, unless they are of such construction, or in such a position as to be equally safe as if they were protected.

(4) Tappet, twill motion and barrel motion wheels on all looms, whether placed underneath or at the side of looms, shall be fenced, unless they are safe by

position behind the balance wheel, with the ingathering point on the side next the slay.

(5) Overhead driving shaft on jacquard looms shall be fenced

(6) On new looms finger-room (one inch) shall be provided between the set-screws on the heald shaft and the top of the loom.

> *Note:* Agreed to for old looms, also, where space can be provided by the adjustment of bracket and where the distance between the healds and the slay suffices.

(7) There shall be a space of not less than one inch between the connecting rods driving the dobby and the framework of the loom, and between the stay and the picking-stick a space of not less than two inches.

(8) No weight shall be suspended from the weight rope, or hooked on to the top of another weight, and levers shall not be allowed to project in such a way as to obstruct the alley.

This rule shall only be deemed to apply to the bottom beam.

Plaiting Machines:

The spur wheels driving the bottom shaft shall be fenced.

III. Spacing of Looms:

In new sheds there shall be at the backs of the looms a space of at least a foot between the flanges of the beams, and in the alleys a space of not less than 2 feet 6 inches between slay and slay. Provided that in new sheds with looms over 72 inches in width, in which overhead trolleys for the beams are not provided, there shall be a space of 15 inches left between the flanges of the beams.

IV. Cleaning Machinery:

Women, young persons, and children shall not clean underneath any loom while it is in motion.

V. Lifting of Heavy Weights:

(1) Women, young persons, and children shall not be employed to lift, carry or move anything so heavy as to be likely to cause injury to them.

(2) Women, young persons, and children shall not assist the overlooker in lifting beams into the looms.

VI. Lighting of Dark Passages and Stairways:

Passages and staircases shall be effectively lighted either by natural or artificial means.

CHAPTER V

LIGHT AND ILLUMINATION IN FACTORIES

The Importance of Light in Factories. Light is an essential working condition in all industrial establishments and is also of paramount influence in the preservation of the health of the workers. There is no condition within industrial establishments to which so little attention is given as proper lighting and illumination. Especially is this the case in many of the factories in the United States. A prominent investigator who had extensive opportunities to make observations of industrial establishments in Europe as well as in America, states: "I have seen so many mills and other works miserably lighted that bad light is the most conspicuous and general defect of American factory premises. Germany and England are vastly more advanced in this respect than America." *

My own investigations for the New York State Factory Commission support this view. In these investigations it was found that 36.7 per cent of the laundries inspected, 49.2 per cent of the candy factories, 48.4 per cent of the printing places, 50 per cent of the ice cream plants and 64.8 per cent of the chemical establishments were inadequately lighted. There was hardly a trade investigated without finding a large number of inadequately lighted establishments.

According to another report, one-third of the shops in the cloak and suit industry of New York City were found to be inadequately lighted and artificial illumination was needed during the day.†
Inadequate and defective light is also complained of in practically every report of the factory inspectors in the different states.

An inspection of a large number of establishments in European countries has convinced me that light conditions are very much superior in these countries than in the United States. However, it would be wrong to state that lighting conditions in most of the factories abroad are perfect. The factory inspectors of England frequently complain of the bad lighting of factories, a fact which led

* Arthur Shadwell: Industrial Efficiency, Vol. II, p. 3.
† First Report of The Joint Board of Sanitary Control.

the English factory department to make a special report on the illumination of factories and workshops, which showed that there was a great deal of room for improvement. The same complaint comes from the factory inspectors of France. A prominent authority on the subject remarks that " the shops in France are lighted just as much as is absolutely necessary for production, not as much as is necessary for hygienic purposes; but how many factories are not even provided with sufficient light for production itself? " *

It is very difficult to determine just what percentage of industrial establishments is properly lighted. As a rule, where factories and workshops are constructed in isolated places, where most of the establishments are in one-story buildings, and where there is no congestion, lighting conditions are much better.

What are the consequences of defective lighting of industrial establishments? The consensus of opinion of all competent observers and investigators is that defective lighting of industrial establishments has an important bearing (1) on the cleanliness, cheerfulness and salubrity of the workplace, (2) on the efficiency of production, (3) on the number and character of accidents in industrial establishments, (4) on the causation of eye strain, (5) on the causation of certain eye diseases, and (6) on the general impairment of the health of the workers.

Cleanliness in a workshop is directly dependent upon the amount of light within the factory. As a rule, a dark shop is also a dirty shop; a light shop is usually a clean shop. Not only is a well lighted shop cleaner but it is also brighter and more cheerful. There is nothing so inimical to dirt as plenty of light. Light, and especially sunlight, has a direct influence upon the destruction of various bacterial organisms, especially tubercle bacilli. Moreover, there is a certain psychological effect of plenty of light in a factory upon the cheerfulness and well-being of the workers.

As to the increase of efficiency in production in all well-lighted shops, there is the testimony of a great many investigators that improved illumination means " a sensible increase in production and an appreciable decrease in seconds and spoilage." † R. Thurston Kent demonstrated that good illumination has a very important bearing on the time taken by an industrial process.‡ · " Summer-made cotton goods used to demand higher prices than winter goods, their quality being superior because of the better lighting conditions

* Hygiène Industrielle, Bruardelle. p. 183.
† Traveler's Standard, Vol. I, November, 1913, p. 287.
‡ Report quoted in Illuminating Engineer, London, No. 9, September, 1912, p. 422.

under which they were made."*   It is also reported that "the
operatives prefer in some places to work by night, since by working
on piece-work they could make more money than in the day time
because of the better illumination." †

The relation of inadequate factory lighting to the occurrence
of accidents has been proven over and over again. In a statement
issued by the Travelers' Insurance Company, the following assertion
is made: "It is generally estimated that approximately twenty-
five per cent of the avoidable accidents are due directly or indirectly
to poor illumination."

Many statements were made before the Departmental Committee
on Accidents to the effect that "defective lighting is a prolific cause
of accidents." In a recent discussion (of the Illuminating Section
of the Safety and Sanitation Conference) the importance which
good lighting played in securing safety was emphasized by a quotation from the report on the iron and steel industry prepared under
the direction of the Commissioner of Labor and submitted to the
United States Senate, in which a comparison of the day and night
accident rates for the six years included between 1905 and 1910
showed that in the mechanical departments the night accidents
exceeded those in the day by 118.3 per cent, and that the night
accidents in the yards exceeded those during the day by 127.6 per
cent. As all the conditions for night and day work were practically
the same excepting the illumination, this great increase in accidents
was ascribed by the Commissioner to poor illumination.‡

The International Harvester Company found that numerous
accidents resulted from bad lighting, and hence a general standard
was adopted. For general machine-shop lighting, $\frac{1}{4}$ candle-power
per square foot of floor area is the minimum, and in foundries where
smoke and vapor absorb much of the light, $\frac{1}{2}$ candle-power per
square foot. Tungsten lamps (100 watt) in enameled bowl-shaped
reflectors hung $10\frac{1}{2}$ feet above the floor at intervals of 18 feet give the
desired light. Wherever a more intense light is needed, as for
example on a machine tool, an 8-candle-power lamp under an
enameled cone shade is hung at the requisite angle. One of the
advantages to the company has been the reduction of defective
product. It is also claimed that the number of accidents has
greatly decreased.§

* Practical Considerations in Cotton Mill Illumination, National Association of Cotton
Manufacturers Transactions, 1912, p. 285.
    † Quoted by F. B. Ray, Industrial Engineer, Vol. II, p. 171.
    ‡ Quoted by Lighting Journal, Vol II, No. 1, January, 1914, p. 19.
    § United States Department of Labor Bulletin No. 123, p. 14.

The relation of defective light to eye strain has been discussed by a number of observers. Their reports state that defective light during work undoubtedly causes eye strain. All prolonged work and close application involving constant use of the eyes cause fatigue of the muscles of accommodation. Even when work is performed with plenty and good light, the long hours of labor, the close application to the work and the concentration of the eyes of the worker on the material are bound to cause fatigue and eye strain. Especially is this the case where the light is either inadequate or improper.

In the report of the medical factory inspector of the New York State labor department,* the inspector makes the following statement:

" I have found that a large number of women and young workers, especially girls, are employed in basements and cellars where the illumination throughout the entire day is by artificial means. This has an important bearing not only upon the condition of the eyes of the worker, but also upon the health, being a frequent cause of anæmia. I have also observed that in many instances where natural light is used, machinery is so placed as to obstruct this light, and thus the duties of the workers must be performed in semi-darkness which increases the number of accidents notwithstanding the guards."

That eye strain is not only harmful to the eyes but also to the general health of workers, has been clearly proven by the investigations of Dr. G. M. Gould and others who have traced the headaches, anæmia, backaches and the failing of general health of employes to eye strain caused by defective light.

As to the influence of bad lighting conditions upon the eyesight of workers, upon the causation of myopia and other diseases, there is abundant evidence in the reports of various investigators. Ramazzini, in 1700 A.D., remarked that many workers suffer from nearsightedness, especially those who do delicate work; such as type setters, watchmakers, jewelers, goldsmiths, embroiderers, draughtsmen, etc. In the investigations made by German scientists it was proved that certain workers, especially type setters and others, suffer from a high degree of myopia.

According to Froelich, 42 per cent of the type setters, according to Cohen, 51 per cent, according to Overweg, 48.9 per cent, according to Hazelberg, 48.8 per cent of type setters were myopic.† Accord-

---

* Tenth Annual Report, 1911, p. 71.
† Walter: Augenkrankheiten in Weyl's Handbuch der Arbeiter-Krankheiten, p. 700.

ing to Overweg, 47.7 per cent of engravers, according to Cohen, 45 per cent of lithographers had myopia. According to Walter, 75 per cent of weavers had the same defect. According to Netolitzky, house weavers and needle workers are apt to have weak eyesight, myopia and cataract.

Certain diseases, such as cataract, nystagmus and others are due either to defective or too glaring light. Thus, glass workers are

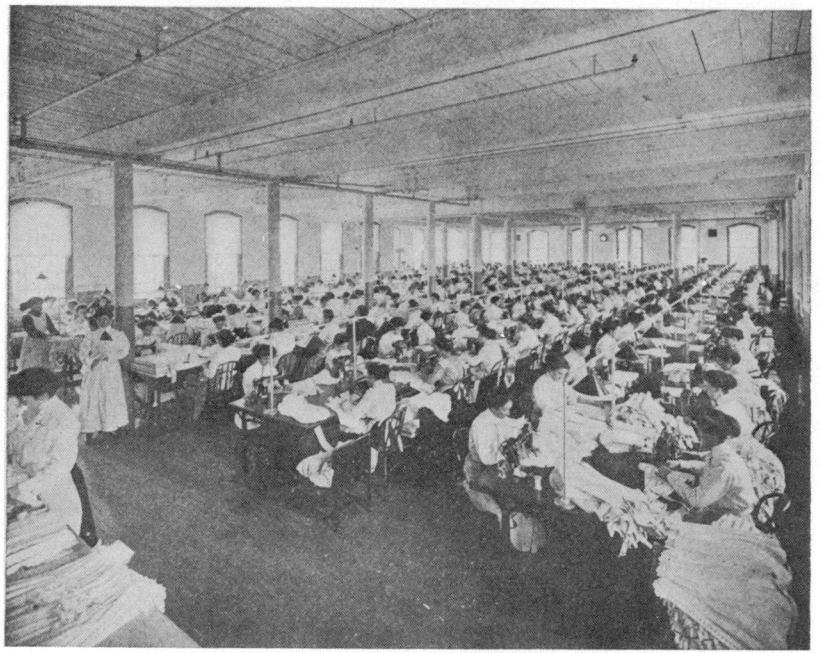

Courtesy Royal Worcester Corset Co.

Window and Reflected Light from Walls and Ceilings.   Localized Illumination for Each Table.

said to suffer from cataract. Formerly the injurious influences of glaring light were ascribed merely to the influence of light rays; now it is stated that they are due to the presence of ultra violet rays.* Workers at white goods, bleachers, engravers, polishers, tinsmiths, zinc molders, glass workers, steel makers, testers of arc lamps, etc., who work on materials reflecting glaring light very often suffer from retinitis, from other eye lesions and sometimes from the formation of cataracts.

* Walter, p. 680.

According to Dr. Court, nystagmus, from which a great many miners suffer, is due to insufficient light or too much eye-strain. Intense light causes dazzling and glare which injuriously affects the conjunctiva of the eye. The physiological effects are fatigue, strain, tears, redness of conjunctiva, stone blindness, seeing red, ophthalmia, and, at times, cataract.*

It is hardly necessary to cite any additional proof of the baneful influences of defective lighting in factories upon the workers and their health in order to prove the contention that industrial establishments should be adequately and properly lighted.

What is adequate and proper light? This is an important question which, however, has not as yet been fully answered. Almost all industrial codes and labor laws contain a provision that every industrial establishment must be *properly* and *suitably* lighted. No definite standards, however, are set to explain just what suitable lighting in a factory means. To this lack of standards of lighting in factories is due much of the present defective lighting in such establishments. The reason for the absence of such standards is that many of the lighting and illuminating engineers themselves have not come to definite conclusions as to the proper standards for the various conditions found in industrial establishments.

Of course, it is a matter of great difficulty to set definite standards for the conditions existing in industrial establishments in relation to light. There are so many factors which have to be taken into consideration, such as the personal factor, individual health of the operatives, condition of their eyes and eyesight, the construction of the workshop, its proximity to other buildings, the character of light, natural or artificial, the kind of work which is being done, the materials which are worked with, the duration of the work and a great number of other factors too numerous to mention. It is almost impossible, therefore, to set definite standards which would be applicable to all establishments or to all kinds of workshops. It is necessary to take into consideration local conditions in each workshop and set a standard for every industrial establishment; and, indeed, for every part of each industrial establishment. The standards would also vary according to the different kinds of light, such as daylight, artificial (direct, indirect and semi-indirect), and according to the various kinds of artificial lights, as well as to the different kinds of work and materials manipulated.

---

*.Augenschedigung durch Intensieve Belichtung, Zeitschrift für Unfallverhütung, etc. p. 61, 1911.

Courtesy National Lamp Works, General Electric Co.

Illumination in a Weaving Room.   (One 60-watt lamp for each group of four looms.)

The quantity and intensity of light may be considered in relation to the special place of work and to the surface upon which the work is performed. The quantity of light will depend upon the source and the kind of light which is let into the factory, and the adequacy of light will also depend upon the kind of material upon which the work is performed. Mr. Wilson, who has made the light investigations for the factory department of England, distinguishes two kinds of work, which he names respectively inspective and detective, according as the work entails continuous application of the eye to one point or small area, or consists merely in keeping general watch over a given process, actual labor being demanded only when some fault occurs. " The making up of clothing, handkerchiefs and type setting," he says " belong to the inspective class; while cotton and flax spinning and preparing belong to the detective class." The work of a watchmaker, jeweler, or draughtsman requires very much more light than the work of clothing or any needle workers. The work of a hand type setter, for instance, may also be divided into several kinds. It requires more light to decipher some of the manuscripts which the type setters have to set up, and certainly much more light than that which is necessary on the type stick itself. Proof-reading may require more light than any of those mentioned.

The surface brightness or the intrinsic brilliancy of a surface receiving light will depend not only upon the source of the light but also upon the kind of surface. According to Wilson, in a linen weaving shed the illumination intensity on brown cloth was found to be 3.4 foot-candles; while the surface brightness was only 1.0 foot-candle. This means that the brightness of the brown cloth illuminated with 3.4 foot-candles was the same as that of white cloth illuminated by one foot-candle, showing the difference in the necessary intensity of light for different colored materials.

Illumination is usually measured by photometers and is expressed in terms of a unit of illumination intensity and known as foot-candles. A foot-candle, or as it has been sometimes written a candle-foot, is the unit of illumination intensity, and is defined as " the direct illumination given by a standard candle one foot from the object illuminated."* It is very difficult to give a popular idea of this unit, but it may perhaps be said that very roughly one foot-candle corresponds to the minimum illumination intensity which allows small print to be read for a time without fatigue,

* Bell: Art of Illumination, p. 5.

0.1 foot-candle corresponds to the minimum illumination of a well-lighted street and 0.01 foot-candle to that of a badly lighted street. Cohen states that ordinary writing and reading need 10 meter-candles (1 foot-candle). On cloudy days the daylight indoors varies from 12 to 19 meter-candles, and on clear days from 22 to 70 meter-candles. He recommends a minimum illumination intensity of 2.5 foot-candles for schools. In the investigation made by Wilson in various factories, the illumination intensity in foot-candles was in some places as low as 0.01; while many other establishments had an illumination intensity up to 36 or more foot-candles.

Courtesy National Electric Light Assn.

An Example of Localized General Illumination.

60-watt tungsten filament lamps with porcelain enameled reflectors located 7 feet, 6 inches above the floor.

In Germany an illumination intensity of 10 meter-candles is considered sufficient to write and read by. For finer work 15 to 50 meter-candles are required. In Holland the law requires a minimum intensity of 10 bougie-meters (1 foot-candle) to be maintained and in some special industries such as sewing, embroidering, knitting, printing, etc., an intensity of 15 bougie-meters (1½ foot-candles) is required.

One of the most common light defects is the presence of glare.

Wilson defines glare as " the dazzling effect of a powerful light."
According to Professor L. Weber of Kiel:*

" A system of illumination may be described as glaring when it
exceeds any of the limits specified in the following, namely:

(a) If the ratio of the intrinsic brilliancy of the source of light
to that of the illuminated surroundings exceeds a certain
limit.   This ratio should not exceed a value of about 100.

Courtesy United Gas Improvement Co., Phila.

General Illumination from Gas Arc Lamps with Opal Globes, and Local Lighting over Sewing Machines with Reflex Incandescent Mantle Gas Lamps
Equipped with Opal Cone Reflectors.

(b) If the absolute intrinsic brilliancy of the source exceeds a
certain value.   The brilliancy of the open candle flame
(about 2.5 candles per square inch) might be taken as a
safe limit.

(c) If the angle between the direction of vision of the eye when
applied to the work it is called upon to do (e.g., when
gazing at a desk, blackboard or diagram on the wall,
etc.), and the line from the eye to the source of light is

* Quoted by Wilson.

too small. This minimum angle may be provisionally
assumed to be 30 degrees.

(*d*) When the extent (apparent area) of the illuminating body
is too large. The source should not subtend an angle
of more than 5 degrees at the eye.

Courtesy Royal Electric Co., Philadelphia.

Local Lighting of Sewing Machines in a Shirt Waist Factory.
(Aluminum finished metal reflectors with 40-watt Mazda lamps.)

In order, therefore, that a lighting system should be free from
glare, it is necessary that

(1) No source of light of intrinsic brilliancy should be so located
that it can readily be seen except at considerable distance.

(2) No considerable amount of light even from a well diffused
source should be allowed to enter the pupil of the eye
directly when it is focussed on the work; this usually

requires that no light source, unless remote, be visible when the head is inclined toward the working surface.

(3) It is desirable that the area within the field of vision be uniformly illuminated; at least, the brightness of any portion of this area should not be materially greater than that of the object under observation.

(4) Specular reflection should be guarded against so far as possible. Where the position of objects worked upon is fixed and the greater portion of the work is in one plane, lamps can be so placed as to avoid specular reflection in the direction of the eye. In the majority of operations in industrial plants, however, such conditions do not exist and one should direct his efforts toward producing conditions which will allow the operator to shift his position in such a manner that direct reflection cannot reach the eye.*

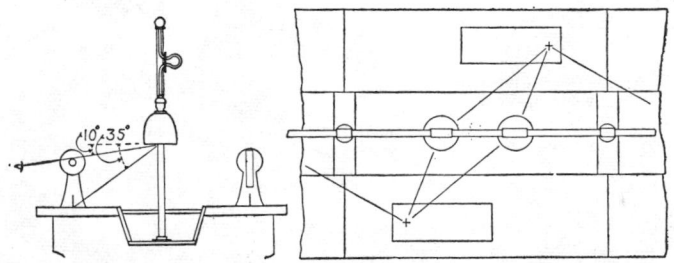

Courtesy Royal Electric Co., Philadelphia.

Plan and Elevation Showing Relative Positions of Lamps and Sewing Machines.

Natural Light. Most of the work in factories is performed during daytime by the aid of natural light. This light comes from direct rays of the sun or is reflected from various surfaces and diffused throughout the interior of the factory buildings. The great value of natural light is in its disinfecting properties and its general beneficent influence upon the health of persons. Its color is also pleasant for the eyes. The illumination given by daylight is general, in that it is spread throughout the whole room. The only disadvantages of daylight are that it is not always uniform, that its intensity depends upon the seasons, climate, time of the day and conditions of the weather, that it is difficult to increase the amount of light available for local conditions and on special materials where greater intensity of light is necessary, and, that the direct rays of the sun sometimes give too much glare.

* Industrial Lighting, Bulletin Engineering Dept., National Lamp Works of General Electric Company, October, 1913, p. 14.

Daylight is allowed to enter into buildings through openings specially made for that purpose, either on the top or side of the building. The amount of light which enters through an opening made at the top of a building or room is proportionately much greater than that which enters through an opening of the same size at the side of the building. This is due to the fact that when light comes from the top, a greater area of sky is effective, while when the light enters through windows on the side, the effective sky area is usually less and the angle such that direct light is

Courtesy National Electric Light Assn.

Glaring Light in the Eyes of the Workman.

secured only at those locations close to the windows, diffused light reaching the other parts of the interior only as it may be reflected from the floor and other surfaces near the windows. Top light is possible only in buildings where the light is let through either skylights or saw-tooth roofs. Cotton and other weaving sheds and factories are usually built one story in height where space is not costly and have either skylights or the so-called saw-tooth roofs, which give northern exposure and diffuse a very pleasant abundant light.

By far the greatest number of industrial establishments get their light by means of side windows. The amount of light which reaches the interior of buildings through windows depends upon a great many factors, such as the following: (*a*) height of adjoining buildings and the color of their walls; (*b*) the area of the window surfaces in comparison with the floor and other surfaces of the building which are to be lighted; (*c*) the size, depth and width of the building and rooms to be lighted; (*d*) the form and methods of construction of the window itself; (*e*) the surfaces within the factory; and (*f*) the story or place where the light is to enter.

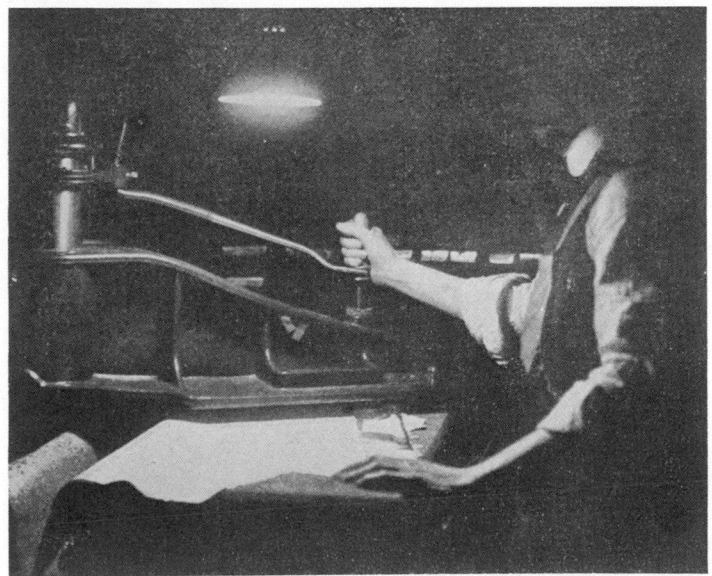

Improved Illumination with Properly Shaded Lamp.

The amount of light entering the windows of an industrial establishment depends upon the character of the obstructions near the building. If buildings of great height are in close proximity to the factory, it is natural that a large amount of light will be intercepted and lost. This is especially the case in concentrated industrial centers in big cities where shops are located in buildings of ten, twelve and more stories in height, and where, therefore, the windows of many buildings are cut off from the light. The wider the space between the buildings and the lower the adjoining building, the more light will naturally penetrate the windows. It is also natural that the lofts of the upper stories will get more light than the shops located in the lower stories of the building, especially those located on the first or second floors or in basements and cellars which may not have any direct sunlight at all.

As most of the light which enters loft buildings in overcrowded cities is reflected light, the color of the surfaces of these buildings is important, as there is more reflection from light than from dark surfaces. In all such buildings the surfaces of the outside walls should be light in color, painted or lime washed.

Courtesy Adler Bros., Rochester, N. Y.

Localized Illumination at the Point of the Needle.

No less importance must be attached to the proportion of window surface to the size of the room to be illuminated. Various standards are set by the industrial codes of different countries prescribing the exact proportion of the window area to the size of the room and to its surface. In Germany the following standards have been adopted by factory inspectors:

(1) 1 square meter of window area to every 30 cubic meters of room space.

(2) A square meter of window area to every 5 square meters of floor space.

(3) From 0.25 to 0.5 square meter of window area for every workplace.

(4) A ratio of windows to room area of 1 to 5 to 1 to 3.

No standards as to the ratio of window area to the surface area of the room are set for industrial establishments in the United States. The New York State tenement law requires windows in tenements to be from one-eighth to one-tenth of the superficial

Courtesy National Commercial Gas Assn.

Localizing Lighting of a Buffing Machine in a Shoe Factory.
(Reflex gas lamp with porcelain enameled angle metal reflector.)

area of the room. In school buildings the window area is from one-fourth to one-sixth of the floor area. It is evident that industrial establishments ought to have as large a window area as possible, and it should not be less than one-sixth of the floor area of the room. Indeed, this is exceeded in many factories, where the walls are all windows with the exception of the steel supporting columns.

The amount of light will also depend upon the height of the room and its width and depth. The rays of the light coming through the window fall at an angle and reach only to a certain distance from the window, and if the depth or width of the room is too great, a large part of the room will not be reached by the rays coming through the window, and may remain wholly or partly dark. The deeper the room, the less uniform the distribution of light. The height of a room is also of importance because the higher the room is, the greater will be the quantity of light admitted, provided the top of the window is near the ceiling.

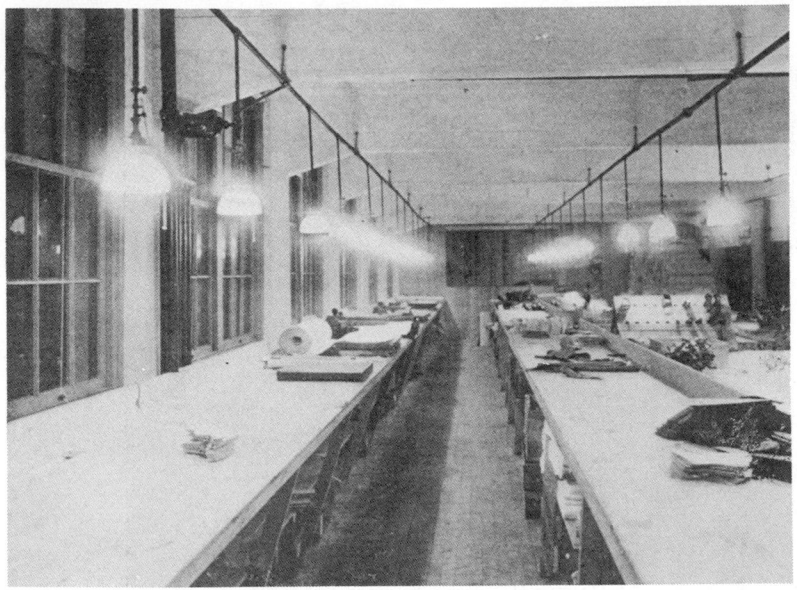

Courtesy National Commercial Gas Assn.

Localized-general Illumination of Cutters' Tables in a Shoe Factory.
(Reflex gas lamps with deep heavy opal reflectors.)

The form of the window and its construction contribute toward determining the amount of light entering it. The larger the panes, the fewer the columns between the panes, the higher the window is in the wall and the nearer it is to the ceiling, the greater will be the amount of light. Light coming from the southeast or southwest is the best; north light is also good. Light coming from many sides is not so good as that coming from two sides opposite to each other.

The kind of window glass is also of importance. The loss of light in plain sheet glass is 4 per cent; double glass, 9 to 13 per cent; milk glass, 35 per cent; green or red glass, 80 to 90 per cent. The glass should also be kept clean, as about 30 per cent of light is lost through glass which is covered with dust and 72 per cent through glass which is very dirty.*

Clear plate glass is the best. A larger amount of light is said to be gained by using ribbed glass, because the rays of light instead of falling directly on the floor are refracted by the uneven, wavy surfaces of the glass and are directed more nearly horizontally

Courtesy Welsbach Co., Gloucester, N. J.

Localized-general Illumination.

(Reflex inverted gas lamps with Holophane glass reflectors, lamps arranged in rows over the center of machine tables.)

further into the room, thus illuminating a larger area within the room than would be possible through the use of plain glass. Still more light may be secured with properly designed prism glass.

Next in importance are the surfaces of the walls, ceilings and floors within the shop. A considerable amount of light is reflected from these surfaces depending upon their color and cleanliness. White and light colored surfaces reflect more light than brown and other colors and should be preferred in all factories.

* Nussbaum: Leitfaden der Hygiene.

Machines and appliances within a factory must be so located as not to interfere with the light. It is best to arrange the work benches and tools so that the light should if possible fall over the backs and heads of the workers instead of coming in front of their eyes. When the direct glare of sunlight is too great it may be modified by the use of shades, or curtains. In most factories some provision must be made for artificial illumination, for those

Courtesy United Gas Improvement Co., Phila.

Localized-general Illumination, Using One Reflex Gas Lamp with Holophane Prismatic Glass Reflector for Each Pair of Machines.

seasons, periods and times of day when natural light fails. Considering the importance of artificial lighting, the cost of labor, the materials of manufacture, and the relative high efficiency of the modern light sources, adequate illumination is to-day exceedingly inexpensive. The cost must be considered in conjunction with the factor of efficiency and the general cost of production.

Artificial Illumination. The exigencies of industry demand the continuation of industrial activity not only during daylight but also when there is no daylight, or when daylight is insufficient or inadequate. Artificial illumination has certain advantages over daylight. Its intensity may be graduated more easily than that of daylight and a greater uniformity, a better local light and improved distribution may also be gained.

The requirements for efficient artificial illumination are (1) that it should be of the required intensity, (2) of a color as nearly as

Courtesy National Commercial Gas Assn.

Localized-general Illumination for Sewing Machine Operators on Gloves.
(One reflex gas lamp with opal dome reflector to each two machines.)

possible to daylight, (3) that it should be uniform and steady throughout the workshop, (4) that it should not cause glare, (5) that it should be so located as to avoid the casting of shadows upon the working plane, (6) that its installation should be safe, (7) that it should add as few impurities to the air as possible, and (8) that it should cost as little as possible.

Reference has already been made to the varying requirements for intensity of illumination for certain industries, establishments

and kinds of work. As to the color of artificial illumination, the
nearer such color is to that of daylight the more hygienic it is considered. Different kinds of illumination give a somewhat different
color spectrum and at times have a predominance of one color.
The white color of an electric arc light or of an incandescent mantle
gas burner is nearer to daylight than other lights. A Cooper Hewitt
mercury-vapor lamp does not contain red rays, but is rich in green,
blue and violet rays. Red rays are accompanied with heat emanations and are largely predominating in most of our present light

Courtesy Edison Lamp Works of General Electric Co.

Localized-general Illumination in a Machine Shop.

(Flat-dome enameled steel reflectors with 100-watt Mazda lamps hung 9 ft. above the floor
for localized illumination and 11 ft. high for general illumination; over the benches.
60-watt lamps with enameled steel bowl-shaped reflectors spaced on 8-ft. centers, 3 ins.
in from the forward edge of the bench and 5 ft. above the bench.

sources, particularly the gas and petroleum flame burners. When
too near the operative their heat may become oppressive. As
to the Cooper Hewitt light, it is claimed that where discernment
of detail is essential this light has many advantages. Many
workers, however, object to the ghastly effect of these mercury
vapor lamps, due to the absence of red rays. In sugar refineries
the blue-green light is found necessary to enable the workers to
find impurities in the white refined sugar, and I found no complaint against its use, although here and there among the workers I found the presence of a conjunctivitis. In a large film

factory where several hundred girls were working for eight or nine hours under red light which was necessary for the delicate film, no complaint was made by the employes and they all seemed to be in good health, and the firm claimed that an examination made by an oculist disclosed no injurious effect upon the eyes.

The uniformity of artificial illumination depends upon the proper location of the lights. The absence of glare is provided for by the proper shading of lights and will be referred to later. The casting

Courtesy National Commercial Gas Assn.

Local Lighting for Engravers and Jewelry Manufacturing.

(Inverted incandescent mantle gas lamps with porcelain enameled reflectors suspended on anti-vibrators.)

of shadows by a light upon the work plane may be easily avoided by proper location of the light as well as by the arrangement of work benches. The safety of the installation for artificial illumination is provided for by various municipal and state fire regulations, as well as the fire underwriters, which regulations are usually well known to those called upon to make the installation.

The means of artificial illumination in most modern factories at the present day are acetylene gas, illuminating gas and electricity. There are few modern factories which are lighted by petroleum oil,

except perhaps some small workshops in the tenement-house districts of large industrial centers. Acetylene gas is made from
calcum carbide in special generators which are placed usually
outside of the establishment and the gas is piped through the building in the same was as city gas. Acetylene gives an intense,
brilliant white light which must be properly shaded in order to avoid
glare. It is used in establishments in rural districts where neither
illuminating gas nor electricity can be provided. Illuminating
gas is used in a large number of factories. Open-flame burners
are so inefficient and otherwise unsatisfactory that their use should

Courtesy National Electric Light Assn.

General Illumination in Composing Room of a Modern Printing Office.

be discontinued. Incandescent mantle burners in all sizes, with
single and multiple mantles, upright and inverted, have been on
the market sufficiently long to prove their economic value. These
mantles give a brilliant light and should be well shaded or used
with opal or other light-diffusing glassware.

Electricity is used in arc lamps, both of the flame carbon and
older enclosed carbon types; the latter, however, are being used
less frequently, due to their comparative inefficiency. Incandescent electric lamps are used more frequently; the older form, with
the carbon filament, gave a light of low intensity, the sizes in use

ranging from eight to thirty-two candle-power. These lamps are rapidly being replaced with the metal-filament incandescent lamps, the tungsten or Mazda lamps, by which higher intensities at about one-third the former cost may be secured. These lamps are available in a wide range of sizes and while somewhat fragile when first introduced some years ago, they are now amply strong for factory use.

Methods of artificial illumination in industrial plants may be divided into three classes, according to the kinds and positions of the lamps used: general, localized, localized-general.

Courtesy Lighting Journal, N. Y.

General Illumination for Hand Ironers in a Laundry.

(Deep-bowl metal reflectors with interior finish of aluminum paint with 150-watt Mazda lamps spaced on 20-ft. centers, 11 ft. above the floor.)

General illumination in factories is gained by the use of comparatively large units placed near the ceiling and gives illumination throughout the whole workroom. The advantages of this system are that it costs comparatively little for installation as well as for maintenance and in many locations this system is economical and otherwise satisfactory. It is especially adapted for large, high, open workrooms where a general distribution of light is more necessary than a local centralization of light in special places. Indirect lighting fixtures are also used for general illumination. These are fixtures using opaque reflectors underneath the lamps which direct the light upon the ceiling from where it is reflected throughout the room. This system should be used only where the ceiling and wall surfaces are of a light color and can be kept clean. While indirect light is well diffused, much of the light is absorbed by the ceiling and wall surfaces and it is therefore not as economical as direct lighting. Semi-indirect lighting is very similar to indirect lighting with the exception that in place of an opaque reflector, a translucent reflector of heavy opal or some such material is used. With these fixtures direct light is received from the enclosing bowl together with indirect light from the ceiling surface. In the past arc lamps, both gas and electric, were used for general llumination. The large tungsten units are at present being used in preference to arc lamps and in many installations where color discrimination is not a factor, mercury-vapor lamps are rendering satisfactory service.

The opposite of general illumination is localized lighting. It is provided for by lamps of low candle-power and intensity, which are placed directly above or near the work upon which the light is to be thrown. Such light is hardly ever used without some other illumination for the reason that local lighting alone leaves the general factory dark, and the difference between the intense local light and the general darkness throughout the room is not good for the eyes. Local lights may be used with benefit in certain work such as sewing on a machine or in other trades where close application is needed. Small lamps with flexible stands may be then placed near the operative, or special, low candle-power incandescent bulbs may be installed near the machines, as shown in the several illustrations.

Perhaps a better form of illumination is what is called localized-general illumination, which is gained by the uniform spacing of tungsten filament incandescent lamps or incandescent mantle burners of a desirable intensity. Various size lamps are used in different locations throughout the shop to increase the intensity of illumination for various machines or benches, or to reduce it in other locations where a high intensity is not desirable. This results in a very satisfactory arrangement. It is best when using such lamps to install them with permanent, well-constructed fixtures, and arrange them so that the workers cannot handle them or adjust them according to their notions. The distribution of these lamps about eight or nine feet above the floor is best for general purposes in factories with ceilings not more than twelve to thirteen feet above the floor.

The quantity of light from tungsten lamps varies with the size of the lamps, which range from 10 to 1000 watts. For general illumination the larger sizes are used, the 500- to 1000-watt lamps being adapted for high ceilings. For local illumination, lamps from 15 to 40 watts are used; while for localized-general illumination lamps of 60 to 150 watts are used. Tungsten, or as they are most generally called, Mazda lamps are rated at an efficiency which will result in an average useful life of 1000 hours, at which point the light output should be about 80 per cent of the initial, beyond which point it is cheaper to substitute a new lamp. The average useful life of these lamps is more than twice that of the old carbon lamps.

The light of the tungsten lamp is white or in color and is pleasant and agreeable to the eyes. These lamps give a brilliant light and are suitable to all kinds of rooms and buildings. The maximum intensity of light emanating from tungsten lamps is at right angles to the filament. With the lamp hanging pendent, this maximum is in a horizontal direction and can be redirected with suitable reflectors downward on to the work bench or otherwise directed as may be desired for a general distribution of light over the whole floor space. It is an economical lamp, consuming from 0.6 watt in the larger sizes to 1.25 watts in the smaller sizes per mean horizontal candle-power and is made for use on all commercial lighting circuits from 100 to 130 volts and 200 to 260 volts.

Single lamps of large wattage are preferable to clusters of smaller lamps giving equal light.

Almost all kinds of lamps must be provided with shades and reflectors to modify their intensity and protect the eyes of the operatives from the harmful brilliancy of the lamp filament or incandescent mantle and from glare. There is perhaps no worse form of illumination than that from an unshaded lamp at close range, covered only with the common wire basket or guard which is supposed to protect inflammable materials. Practically all of our modern light sources if in close proximity to the worker, are apt to result in too much glare and whether in general, local, or localized-general illumination, some form of shade or reflector should be used. The reflectors are also necessary to redirect the light rays and insure an installation of reasonable efficiency. Reflectors are made of various materials: glass, metal with porcelain enamel and white enamel paint on the inner surfaces. The kind and shape of reflector to use depends upon the location and position of the lamp and the manner in which the light is to be distributed. Wherever reflectors are used, it is preferable from the standpoint of maintenance to use one type throughout the shop or room.

Opal or prismatic glass reflectors have been used to a considerable extent. These reflectors result in the illumination of the ceiling and walls as well as the work places.

The common type of reflector used in many industrial establishments is one which evenly distributes the light over the working plane and for many locations the best reflectors are of steel with white porcelain enamel finish; they do not corrode, are not affected much by gas and smoke and are strong enough for all purposes.

The latest orders of the Wisconsin Industrial Commission in respect to shop lighting are of interest. They are as follows:

Artificial Light Where no Gas or Smoke. Each place of employment in which hand or machine operations are performed, must be supplied during the working hours, when daylight is not available, with artificial light equivalent in amount, for each 4 square feet of floor space, to not less than the light produced by a one candle-power lamp hung 10 feet from the floor.

Artificial Light Where Gas and Smoke. In foundries, forge shops and other industries where there is smoke and gas which obstruct the light, sufficient artificial light must be supplied to overcome the obstruction and to furnish the standard amount on the floor space specified above.

Warehouses and Storage Places. Each place of employment in which hand or machine operations are not performed, such as warehouses, vat rooms and storage places, must be supplied during the working hours, when daylight is not available, with artificial light equivalent in amount for each 8 square feet of floor space, to not less than the light produced by a one candle-power lamp hung 10 feet from the floor.

In each place of employment where fine or close work is being done, such as fine lathe work, engraving, typesetting and drafting, and where the standard of light specified above is not sufficient to prevent injurious eye strain, sufficient light must be provided in every case to avoid unnecessary eye strain.

Note. In many cases it is advisable to provide individual lights for each machine, bench or table. It is exceedingly important that these lights be equipped with proper reflectors which can be kept clean, and which so reflect the light that the eyes are not subjected to the glare of the light, and eye strain is avoided.

CHAPTER VI

FACTORY SANITATION

LIVING as they do for nine, ten and more hours daily within the walls of the factory, workingmen are profoundly affected in their health, in their habits, and in their personal appearance, by the conditions under which they work in these factories. A sanitary shop is one in which the health of the workers is well conserved and which is cleanly, cheerful and efficient. The sanitary care of a factory and the provision of necessities and comforts for the use of employes are indispensable to industrial efficiency.

The conception of factory sanitation includes all those measures, provisions and appliances in an industrial establishment which are needed for the preservation of the health of the workers and the prevention of disease. Practically, however, the scope of factory sanitation is limited to provisions for drinking water, washing and dressing facilities, disposal of refuse, sewage and wastes, and the preservation of general cleanliness.

The following is a classification of those items of factory sanitation which will be discussed in this chapter:

(1) General Cleanliness.
    (*a*) Removal of dust from surfaces.
    (*b*) Removal of accumulated dirt and rubbish from shop.
(2) Provision of Certain Necessities and Comforts.
    (*a*) Drinking water.
    (*b*) Dressing rooms.
    (*c*) Washing facilities.
(3) Disposal of Refuse, etc.
    (*a*) Disposal of sewage.
    (*b*) Disposal of odors, smoke, gases and fumes.
    (*c*) Disposal of factory wastes.

General Cleanliness. In spite of the importance of cleanliness to the efficiency and health of the workers, this matter is much neglected by employers and employes. As one who has made official inspections of a great many thousand industrial establish-

259

ments throughout the United States as well as in various countries abroad, I can testify that there is hardly a part of factory sanitation which is so much neglected as general cleanliness in a shop. This is true not only of one state or industry, but is general in the establishments in many different countries, except, perhaps, in Germany where the industrial establishments seem to me to be the cleanest of any I have seen.

The walls, ceilings, floors, fixtures and machinery, are apt to be covered by much dust and dirt in every factory not having artificial or local ventilation. The layers of dust when covering lighting fixtures, reduce the amount of light in the factory and when deposited upon the walls and ceilings, greatly reduce the light reflected from the surfaces. The walls and ceilings are not only apt to be covered with dust, but are frequently marred by grime and dirt which adhere to them for a long time, and indicate that these surfaces are only cleaned at long intervals. In all labor codes and factory laws there are rules and regulations requiring the owner to clean the walls and ceilings and to limewash them at certain intervals and at the order of the factory inspectors. Owners of industrial establishments would find that it would pay them to have the surfaces of the walls and ceilings frequently cleaned and painted a light color, as this increases the light within the establishment and pays in increased production and efficiency. Of course, there are a number of large industrial establishments which endeavor to keep all the surfaces within the factory in a clean condition. This is accomplished by the hiring of a special cleaning squad and putting the responsibility of the general cleanliness of the shop upon special persons. With motive power present in practically every workshop, there is no reason why a system of vacuum cleaning, which would do the work of cleaning efficiently, cannot be installed and maintained in every industrial plant. I believe this would pay for itself in a very short time.

The cleaning of floors is usually much neglected in ordinary factories. The cleanliness of the floor depends a great deal upon the material of which it is constructed; but whatever the material may be, the difficulties of cleaning it are not insurmountable. Perhaps the best method of cleaning floors and also walls and ceilings is by means of a hose with water under pressure. Of course, this can be done only in places where the water will not injure the machinery or the materials in the manufacturing plant. In plants where deleterious poisons such as lead are employed, the cleaning of the floor should be done by means of hot water and scrubbing brush; where much organic matter is used, with some disinfectant, such as a solution of lysol, carbolic acid, etc. Floors should be free from cracks, crevices, ruts, etc., which must be repaired as soon as noticed. The dry sweeping of floors is objectionable, especially when done during working hours, as it raises dust which spreads upon materials and is inhaled by the workers.

In an investigation of 5124 workshops which was made by the New York State Factory Commission during 1911–12, the general cleanliness was considered good in only 41.9 per cent of the shops, poor in 34.2 per cent of the shops, and bad in 19.2 per cent of the shops. As to the industries in which the greatest percentage of unclean shops was found, 93.1 per cent of the shops in which human hair goods were made, were very dirty, 82.2 per cent of places where mineral water was manufactured were in the same condition, 80 per cent of the ice cream shops, 76.6 per cent of the candy and 50.8 per cent of the bread and bakery establishments investigated were also in a bad sanitary condition.

Of great importance to the general cleanliness of a shop is the prompt and efficient removal of all rubbish, sweepings, clippings, etc. Labor codes usually have regulations requiring the daily removal from buildings of all kinds of waste materials, and the provision of receptacles of fireproof material in which the rubbish, sweepings, clippings, etc., should be deposited in order not to litter the floors and other surfaces with this material. There are a number of forms of receptacles which are available for this purpose. Incinerators and destructors may be easily installed in every plant and greatly facilitate the work of destroying all waste matter. Where clippings, or rubbish, may be of some value, they should be stored in proper receptacles or pressed into bales and removed daily.

The habits of a great many workers are such that it is very difficult to induce them to deposit all rubbish in the receptacles provided, instead of throwing waste matter upon the floor. A system of education in sanitary matters is necessary in order to persuade employes to conform to the general rules of sanitation and to gain their cooperation in keeping the place clean.

In view of the possible presence in every workshop of one or more employes who are victims of tuberculosis, the disposal of sputum and also the proper cleaning and disinfection of cuspidors should not be neglected. The mere prohibition of spitting is insufficient, and the posting of notices and signs has not much effect.

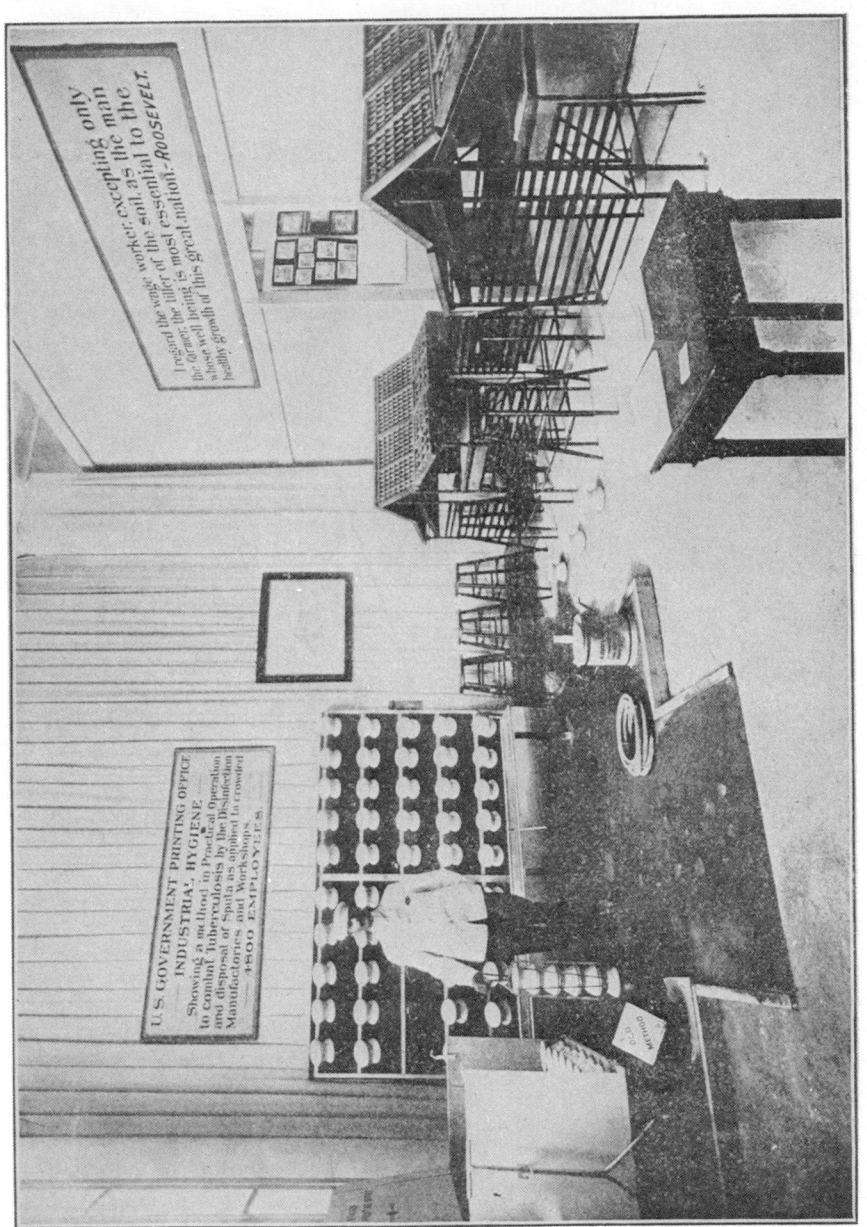

Methods of Cleaning and Disinfecting Cuspidors used in United States Printing Office.

Suitable cuspidors should be provided and it is necessary to have a sufficient number of them in order to prevent the employes from spitting upon the floors. I have seen some cuspidors in France made in the form of a porcelain or enamel iron bowl permanently attached to a waste pipe, trapped and provided with a water-supplied faucet. Hard vitrified china is probably the best material because of the possibility of the use of bichloride of mercury or some other corrosive poison as a disinfectant. The cuspidors should be so designed as to permit easy cleaning and self-draining, should contain no angles to interfere with the cleaning process, and should have a wide neck so as to permit cleaning them with a hose if necessary. They should contain some disinfecting solution, as it has been found that it is difficult to clean these cuspidors properly if they contain no such solution. Cuspidors may also be filled with sawdust.

In the United States Government Printing Office, Dr. Manning has devised a sanitary clutch which picks up the cuspidors, one above the other, in " nests " of five, without the hands of the cleaner in any manner coming in contact with the infected or soiled cuspidors, thus entirely avoiding the irksome, repulsive features which characterize the methods of washing spittoons in vogue at present, and greatly minimizing the danger of infection. The vessels thus collected are carried by means of the clutch to specially designed wooden, zinc-lined box trucks with detachable sides. Each truck is capable of holding 175 cuspidors for transmission to the sterilizing chamber. After the trucks are filled they are transmitted from the respective floors to the basement on a freight elevator and wheeled directly into the sterilizing chamber. The contents of the cuspidors are emptied into a trough connecting with the sewer by means of short forceps which grasp the lip of the cuspidor. After the vessel has been made thoroughly clean and sterilized by immersion in boiling water, the operator, still grasping the forceps, presses the vessel into the steel spring clutch on the rack, where it drains and dries, as shown in the photograph. It is then washed with a solution of bichloride of mercury sufficient to kill the most resistant disease germs.

Water Supply for Drinking Purposes. Every industrial establishment needs an adequate supply of water for drinking purposes. The quantity of water needed must be sufficient for all seasons and conditions. The sources of supply do not depend upon the manufacturer, when the industrial establishment is located in a city where water is received from the public supply system. In factories located in rural communities the question of the water supply is of great importance, as the ordinary sources, such as nearby rivers or lakes, are liable to be contaminated with sewage, factory waste, sludge, etc. In such cases it is necessary for the employer to get water from a carefully selected source, uncontaminated by sewage and organic matter. The supply of water is usually conducted through pipes, pumped to the highest part of the factory into tanks,

Courtesy Eastman Kodak Co.

Drinking Fountains.

and supplied from those tanks to the various parts of the building. The tanks should be properly constructed, covered and guarded against contamination and frequently cleaned. The hardness or softness of the water is of importance for industrial as well as for drinking purposes. The hardness of the water depends upon the presence of carbonate of lime and of sulphates and chlorides. Temporary hardness, which may be driven off by boiling, is caused by carbonate of lime; permanent hardness depends upon the presence of chlorides, sulphates, salts of magnesium, etc., and cannot be removed by boiling.

Water for drinking purposes should be purified, and the best methods are filtration and distillation. In filtration the water passes through a material which is capable of retaining some or all the impurities. The value of a water filter depends upon (1) the character of the filtering medium and its ability to retain and remove from the water as many impurities as possible, (2) the rapidity and thoroughness of the filtering process, (3) the ready cleaning of the

Courtesy Standard Sanitary Mfg. Co., Pittsburgh.

Bubbling Valve Drinking Fountain.

filtering media, and (4) the simplicity, cheapness and accessibility of the filter. In the Berkefeld filter, infusorial earth is the filtering medium. It is pressed in the form of hollow tubes. The water is forced up through the fine pores of the filter and flows out at the top. It is claimed for this filter that when new it will remove all organic matter and bacteria from the water. The filter is made in various forms and sizes, and may be attached to the house sink faucet. The filtering tube must be frequently removed, sometimes more than once a day, and the dirt accumulated upon the surfaces washed off, otherwise the filtering process becomes slower and slower and stops when the pores of the tubes become clogged.

In establishments where there is reason to suspect that the source of the water supply is contaminated, the best purification method is distillation. There are many distilling apparata for water which may be conveniently and cheaply installed in the factory. During the summer, it is necessary for the comfort of the employes to cool the water, and, in a great many of the better class factories, water coolers, in which water is cooled by means of ice or by the ammonia process, are provided.

In large industrial establishments, a water-cooling plant of the mechanical refrigeration type may be installed, and the cooled water supplied to the several floors through well-insulated pipes. A small rotary pump will keep the water in circulation, flow and return pipes being provided, so that cold water will be on tap as soon as a faucet is opened. In large plants occupying several buildings and spread over several acres of ground, the drinking fountains should be scattered over the premises so they will be available without loss of time. Wherever a bubble fountain is set up under such conditions, a separate cooler will be necessary, as it would not be economical or practical to pump cooled water to all parts of the plant from a central station on account of the expense of insulation, or the alternative of great loss of cold. The most practical solution is to have a coil of tin pipe in an ice chest or cooler near each fountain, to cool the water used there. These cooling coils may be placed in any convenient place nearby, or in an ice cellar built in the ground alongside of the fountain and covered with an iron manhole cover.*

Drinking water fixtures should be located on every floor, accessible to all employes and at not too great distance from any part of the room, so that the employes need not waste too much time in walking to and from the fixtures.

The old method of providing a single cup for all the employes is condemned by all sanitarians. It has been proved that the common drinking cup is a carrier of infectious disease, and its use is prohibited by many sanitary codes. The substitution of individual or paper cups for the common drinking cup is better, but it is not practicable in large industrial establishments. Drinking fountains so constructed that the water flows at all times, and drinking is

* J. J. Cosgrove: "Factory Sanitation," Standard Sanitary Manufacturing Co., p. xx–xxi.

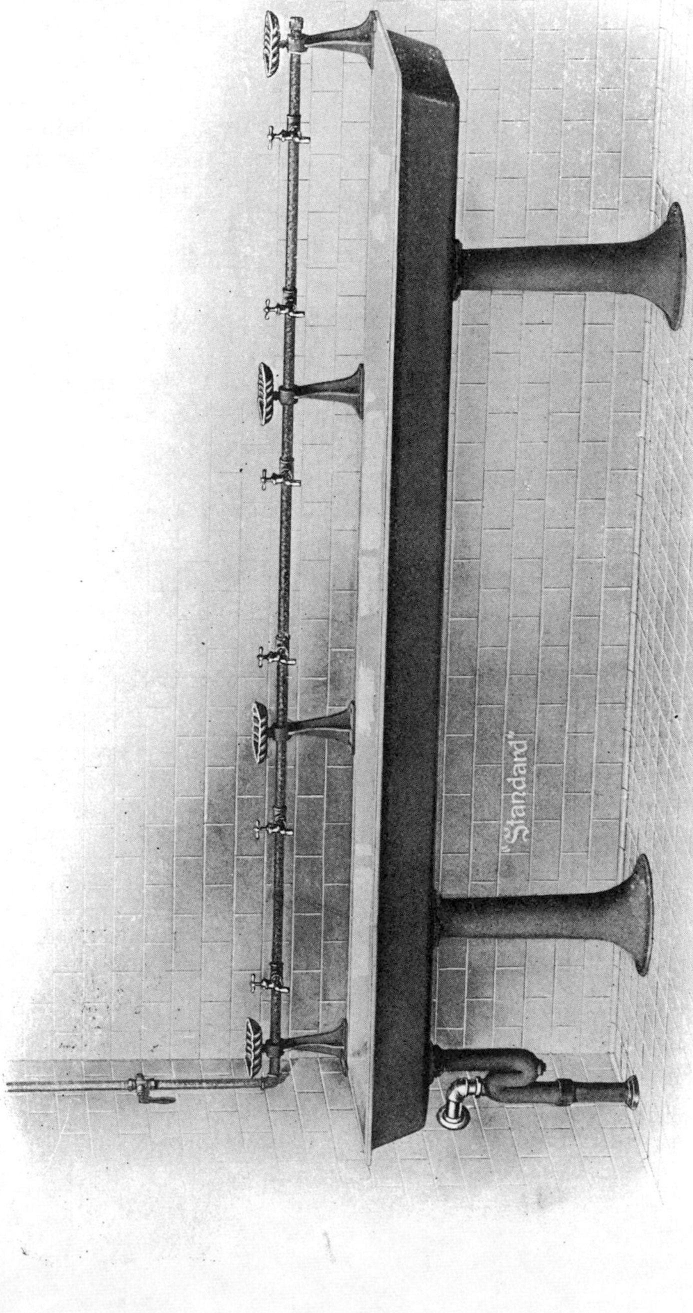

Courtesy Standard Sanitary Mfg. Co., Pittsburgh.

A Factory Wash Sink.

possible without contaminating any stationary fixture, are now regarded as best from a sanitary standpoint.

Sanitary drinking-water fountains sometimes called bubble-
valve fountains must be so constructed that the person using them
drinks from a stream or jet, and cannot put his lips on the outlet
for water. Every fountain must be so arranged that waste water
will be carried away without slopping.

Washing Facilities. There is much dust and dirt in every industrial establishment, and almost all work soils the hands and other
exposed parts of the bodies of the workers. Some materials are
injurious to health, and others, such as arsenic, are virulent poisons
when absorbed by the body. It is therefore essential for general
cleanliness as well as for the prevention of disease that ample
provision be made in every industrial establishment for washing the
hands and other exposed surfaces of the body.

Very inadequate provision is commonly made for washing
facilities in this country, and very little attention is paid to this important sanitary subject by employers. In an investigation made
by the New York State Factory Investigating Commission, the
inspectors found washing facilities inadequate in 71.8 per cent of
the shops. In a large number of establishments the washing facilities were located in a distant part of the building, and it required
considerable time for the employes to reach them. This inconvenient location of washing facilities shows general inefficiency in the
management of the shop, and is a direct source of waste of time
and energy. As Mr. Cosgrove well says:

" The necessity for modern sanitation in the factory does not
rest entirely upon the value of sanitation for hygienic reasons, but
is made imperative by the fact that money is saved, production
cheapened, cost of maintenance lessened, better employes secured,
and their efficiencies enhanced, by the proper number and distribution of sanitary appliances. If, for instance, in a factory
employing 500 men, each loses 3 minutes a day walking an unnecessary distance to water-closet or urinal, or waiting in line at the
toilet convenience for their turns, it would mean a loss each year
of over three working days for one man. Allowing an average wage
of $2.00 per day and 300 working days in the year, then the loss
from this cause alone would be $1800, annually, or an amount
sufficient to pay interest at 5 per cent on $36,000 for extra equip-
ment." *

It is absurd for employers to blame their employes for lack

* J. J. Cosgrove: "Factory Sanitation," Standard Sanitary Manufacturing Co., p. vii.

of cleanliness, if these employers do not provide proper washing facilities. In some of the factories I inspected, the washing facilities were so crude and antiquated, that no one could blame the employes for refusing to use them.

Whether the wash basins should be put in the shop or in separate wash-rooms is a matter which must be decided according to the needs of the establishment. Wherever there are a large num-

Courtesy Adler Bros., Rochester, N. Y.

Dressing Room with Sanitary Washing Arrangements and Individual Lockers.

ber of women, it is essential to provide separate wash-rooms properly lighted and ventilated and kept in a clean condition. The number of wash basins with faucets for the employes depends very much upon the character of the work, and in some industrial codes the ratio has been set at one faucet with wash basin for every 15 employes.

It is to be regretted that there are so few establishments where hot water is supplied in the wash-rooms or for the wash basins. New York and several other state industrial codes require hot water supplied in all establishments where lead or other poisons are

being worked with. Hot water, however, should be supplied in
every establishment, for the reason that it is difficult to cleanse
the hands without it, and many employes fail to use the washing
facilities because of the absence of hot water. In foundries and
similar shops, common sink troughs with separate faucets for every
ten-foot space may be used; but these sinks should be made of
white enameled iron, or of earthenware. In other establishments

Courtesy Pierce Arrow Motor Car Co.

Individual Wash Basins for Employes.

it is best to have individual wash basins. Sinks and wash basins
should be made of vitrified glazed earthenware or enameled iron.
If there is not sufficient daylight in the neighborhood of these
fixtures, artificial illumination should be maintained.

A supply of soap is a necessary adjunct, and the complaint of
many employers that this is costly because employes misappropriate
the pieces of soap, may be met by supplying tilting soap powder
dishes or soft green soap which is very good for washing purposes.
The common towel, especially the roller variety, is to be condemned,

and individual or paper towels should be furnished.   Of equal importance with the provision of washing facilities is proper supervision by the factory authorities to make sure that they are used. There are very few factories where the washing up at noon is compulsory or supervised by foremen. This is absolutely necessary in some establishments, especially where injurious substances are employed.

One of the reasons why plumbism is being eliminated in the Pullman car shops at Pullman, Illinois, is the stringent lavatory supervision at the noon hour.   Ten minutes before the noon hour the bell is rung and all employes are compelled to go to the central wash-rooms, where they are furnished with individual nailbrushes, soap and towels, and where they spend five to ten minutes in the process of washing, this process being supervised by foremen.   I was not surprised to learn that since the introduction of this " washup " system, the number of persons suffering from lead poisoning in the Pullman Company has been reduced from seventy-seven in July, 1911, to none in July, 1912.   The mere provision of wash basins and water is not sufficient to insure the proper cleansing of the hands, which is so necessary to the health of the employes in certain trades.

Dressing Rooms. Much of the work performed in industrial establishments soils the clothing worn by the workers.   It is therefore necessary to provide places in which workers may take off their street clothes, don their overalls or other special clothes to be worn while at work, and change their clothes at the end of the working day.   In establishments where there is much humidity, dampness or water, or where poisonous substances are being worked with, it is absolutely necessary to have special overalls, aprons, shoes and caps provided.   There is hardly an establishment where a dressing room is not needed.   In some establishments not only a dressing room but a laundry and drying room are also necessary.

In this, as well as in other sanitary matters, there is a great difference in the attitude and practice of employers.   While some manufacturers install and maintain splendid dressing rooms with proper light, ventilation and comforts for their employes, others consider this matter unimportant and cither make no provision whatever for this purpose, or locate the dressing rooms in cellars, basements or some dark nooks and corners unfit for any other purposes.

Dressing rooms should be separate for males and females;

should be, if possible, located in different parts of the floor and should be enclosed by solid partitions and walls extending at least to a height of seven feet. Dressing rooms should be separated from toilet and water-closet apartments by solid partitions extending to the ceiling. Every dressing room should have at least one window of suitable size opening to the outer air, and should also be provided with artificial illumination.

Dressing rooms must be always well ventilated, as it is neces-

Courtesy N. Y. Telephone Co.

Individual Lockers for Employes.

sary to have plenty of air in such a room. Provision must also be made for the proper cleaning of all dressing rooms by employes specially designated for this purpose. Every dressing room should be kept heated in winter to a temperature not less than 50° F. The walls and ceilings should be painted a light color and kept clean. Dressing rooms should be provided with separate clothes hooks for every person employed, or special clothes lockers for each employe. In a number of factories a steel locker is provided for each employe, divided into two parts, one for the working clothes and the other for the street clothes. There are several such lockers on the market. Most of them are very good and comparatively cheap. In some industrial codes a standard is set for the size of the dressing rooms, especially those for the use of females. The size, however, of the dressing room is not of so much importance as its proper construction and the installation of lockers.

Bathing Facilities. In some establishments, because of the

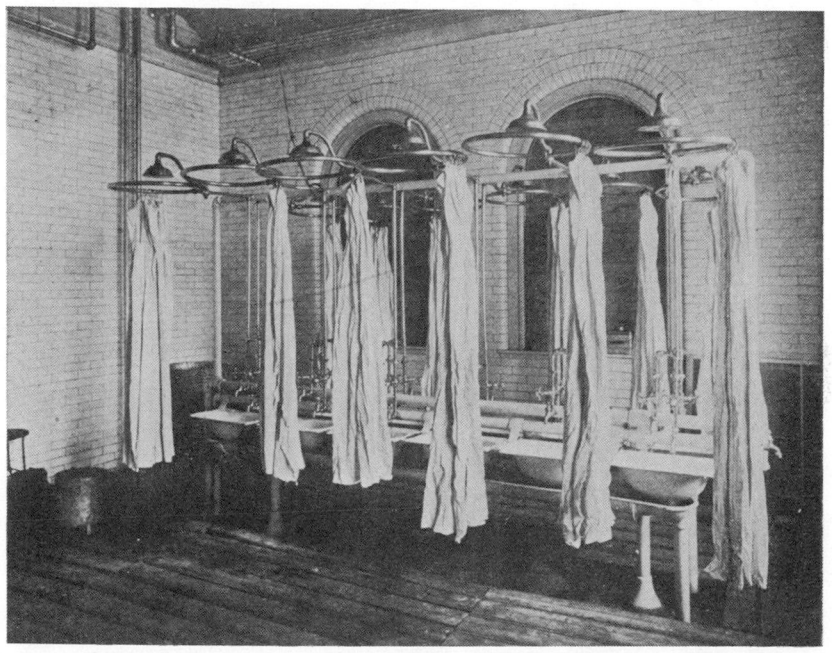

Courtesy Utica Drop Forge and Tool Co.
Bathroom for Employes Finished in Glazed Brick.

dust or dirt, injurious poisons, or penetrating colors used, bathing facilities for the employes to use after their work become necessary. The number of employers who provide bathing facilities in their establishments is small, even in those industries where such fixtures are absolutely needed. Some employers have installed fine shower or tub baths in their factories, others are satisfied with any makeshift fixture. I remember one large factory in Buffalo, N. Y., where aniline colors are made in which the owners were compelled to install bathing facilities because the street car companies refused to allow their employes to ride on the cars after their work without having bathed. In this plant, the bathing facilities provided for the three or four hundred workers were in the form of three huge tanks filled with dirty, slimy water. Each tank was used by one hundred or more employes, and the water was changed but once a week. The reluctance of the employes to use fixtures of this kind and their contempt for such so-called "welfare work" may be readily justified.

The location of the bathrooms is of less importance than that of dressing rooms, and there is no reason why the basement of the fac-

Courtesy Joint Board of Sanitary Control.

Broken Plumbing and Darkness Create Conditions such as These.

tory building should not be used for this purpose. The floors, walls and surfaces of bath rooms should be made of impervious material. Each fixture should be separated by partitions, as many employes object to using the common battery of bath-tubs located in one undivided room. Most of the baths provided are of the shower form, which are cleaner than tubs. Shower baths also take up less space and can be more quickly and frequently used.

Plumbing and Plumbing Fixtures. In all factories proper provision should be made for a water carriage system of plumbing whether there are sewers located in the street or not. The installation of plumbing fixtures in factories is usually under the supervision of municipal authorities. All plumbing pipes, vertical as well as horizontal, should be made of extra heavy cast iron, but the usual plumbing pipes are too large for the purpose. Unless very large quantities of water and waste are sent through the pipes, soil and waste pipes may be four or five inches in diameter for all buildings under six or seven stories in height. My opinion is that in most places the soil and waste pipes may be conveniently merged into one, and only one pipe used for the waste and for the water-closets and urinals. The elimination of the vent system upon which most plumbing codes insist, would also reduce the expense, waste and the defective conditions at present existing. The one pipe system of plumbing is at present approved by eminent sanitarians.

The house drain should be made of extra heavy cast iron, six or eight inches in diameter, and it is best to have it exposed. The pitch of the house drain should not be less than one-half inch to the foot and the house drain should be provided with a main trap having a tide valve and a number of hand holes for cleaning purposes.

Toilet Accommodations. No part of an industrial establishment is so neglected as the toilet accommodations. In many cases they are located outside of the factory, and sometimes quite a distance from it, causing the loss of much time and also endangering the health of the employes.

In the investigations made for the New York State Factory Commission, the toilets were located in yards in 186 of the establishments inspected. In some chemical establishments I found the toilets 150 feet from the central part of the establishment. In 795 shops, the toilets were located in halls and usually kept in a grossly unsanitary condition. Many of the toilets were not separated for the sexes and were of an obsolete and crude type. In a large number of factories in rural communities the unsanitary privy is still being used, and in a large chemical factory in New Jersey the toilets consist of nothing but a ramshackle frame shed over a canal, with only a narrow board for a foot rest. School sinks and trough closets are still found in some factories, and in one of the largest sugar refineries old trough closets are still in use. In a shoddy mill in a city in Central New York State, the owner, a " member of the local health board," entirely neglected to provide any water-closet accommodations for his thirty or forty employes. His substitute for proper toilet accommodation was a wooden barrel in a sub-cellar of his establishment. Where the toilet accommoda-

tions are of a better type, they are so neglected that their condition
is unspeakably dirty.   The illustrations on pages 274-277 are from

Courtesy Joint Board of Sanitary   Control.

A Broken Fixture in Use in a Tenant Factory on the East Side of New York City.

photographs taken of actual conditions in the garment industry in
New York City.

Even in European countries where there is usually more regard
for factory laws, I found the condition of the toilet accommodations
very bad, especially in France and Belgium.   In many factories in

these countries the fixtures in use for toilet accommodations were simply openings in the floors connected with sewers, no seats or any fixtures at all being used above the floor. Privacy is very much neglected in these countries, and in many establishments I found toilet rooms used by both sexes.

All industrial and sanitary codes demands separate water-closet compartments for the sexes in every factory where men and women are employed. All toilet rooms should be located within the factory building and be convenient and accessible to the persons using them. It is best to provide toilet rooms on every floor of the establishment; but in no case should the workers on more than

Courtesy Joint Board of Sanitary Control.

Toilet in a Tenant Factory on the East Side of New York City.

two floors be allowed to use a toilet room on one floor. Toilets should invariably be located on a floor where a large number of employes are working.

The location of toilet rooms in halls is not recommended. Each toilet room should be properly screened and provided with a vestibule and the entrance should not open into the room where most of the workers are employed. It is best that toilet rooms for males and females should be in different parts of the building. Where they are placed together they should be separated by solid plastered or other sound proof partitions extending from floor to ceiling. The doors of every toilet room and of the water-closet compartments should be self-closing. The outside partitions must be airtight and must extend to the ceiling.

The floor of every toilet room and the side walls to a height of six feet should be constructed of material impervious to moisture and with a smooth surface. Such material may be asphalt, non-absorbent cement, tile, glazed brick or other water-proof material. Where more than one water-closet is installed in a toilet room, partitions not less than six feet and not more than seven feet in height should be provided between each closet. A space of six to fourteen inches should be left between the floor and the bottom of such partitions. All toilet rooms should have a window or windows opening to the outer air. Where this is impossible, the toilet room should be ventilated by means of shafts of sufficient dimensions and height to carry away the foul air from the room. Each toilet room should be lighted by means of windows or artificial illumination and properly heated. Walls and ceilings should be painted a light color and frequently washed and cleaned. It is best to employ a special caretaker for cleaning the water-closets. Sanitary codes prohibit the use of trough water-closets, latrine or school sinks, and require individual water-closets with flush rim bowls made of vitrified glazed earthenware, set entirely free and open without any enclosing woodwork.

Every water-closet should be installed with connections through the floor and should be set on a floor slab of slate or other material impervious to moisture, not less in size than the base of the water-closet set thereon. An evenly laid and solidly tiled flooring on a strictly fireproof floor construction is better, provided a suitable template of slate or marble of the full size of the floor flange is intalled to furnish a solid bearing for the fixture. Every bowl installed must be so constructed that the space behind and below may be easily cleaned. The seat of every water-closet should be made of wood or other non-conducting material and finished with varnish or other substance which will make it impervious to moisture. Every water-closet or group of water-closets must be flushed from a separate water supply cistern, the water from which is used for no other purpose, connected so as to keep the water supply free from contamination. Flushing cisterns usually have a capacity of at least eight gallons and are so constructed as to use not less than three gallons of water at each discharge. The discharge must be of sufficient force to clean the bowl at each flush. Long hopper closets, the so-called Philadelphia hopper type, as well as the pan, plunger and offset closets should not be used. There is much objection to the use of range closets, and it is best to provide individual closets in all factories where this is possible. Where range closets must be used, separate bowls should be installed and not more than ten bowls supplied from every flush tank. The bowls should be separated by partitions and the range closets automatically flushed at intervals of not more than one hour with a flush sufficient to remove the entire contents. In some factories the flush is operated by the opening or closing of the door of each compartment or by the raising of the seat of the closet. These con-

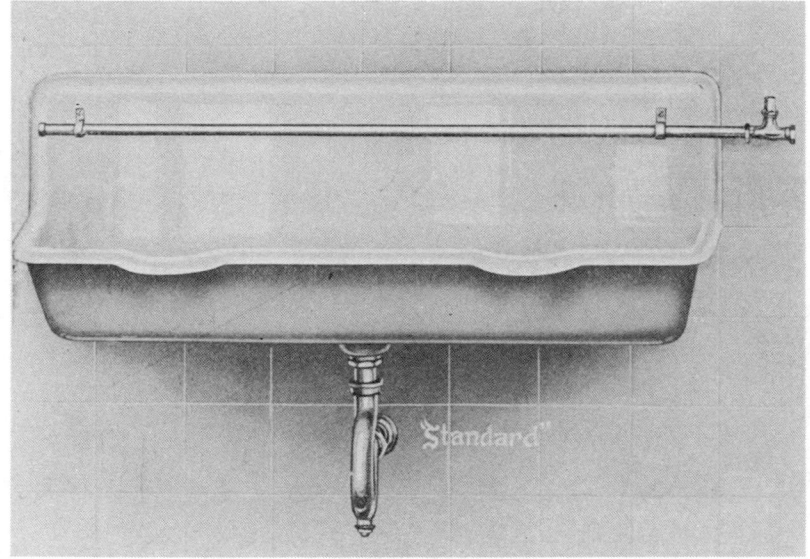

Courtesy Standard Sanitary Mfg. Co., Pittsburgh.

A Sanitary Urinal.

trivances are installed to obviate the results of neglect on the part of the worker to pull the chain or lever of the flushing tank. In a number of modern factories flushometers are installed and used with good results. These flushometers are only of value when the water pressure in the pipes is more than twenty-five pounds; otherwise flushing tanks should be insisted upon.

Urinals should be provided on every floor where a large number of male employes are at work. These fixtures should be made of a material which is non-corrosive and impervious to moisture. All urinals made of cast iron or galvanized iron or sheet metal should be discarded, and replaced by urinals made of porcelain or smooth

Well Arranged, Sanitary Water-closets.
(Note ventilating ducts near ceiling.)

Courtesy Standard Sanitary Mfg. Co., Pittsburgh.

earthenware material. The sides, back, base and floor of urinals should be impervious to moisture, and made of slate or tile. Urinals should be flushed in the same manner as water-closet flush tanks.

The number of urinals and water-closets which should be provided in a factory is important. Most of the codes in European countries as well as in different states in this country provide for a ratio of twenty-five workers to one water-closet fixture. Some codes require one fixture for 20 males or 15 females. In view of the fact that a fixture is not used more than from three to four times a day by each employe, the above ratio seems to be adequate for all ordinary purposes; and there is no necessity for any larger proportion of fixtures, the more so that with every increase in the number of fixtures there is increased probability of their abuse and contamination.

Of greater importance than the number of fixtures are provisions for their cleanliness. In large establishments a special person should be engaged to supervise the cleaning of these rooms and fixtures. It would perhaps also be advisable to provide in every toilet room used for females, a supply of sanitary napkins and also a receptacle for these to be thrown into. A sufficient supply of paper should also be provided.

Lunch Rooms. Most of the industrial codes require a pause of from forty-five to sixty minutes during noon hour, but no provision is made for a place within the factory where the employes may eat their midday lunch. The consequence of this omission in the factory laws is that workers eat their lunch at the machine tables, very often with soiled hands, and often soil the materials with which they work, leaving crumbs and parts of vegetables, fruit and other organic matter around tables, chairs, and work places. Where there is much dust or where poisonous materials are being worked with, the eating of lunch within the shop is injurious to health and may cause disease. Some industrial codes insist upon separate lunch rooms in certain dangerous trades. In a number of establishments the employers have voluntarily provided lunch places, although the location of such places is often poor and the condition in which they are kept is at times very bad. In a large cordage mill in Central New York, belonging to a big corporation, I found the restaurant or lunch room located in a corner of a semi-dark basement. The firm complained that the lunch room was not appreciated and not used by their employes, and were

rather indignant at my remark that I did not blame the workers
for refusing to use such a lunch room.

Sewage Disposal. Where there is no general sewage system,
the problem of efficient disposal of sewage is often very difficult
of solution. As most factories established in such localities are
constructed on a large scale, effective and efficient methods of
sewage disposal should be installed at the same time that the
factory is constructed.

No factory in which more than ten or fifteen workers are employed should resort to the use of the old time privies and cesspools
for sewage disposal. In its primitive and common form the privy-
vault is nothing but a hole dug in the ground near or at some distance from the house; the hole is but a few feet deep, with a plank
or rough seat over it, and an improvised shed over that. The privy
is filled with the excreta; the liquids drain into the adjacent ground,
which becomes saturated and contaminates the nearest wells and
water courses. The solid portion is left to accumulate until the hole
is filled or the stench becomes unbearable, then the hole is either
covered up and forgotten, or the excreta removed and the privy
is used again. This is the privy system so often found near the
cottages and mansions of our rural populace, and even in towns.
The terrible ravages of the hook-worm disease in the South are
mainly due to soil pollution from unsanitary privies.

The principal parts of a privy are: the shed, the seat, and the
receptacle into which the excreta is dropped. The shed in a sanitary privy should be made of tightly fitted boards with windows
properly screened and doors well closed in order to prevent insects
and flies from gaining access. The seat should be so arranged as
to be convenient for use and should be free from the contamination
of excreta. The receptacle, or the place into which the sewage
is dropped, should be made water-tight by being lined with cement
or some other non-absorbent material. The sewage when dropped
into this water-tight receptacle will remain there and must be
removed from time to time. A still better method is to place in
such water-tight receptacles a tight portable pail which is hung
on a hook from the seat. The sewage is dropped directly into the
pail, which may be removed as soon as it fills up, the sewage being
cremated or disinfected and the pail cleansed, washed and disinfected and returned to its place. For the purpose of removing
these pails and cleaning the vault beneath the privy, each part of the
privy should be provided with a sling cover so as to be accessible.

Cesspools may be used when there are no sewers and the factory is provided with fixtures and pipes to carry the sewage outside to a point sufficiently distant from the factory. "Leeching" cesspools which allow liquids to drain into the ground are open to the same objections as privy-vaults. When cesspools are water-tight they must be emptied at periodical intervals or provided with automatic ejectors and siphon apparatus to discharge the contents.

It is much better for industrial establishments to discard the use of privy vaults and cesspools and to employ one of the modern methods of sewage disposal through chemical and biological treatment. The accumulation of the sewage matter collected in cesspools or tanks may be disposed of either by irrigation of nearby lands through a system of underground earthenware pipes or through chemical precipitation and filtering and separating the solid matter, which is then either destroyed by burning, or is utilized for fertilizing purposes. The new bacterial treatment of sewage may also be resorted to, as it is at present being introduced into the sewage disposal systems in a great many towns and cities.

Noises, Odors, Smoke, Gases and Fumes. Certain industrial plants frequently become a menace to the comfort and health of the neighborhood and are regarded in municipal and sanitary codes as "public nuisances." The nuisance caused by these factories is due either to excessive noise, or smoke or bad odors or to gases and fumes given off from their chimneys, which are sometimes harmful to health as well as injurious to the vegetation around the factories.

There are some factories whose rumbling noise may be heard for half a mile. Boiler factories and other metal-working establishments are especially noisy. The noisiest factory I ever visited was the cutlery factory of the famous Henkel Bros., in Solingen, Germany, an establishment which has been in existence for several centuries. The noise in one department of that factory was so terrific that it could be distinctly heard half a mile from the place, although the whole city of Solingen is full of cutlery factories, and the general noise produced by them is great enough. I was told that every worker in this branch of the factory becomes deaf a short time after beginning to work there.

The methods of lessening noise present a technical problem, which may be solved in many factories. Where excessive noise becomes a public nuisance, municipal regulations require plants causing it to be maintained outside of the city limits and at a distance from human habitations.

The black smoke belched from the chimneys of industrial plants using soft coal is apt to be injurious to the vegetation as well as to the inhabitants of nearby villages and cities. The composition of smoke as it leaves the chimney depends upon the character of the fuel burned as well as the methods of combustion. Black smoke consists of carbon mechanically suspended, and also of gases such as carbonic acid, carbonic oxide and hydrogen sulphide. Wood and bituminous coal give off very abundant black smoke. When furnaces are of adequate capacity, with grates having a large area, with coal spread in a thin continuous sheet, supplied with the requisite amount of air, the production of smoke is greatly diminished. Other remedies for preventing factory smoke are the construction of very tall chimneys, and the use of smoke-consuming devices. There are a number of patent smoke-consuming appliances, most of them based on the principle of a more thorough and complete combustion of all the particles of carbon in the fuel. The better the combustion within the furnace, the less will be the waste and smoke from the chimney.

A number of manufacturing plants emit foul or offensive odors, which are at times harmful and at all times unpleasant and interfere with the comfort and health of the neighboring inhabitants. These odors are due either to decomposed organic matter or to chemical dust, gases and fumes, which may be still more unpleasant and harmful. Organic odors are perceptible in establishments where animal substances are utilized; such as slaughtering houses, fat rendering establishments, soap-making factories, tanning of hides, manufacture and utilization of animal substances, manufacture of vegetable substances, etc. In the manufacture of illuminating gas, alkalies, ammonia, bleaching powder, soda, glass, smelting, lead paint, drug manufacture, etc., odors, gases and vapors often escape and become offensive.

To prevent the nuisance caused by such offensive trades a thorough study must be made of each separate process in each manufacturing plant. Methods of prevention may be summarized as follows: (1) general cleanliness; (2) removal of all noxious matter by either destroying or utilizing same; (3) storage of all offensive materials in closed and tight vessels; (4) substitution for offensive processes of less offensive ones; (5) the use of plenty of water to insure cleanliness and drainage; and (6) the destruction of all offensive odors, etc., by passage through condensers and thence into fire pits where they are consumed.

The prevention of gases and fumes may be accomplished by some of these methods, or by dilution of the gases and fumes with air, condensation of the gases by passing them once or several times through condensers filled with water or through scrubbers filled with wet coke; and by absorption of all gases in fire pits where they are destroyed by the action of fire or by passing them through neutralizing substances which differ for each gas or fume.

Disposal of Factory Wastes. Besides the wastes which have already been referred to, there is, in many manufacturing establishments other industrial, waste either in solid, semi-solid or liquid form. When waste is in solid form, its removal, destruction or utilization is not difficult when the means of transportation and utilization are at hand. It may also be burnt in special incinerators.

A more difficult problem is presented by semi-solid and liquid industrial wastes. The cheapest and most common method of disposing of such wastes is by sludging them into nearby lakes, rivers and water courses. That such practice is very objectionable is attested by the protests which have been made by villages, towns and communities on or near the lakes, rivers or water courses, and by the appointment by various governments of commissions to investigate river pollution and to find remedies for the abatement of this nuisance. So great is the pollution of streams by manufacturing waste, that practically every community prohibits the disposal of industrial wastes into water courses which are needed for bathing and drinking purposes.

The pollution of rivers is especially objectionable in the case of factories which discharge organic matter and poisonous materials into the water courses. Among the industrial establishments which usually have offensive waste are woolen mill factories, tanning and fellmongering, brewing and distilling, bleaching and dying, paper making, aniline color works, dyeing establishments, general chemical works, etc. All these industrial establishments send out large volumes of foul and offensive waste, which contaminates and pollutes the waters of rivers and lakes.

The proper disposal and treatment of factory wastes is a mechanical, chemical and biological problem which must be solved by different methods in each industrial establishment, according to the materials used and wastes produced. The following are the principal methods used for this purpose: the liquid or semi-liquid wastes are reduced in volume by separation, sedimentation, settling, straining or filtering. The liquid wastes are separated from the semi-solid and solid constituents, and if the liquid wastes have no deleterious matter in solution they may be discharged into nearby water courses. The semi-solid or solid wastes may be reduced in volume by pressing and may be destroyed by heat or utilized in some other form. It is possible also to treat waste chemically by neutralization.

CHAPTER VII

EMPLOYERS' WELFARE WORK

I

THIS is an era of industrial welfare work. We hear of welfare work in every industry, in almost every factory, in every state and in every country. Employers boast of the welfare work in their shops, the workers discuss the forms of welfare activities carried on in the industrial establishments in which they work. The National Manufacturers' Association devotes a great part of its activities to the discussion of the benefits of welfare work. The National Civic Federation has a special department on welfare work. There have been many exhibitions of welfare work—national and international.

There is as yet great confusion in regard to the conception and definition of welfare work. What is welfare work and what is it not? Where does it begin and where does it end? An employer who introduces some new system of wage payment by which he gives one penny bonus for every ten cents additional work done by his employes, regards this as welfare work. As welfare work is also regarded the increase by another employer of the wages of more than ten thousand employes from an average of less than $2.50 per day to a flat rate of five dollars per day. Any improvement in the factory may be called welfare work from simple arrangements for light and cleanliness in the workrooms, which scarcely conform to the minimum required by law, up to the most elaborate systems for providing rest, food, shelter, education, insurance, old age pensions, etc., which in fact take charge of every waking and sleeping moment of the worker from the time he enters the factory until his death, and pursue him even afterwards in the shape of pensions, benefits and supervision of his family.

In the multiplicity of forms in which welfare work appears and in the great extent of undertakings and institutions created for the improvement of the condition of the workingmen and of the working class, there is urgent need of a criterion by which all these efforts for the industrial welfare of the worker may be judged and by which their forms and aspects may be clearly defined.

In defining welfare work, it is necessary to exclude all those activities which are really outside its scope and real intention. Only *employers'* welfare work will be considered in this chapter. This excludes all improvements of working conditions undertaken by the state, by municipalities or by private social organizations, such as municipal housing, tenement inspection, parks, playgrounds and municipal bath houses which are provided for the whole population.

We also exclude from welfare work any efforts made by the workers themselves for their own improvement. Such efforts, whether they appear in the simple form of libraries, or cooperative societies, etc., are clearly outside of the sphere of welfare work, which is done by the employers themselves.

We also exclude all those forms of industrial improvement which the employers are *compelled* to introduce into their industrial establishments by the state or municipality or their own trade associations. Thus the minimum sanitary and industrial standards established by legislation cannot be included in the conception of employers' welfare work. Under this limitation what is termed welfare work in one state may not be welfare work in another state. For instance, the backing of chairs in a factory is regarded as welfare work in all those states and countries where this is not one of the provisions of the labor code; while it is merely a legal standard where it is found on the statute books. The granting by the employer of an hour and a half pause during the day (an hour during noon and a quarter hour each in the forenoon and afternoon) is regarded as welfare work in the United States, but not in certain European countries where this is the legal standard for women and minors.

The next important limitation of welfare work is its aim and purpose. We limit the definition of welfare work to that which is done for the sole purpose, or, at least, *in a large measure*, for the benefit of the workers themselves. We cannot, for instance, regard as welfare work the installation of a mechanical ventilating plant by a film factory in their film department, where this is done because of the necessity for excluding dust and not primarily for the benefit of the health of the employes; even though they may be benefited secondarily. That the installation was not for the benefit of the workers, is shown by the fact that no mechanical ventilation of this kind was installed or maintained in the other departments of the factory.

On the other hand, the mere fact that the installation of an industrial improvement results in benefit to the employer himself by increasing the efficiency or health of his workers, does not exclude certain activities from being regarded as welfare work. Thus, for instance, the fact that the eight-hour workday, when introduced in the Zeiss Works resulted in an increased output, does not exclude the eight-hour workday from the category of welfare work; nor will Ford's attempt to introduce an eight-hour shift fail to be regarded as welfare work because it has already shown an increase in the output in the factory and a greater efficiency in the works. The chief criterion in judging industrial improvements voluntarily introduced by employers should be whether the *general purpose* is the improvement of the condition of the workers rather than increase in production.

Finally, the term welfare work must be limited to all such activities as are instituted by employers for their own workers and their immediate families; for it is evident that all work done by employers for workers of other establishments or for the general public is *social* welfare work and not *employers'* welfare work.

The definition, therefore, of welfare work to which we shall limit ourselves is the following: All devices, appliances, activities, and institutions voluntarily created and maintained by employers for the purpose of improving the economic, physical, intellectual or social conditions of the workers in their industrial establishments.

Why do employers voluntarily undertake welfare work? What are their motives? What are the principles by which employers are guided in their attempts at improving the conditions of the workers? Is the large increase of welfare work in modern industry due to the moral awakening of the rich, to the increase in the philanthropic spirit of the class of employers, or is it due to the fear of a social upheaval, to the dread of organized labor, to the terror of the spectre of the coming social revolution? Are the motives back of welfare work pure philanthropy, or pure selfishness and desire for efficiency; or are they inspired by the recognition of the principles of industrial justice?

The earliest examples of welfare work were simply an expression of the feeling of responsibility and kindliness of the employer toward his working people. It was an extension of the friendly relations

that existed in the small workshop between the master who worked
with his hands as well as directed his workers. It was natural
for some employers in the earlier factories to have intimate relations with their workmen, to feel a deep interest in their welfare
and to do everything possible to improve their conditions. Hence,
from the time of Robert Owen, who was the first to introduce extensive economic, educational and general welfare work in his mills
at New Lanark, down to the present time, much welfare work is
due to this benevolent spirit of the employer.

The philanthropic motive for welfare work was probably the
dominating one at the beginning of the modern factory system during the period when the employing class as a whole strictly adhered
to the *laisser faire* policy, but this motive gradually diminished in
strength with the rise and growth of corporations, trusts and monop-
olies, when the actual employers and owners hardly ever saw their
factories or knew the workers in them.

Undoubtedly, in the motives for welfare work, especially that
done by large corporations, an element of *fear* is present. The spread
of labor unionism, the rise and growth of radical and socialistic
political parties, the awakening of class consciousness among the
working people, the bitter strikes, lockouts and labor wars so frequent
within late years undoubtedly operate strongly for the introduction
by large and powerful corporations of certain forms of industrial
welfare activity.

The third motive for industrial welfare work, is so-called " efficiency." By this is meant the fact that most, if not all, of the
improvements which are voluntarily made by employers for the
benefit of their workers more than pay for themselves through
increased efficiency of the workers and increased output. Efficiency
engineers and employers now assert that they undertake welfare
work not through charity or fear, but because it pays.

The general manager of the International Harvester Company,
in speaking to his welfare board, said that he held them responsible
to the management " not for sentimental results or for actions
outside of the scope of pure business, but for results inside the
scope of pure business, which will make the company a leader among
industrial corporations."

Welfare work not only pays, but pays especially because it
prevents labor disputes. Under the title " Welfare Work as a
Way to Prevent Labor Disputes," a writer in the American Academy
of Political Science discusses the part played by welfare work in

keeping the workers at the Winifrede Mine in the Kanawah district loyal to the employer when the rest of the miners in neighboring districts went on strike. It is also said that the employes of the McCormick plant of the International Harvester Company refused to strike when the operatives of the Deering works struck, because of the extensive welfare work in the former plant. Many employers when writing or speaking of their welfare work to other employers of labor repeatedly assert that their welfare work pays because their workers do not usually join labor unions and are less willing to strike or make " trouble."

Finally, the fourth motive for welfare work, that of " industrial justice," is at present gaining more and more ground and is spreading among the better class of employers. Many employers have come to the conclusion that the present wage system is unjust to the workers and results in much hardship, and that it is their duty as a class to do everything within their power to make some return to the workers and to improve their condition. This new policy of the " square deal," and industrial justice is already becoming a basic principle in the platforms of great political parties and is probably destined in time to dominate all other motives for welfare work.

The introduction and extension of employers' welfare work has not been accomplished without much opposition, some of it from political economists and philosophers, some from employers, and much from the workers and the leaders of labor organizations.

It is but natural that the old time economists, who opposed state interference and paternal government, should object to all voluntary efforts by employers to give their employes anything to which they are not entitled by law or by economic determinism.

Nor do all employers favor welfare work. Some are opposed to the efforts of neighboring employers because it sets a " bad example " to their own workers, and makes them demand things to which they are not entitled. Others express themselves as opposed to the extension of welfare work because " we do not believe it helps the man to give him something for nothing, nor do we believe he wants it. The men rather resent it." " We believe in giving a man a chance to earn his own recreations," said one employer. " We have regulated our relations with our employes on the principle of doing what logically belongs to the relation of employer and employe. We believe that there are few employers who can safely go into the private lives of their people." *

Of greater consequence is the undoubted opposition to welfare work which is so prevalent among the working people themselves, and especially among the members of labor unions, and those engaged in socialistic propaganda among the workmen. Indeed, the attitude of organized labor toward all welfare work is more than indifferent—it is largely hostile.

What are the objections made by workers and their representatives to welfare work and upon what are they based?

In the first place, their opposition is based upon the fact that most, if not all, welfare work is paternalistic, is given in the form of charity, is degrading and tends to enslave the people. It is that tendency of human nature to look the gift horse in the mouth and the one which is so well expressed in the proverb " *timeo Danaos et dona ferentes* " (though they bear gifts, yet do I fear the Greeks).

The second objection which the representatives of the working class have to welfare work is the motive which they think is behind it all. Rightly or wrongly, they assert that the usual motive of the employer in introducing welfare work in his shop is not the real benefit of his working people but is usually his own aggrandisement, the advertising which he receives because of his benevolence, the political preferment that a benevolent employer is apt to obtain or even the very efficiency and increase in the profits which many of the employers themselves admit is one of their most frequent motives.

Perhaps the most important point in the opposition of the workers to welfare work is the fact that its promoters seem to be opposed to labor organization, and seek to prevent combination, strikes and increase of unionism among workers. This view is justified by the well known hostility to unionism of the great corporations which are famous for their welfare work and their utter disregard of the principles of freedom of organization among their workers. Only two notable examples need be cited here. Perhaps the greatest activities in welfare work in Germany are performed by the Bayer Chemical Corporation at Elberfeld and Leverkussen. Here practically all forms of welfare work are done on an extensive scale, and the general condition of the workers is probably better than in any other industrial center in Germany; and yet I was

---

* Tolman, W. H.: "Social Engineering," pp. 360-361.

personally told by an official of this corporation while inspecting their factory, that they not only discourage unionism and labor organizations among their workers, but discharge every employe in their works who advocates unionism or attempts to organize his fellow workers.

The other example is that of the Ford Automobile Company which, by its recent doubling of wages, has created so much discussion. In a magazine article the fact is noted that Ford is strenuously opposed to unionism among his workers, and that ninety men in one department who were reported to him as attempting to organize were discharged.* The hostility to labor organizations of the United States Steel Corporation, the best recent exponent of welfare work in the United States, is also well known.

The workers also claim that welfare work tends to lower wages and has a tendency to shackle labor with gratitude and diminish its freedom in the bargaining process. Organized labor holds that questions of hours and wages are of first importance and that much of welfare work with its emphasis on rest and recreational facilities, on libraries and lunch rooms, is beside the point. At any rate they are not willing to accept it as a substitute for trade union action leading to shorter hours and higher standards of wages. In many cases the workers feel that welfare work of certain kinds has been undertaken at the expense of wages. This feeling is quite general among organized and unorganized workers. The workers in a certain collar factory in Troy assert that every improvement in sanitation or ventilation in the factory has been followed by a cut in wages. It is certain that wages in collar factories in Troy have been continually cut during the past eight years, and that at the same time, together with cuts in wages, much welfare work has been instituted. Of course, the workers regard this probable coincidence in the nature of cause and effect.

Another objection against welfare work is that most of this work does not result in economic betterment but tends rather to sanitary and so-called social and moral improvement. The workmen resent such activities because they feel that if they are given reasonable hours and decent wages and the minimum requirements for sanitary conditions in the factory, they can take care of the social, intellectual and moral sides of their lives themselves. In a small manufacturing town in Pennsylvania dominated largely by a great industrial corporation, the management donated to the workers

* *Everybody's* for April, 1914.

a handsome library, well equipped, which cost about $20,000. The workers, instead of using this library, collected a fund of their own of $8,000 and established their own library.

The same kind of opposition exists in regard to lunch and rest rooms, which are a feature of welfare work in many factories. In some of these places the workers claim that they get better food at their own homes and that they do not wish the owners to control their expenditures for lunch during their own midday hour. The author of "Betterment," a book written chiefly in praise of the National Cash Register Company, says that he entered a restaurant provided by the firm in which free coffee was served to the employes, and began a conversation with a man who ate his lunch without the coffee. He asked the workman if he didn't like the coffee. The workman said he did. "Then why don't you have some?" The man answered that he was afraid that if he took two cents' worth of coffee he would be expected to do seventeen cents' worth of work for it.

All these objections on the part of the workers, whether justified by actual conditions or not, form the basis of much of the opposition of the working class and their representatives to all forms of welfare activity.

As to the value of employers' welfare work and actual results of such activity upon the improvement of the condition of the working class, there can be only one opinion—that all forms of employers' welfare activities, no matter what their real motives are, do benefit the workers and do improve their condition.

All welfare work is important in the first place as a social experiment, as an example of what can and therefore ought to be done by enlightened employers. Welfare work is an incentive to improve legal sanitary standards. Such standards give only the minimum requirements, and it is only when intelligent employers show the way and prove by example that other improvements are possible and necessary, that the legal standards are raised. Welfare work not only raises the economic, intellectual and social standards of the workers, but it has an immense educational value in paving the way for the general improvement of the condition of the working class, and for the enlightening of the workers as to what may and can be done for them and, perhaps, by themselves.

Employers' welfare work appears in a variety of forms, but may be broadly divided into two groups of activities: first, the raising of the economic standards of the workers, and second, the improvement of their physical, intellectual and social conditions. The forms of welfare work which fall under the two groups are numerous, as may be seen from the following scheme:

I

IMPROVING THE ECONOMIC CONDITION OF THE WORKERS

I. SECURITY AND INCREASE OF INCOME.
   (a) Tenure of employment.
   (b) Minimum wage.
   (c) Profit sharing.

II. INCREASED INCOME FOR INCREASED PRODUCTION.
   (a) Bonus and premium systems.
   (b) Premiums for long service.
   (c) Scientific management.

III. REDUCTION OF COST OF LIVING.
   (a) Cheap rent.
   (b) Company stores.

IV. COOPERATION IN ADMINISTRATION.
   (a) Suggestion systems.
   (b) Shop committees.
   (c) Promotion and discipline committees.

V. SPECIAL PROVISIONS FOR WORKERS.
   (a) Old age pensions.
   (b) Death benefits.
   (c) Sickness benefits.
   (d) Accident and life insurance.

II

IMPROVEMENT OF THE PHYSICAL, INTELLECTUAL AND SOCIAL STATUS OF THE WORKERS.

I. LESSENING DANGERS.
   (a) Shorter hours.
   (b) Pauses.
   (c) Less monotony.
   (d) Vacations.

II. IMPROVING WORKING CONDITIONS.
  (a) Model factories.
  (b) Light, ventilation and heating.
  (c) Greater safety.
  (d) Washing, dressing and bathing.
  (e) Rest rooms.

III. IMPROVED FOOD AND DIET.
  (a) Lunch rooms.
  (b) Restaurants.
  (c) Free food.
  (e) Anti-alcohol.

IV. RECREATION.
  (a) Place for recreation.
  (b) Music.
  (c) Clubs.
  (d) Athletics.
  (e) Outings.

V. CARE FOR HEALTH.
  (a) First aid.
  (b) Emergency rooms.
  (c) Hospitals.
  (d) Physicians and nurses.
  (e) Medical supervision.

VI. EDUCATION.
  (a) Libraries.
  (b) Apprenticeship.
  (c) Shop schools.
  (d) Corporation schools.

VII. SOCIAL IMPROVEMENT.
  (a) Improved housing.
  (b) Garden cities.

II

IMPROVING THE ECONOMIC CONDITION OF THE WORKERS

The relation of employer to employe is primarily an economic one, determined by prevailing industrial conditions. While the interests of the employers and the working classes are close and interdependent, the improvement of the economic condition of the workers is not primarily within the scope of the activities of employers. From the beginning of the factory era, however, we find an increasing number of employers making earnest endeavors to better the economic condition of their workers. These endeavors appear in a variety of forms, which may be arranged in two principal divisions.

The first division includes all those forms of employers' welfare work which are based upon voluntary attempts by the employers to improve the economic conditions of their workers. Such efforts usually react with benefit to the employers by improving their relations with their workers and by increasing the general efficiency and productivity of the whole industrial establishment.

In the second division of this group of welfare activities are included those efforts of employers which are made solely with the purpose of increasing the productivity of the industrial establishment; and the increased benefits to the workers are usually but a partial restitution and payment for their extra efforts and accomplishments. In this division may be included bonus systems and so-called scientific management. These activities can hardly be included under welfare work, although usually regarded as such.

Security and Increase of Income. *Tenure of Employment.* One of the great evils of the wage system is insecurity of employment. The wage worker cannot tell from day to day whether he will retain his employment or not. Some employers have felt the injustice of this insecurity and have endeavored to mitigate it by making long time contracts with their workers, and by giving them adequate compensation in case of dismissal for reasons for which they are not to blame. On the other hand, most employers do not realize the inequity of this arrangement at all. In many factories the worker is required to give a week or two weeks' notice to the employer before leaving; while the employer assumes the right to dismiss a man instantly if he feels so inclined. Moreover, to insure his week's or two weeks' notice, a corresponding part of the employe's wages are kept back by the firm.

It was Ernst Abbé, the founder of the Karl Zeiss Stiftung (Jena, Germany), who first worked out in detail a scheme which meant for the workers practical security of employment; as, by the terms of the " Stiftung " dismissal of a worker becomes very costly. The firm of Freese in Berlin, also assures its workers security of employment in a similar way.

While most thoughtful employers will admit that in unemployment and insecurity of employment lies the greatest evil of the wage system, I know of few American employers who have taken steps to guarantee their workers permanency of employment, conditioned always, of course, on good behavior.

Minimum Wages. Many employers have adopted a minimum weekly wage or a minimum hour rate, regardless of the kind of work done or the skill of the worker. In other industries a certain minimum rate is attached to each different operation, this rate being sometimes arbitrarily determined by the management; and sometimes where the workers are organized, by shop committees on which the workers and management are represented. It is in the former sense, however, that the term is most popularly employed.

The Karl Zeiss Works at Jena have a minimum weekly rate for all workers. J. Crosfield & Sons in their soap factory at Warrington, England, have a minimum wage of twenty-one shillings for all male workers over twenty-one. The Cadbury Company at Bournville, Lever Bros., at Port Sunlight, and Rowntree's factory at York are examples of English establishments which base their wage payments on a minimum wage. The most striking example of the establishment of a minimum wage is in the Ford Automobile Company of Detroit, which lately instituted a five dollar a day minimum wage for all male workers in its employ over twenty-one years of age. A minimum wage, however, is usually fixed at some very small sum and is chiefly used as a basis for the calculation of premiums, bonuses and piece-work.

Profit Sharing. By profit sharing is meant the practice of some employers of adding to the daily, weekly, monthly or yearly wages and income of their workers a certain sum to which they are legally not entitled, but which is voluntarily given to them by employers from their ordinary or extraordinary profits. Profit sharing is usually in the form of a gift, although it also recognizes the principle that the employes are a part of the machinery of the plant, having done their share in gaining the general results, and are therefore entitled to a certain share of the profits of the works outside of their regular wages. A number of employers have adopted some form of profit sharing. Of course, upon a close analysis, it simply means that the employers have beforehand determined upon the distribution of a fixed percentage of the general profit among their employes.

Lever Bros. do not believe in profit sharing. They state that it cannot exist where the worker cannot share the losses as well as the profits. They have a scheme called "prosperity sharing," which consists in setting aside a certain sum of money from the earnings of any prosperous year, to be used as a substantial benefit for their employes, either by building additional houses for their workmen to be rented at low cost, or by providing some form of recreation or education.

In the Van Marken Works at Delf, Holland, a scheme was instituted whereby the workers became the sole owners of the factory. Fifty per cent of the profits were credited to the workmen in proportion to their wages. This sum was then paid into the bank and when it reached the amount of a share, that amount of stock was credited to the worker. At the end of twelve years the workers in the factory had become the sole owners of the capital stock. Such a scheme, which results in the elimination of the capitalist, has not often been copied.

A form of profit sharing which has attracted much attention was first instituted by Sir George Livesey in the London Gas Works. This scheme of copartnership admitted the workmen, consumers and the share holders. The workmen were entitled to an annual bonus of one and one-half per cent on their wages for every penny at which gas was sold below a certain standard, which was arbitrarily fixed at two shillings and eight pence per thousand feet. The men were required to invest one-half of this bonus in the Company's stock. Responsibility in the management of the Company was then given the workers in proportion to the amount of stock jointly owned by them.

American employers are somewhat divided in their opinion as to the value of profit sharing. One of the first firms to adopt it was Brewster & Company, who employed about one hundred men in their carriage factory. In 1869 they instituted a profit sharing scheme. The percentage of profits to be divided was to be determined by committees elected by each department, to act jointly with the managers as a board of control, and also to control conditions of work in their respective departments. Two years after this scheme was instituted, the men struck together with the rest of the carriage makers in New York for an eight-hour day, and the partnership was dissolved.

Many American employers are of the opinion of Mr. Lever, of the Lever Bros. Soap Works at Port Sunlight, that there can be no real profit sharing without a sharing of losses. Other firms share profits on the stipulation that a part of the profit accruing to each employe shall be used to purchase stock in the company.

This is the case with the N. O. Nelson Company of Detroit, Mich. The workers are paid in proportion to their earnings on a time basis. Profit sharing dividends are allowed only to such employes as have saved ten per cent of their full time wages and invested it in the company's stock. Other firms allot a percentage of their profits to their employes in accordance with their behavior. In the Thomas G. Plant Company, employes are divided into three classes for the purpose of profit sharing. The employe's behavior, manners, punctuality, quality and quantity of work, neatness, etc., are all taken into account in determining the class to which he belongs.

The Detroit Graphite Company sets aside a certain sum each year to be divided among its employes in proportion to their length of service in the firm. Employes who have worked five years or over with the company receive five per cent on their weekly wages; those who have been with the firm four years receive four per cent, and so on.

The latest scheme of profit sharing is that which has been adopted by the Henry Ford Automobile Company. Mr. Ford, having found that at the end of 1913 he had a surplus of ten million dollars, decided to divide the surplus among his ten to fifteen thousand employes by practically doubling their wages for 1914, instead of cheapening the product to the consumers.

As to the value of profit sharing, the following opinion of Frederick W. Taylor is of interest:

" Profit sharing as ordinarily applied in competitive establishments practically throughout the world has been a failure. Dr. Elliot is right in saying that profit sharing has been a failure in nine out of ten cases in which it has been tried. The reason for the failure lies fundamentally in human nature; and until you have studied men, lived next to workmen, analyzed their motives, studied their methods of thought and know their outlook, you will fail to realize why profit sharing is a failure. I am not saying that I do not favor profit sharing. I believe in it, but it cannot be the lazy man's profit sharing; it cannot be the ordinary kind of profit sharing. It is the easiest thing in the world to give away one-seventh of your earnings. That is the lazy man's way. There is nothing to it. You have got to get down to every single individual in your place. You cannot pro-rate wages at the end of the year and do justice to your men—you must share the profits with those men who have earned them and not let the fellow who has not earned them get a cent of the profits." *

* Address before the Boston Efficiency Club Branch, Feb. 11, 1914, p. 25.   Published in the Journal of the Efficiency Society, March, 1914.

In other words, Mr. Taylor claims that profit sharing in order to be just, should not be given indiscriminately to all employes, but only to those who deserve it; and then, of course, it is simply a bonus payment to those employes who by their extra efforts have earned higher wages, but do not get them and receive them in the form of profits divided among them at certain periods.

Increased Income for Increased Production. As we have seen, the objections of the exponents of the efficiency system to profit sharing are its indiscriminate use and the reward of those members of an industrial establishment who are really not deserving of their share of increased income. The method of increasing the income of workers usually practiced by these employers is the giving of bonuses and premiums.

Bonuses and Premiums. In addition to wages, many firms, especially those which conduct their business on a piecework basis, offer bonuses or premiums to their workers. Employers state that the bonus system results in a very much larger output and consequent saving of expense. In the Santa Fé machine shops the bonus system consisted in paying a minimum rate of thirty cents an hour, and then allowing a twenty per cent bonus for performing the work within a standard time, which had been previously determined. H. W. Jacobs, the assistant superintendent of the motive power division in the Sante Fé Railroad, says:

" The payment of bonus is made on an efficiency basis. As previously stated, a bonus of twenty per cent of wages is paid for doing work in the standard time, which represents one hundred per cent efficiency. When more time is taken to do the work than allowed by the standard, the efficiency of the workman necessarily decreases, for which a less amount of bonus is paid, the workman receiving only his hourly pay for doing the work. If the work is performed in less than the standard time allowed, more than twenty per cent bonus is paid for the operation, depending on the reduction made in the time."

This bonus system of the Sante Fé was part of an efficiency plan which was installed in the works, operated for two years and then discontinued. The bonus system aims at a large output. By its critics it is stated to be simply a method of speeding up the worker. There is no limit placed on the standard time, which can easily be shortened as the workers are speeded up to maximum production. Under the bonus system a worker might accomplish his job using only a few minutes more than the standard time; but in this case he would receive no bonus, or, as **Mr.** Jacobs subtly says "a less amount of bonus, namely, only his hourly rate," which he would obtain whether he hustled for the bonus or not.

Organized workers are opposed to the bonus system, whether in their own or other trades. Warren S. Stone, President of the Brotherhood of Locomotive Engineers, states that his organization is opposed to the bonus system all along the line. His reasons are primarily the necessity for careful workmanship in the building of locomotives and locomotive machinery. The bonus system with its emphasis on speed and output tends to the scamping of work and therefore results in faults or defects in machinery. Two hundred and ten members of the Brotherhood were killed in 1910 and many wrecks have resulted from invisible defects. "We don't want piece-work and we don't want the bonus system with its attendant incentive for some man to slight his job." *

Payment of premiums is on a slightly different basis from the bonus system; but a time limit is assigned to every job in the same way. The worker accomplishing his task in less than this standard time receives an additional wage in proportion to the time saved. If he saves one-third of the time, he receives one-third of the money which would have been paid for that time, and has the extra hours in which to go on to another job.

Another method is to pay to each employe at the end of the year a percentage on all wages earned within the year. The Lowney Chocolate Company pays a five per cent annual bonus on the wages earned by each employe. The Heinz Pickle Factory divides twice a year a small percentage with its best workers.

Premiums for Years of Service. Many employers take some method for recognizing faithful and long continued service from their employes. The Van Marken Company in Holland gives a silver cross at the end of twelve and one-half years' service, and a gold cross after twenty-five years of work. The Villeroy & Bach Company give a silver medal to each employe after twenty-five years of service and a gold medal after fifty years of work. The Sherwin-Williams Paint Company present each faithful employe who has served them for twenty-five years with a gold watch. Crosfield & Sons pay £5 at the end of twenty-five years' service and £20 at the end of fifty years' service. The Menier Chocolate Company gives extra pay for long service. A worker who has been

* *Human Engineering*, January, 1911, p. 13.

in their employ for twenty years receives £8 for every subsequent year in addition to his regular earnings.

Scientific Management. Not one of the exponents of so-called scientific management in factories has ever claimed that the purpose of the introduction of this new system is the improvement of the economic or social conditions of the workers themselves. Hence, scientific management can scarcely be considered as a form of welfare work.

By scientific management is understood the efforts of a factory management " to obtain the maximum prosperity as a result of the maximum productivity." " The greatest prosperity," says Frederick H. Taylor, " can exist only as a result of the greatest possible productivity of the men and the machines; that is, when each man and each machine is turning out the largest possible output. It follows that the most important object of both the workmen and the management should be the training and development of each individual in the establishment so that he can do at his *fastest pace* and with the maximum efficiency the highest class of work for which his natural abilities fit him.*

Under scientific management, bonuses and premiums have been largely adopted, chiefly in the industries where output and quantity are the chief consideration. Scientific management, so-called, has worked out systems of payment based on (1) a minimum time wage, (2) premiums or bonuses for the saving of time on a job, and (3) special prizes or awards paid to groups of workers, divided in proportion to their individual earnings. There is no doubt that under scientific management the output of the factory is greatly increased, the general prosperity of the works enhanced, the efficiency of the whole industrial establishment is at its highest, the profit of the employer the greatest, and incidentally the wages and income of the workers also increased to a greater or lesser degree.

In so far as scientific management increases the general efficiency of industrial production and brings increased prosperity to the industrial classes, there can be very little objection to this system. The chief opposition to scientific management in factories comes from the workers themselves, from their representatives and from those social workers who dispassionately judge this new efficiency movement in industrial production.

The opposition of the workers themselves is well expressed in

* F. H. Taylor: " Principles of Scientific Management," pp. 9 and 12. [Italics mine.]

the criticism of scientific management by John P. Frey, editor of the *International Molder's Journal*, in an address delivered before the Western Economic Association. Mr. Frey's opposition is based upon the following contentions: (1) that so-called scientific management tends to specialization and converts the workers into fractional mechanics, whose knowledge of a trade or industry is confined to but a few simple operations; (2) that it does not provide an adequate system for education of apprentices; (3) that it does not provide for the advance of the workman in mechanical knowledge, but keeps him endlessly performing the same operation, disregarding the fact that this constant repetition, which in time becomes semi-automatic on the part of the workmen, through its very monotony numbs the mind instead of inspiring it; (4) that if applied to all industries it would prevent development of competent mechanics and produce in their place fractional mechanics who could only work effectively under the groups of super-foremen provided for by the system; (5) that it is unsafe as well as unscientific, inasmuch as its tendency is toward the production of quantity rather than quality. The number of bricks which can be laid in a day is one thing; the strength and durability of the wall is an entirely different matter. The number of steel rails which can be run through the rolls in a day may be an interesting item in the matter of production, but of greater importance to the public is the ability of these rails to withstand the burden of traffic; (6) scientific management fails to adequately understand the human factor and the spirit of American institutions, for it makes of one man a taskmaster without the free consent of the other; (7) that while workmen do not object to experiments for the discovery of the greatest capacity of production by machinery, they strenuously object, and justly, to all efforts to experiment with them in the same way.*

The eminent English sociologist, J. A. Hobson, makes the following objections to scientific management:

" In so far as initiative, interest, variation, experiment and personal responsibility are factors of human value qualifying the human costs of labor, it seems evident that scientific management involves a loss or injury to the workers."

" The basic reason," says Mr. Hobson, for offering a bonus in scientifically managed concerns at the present day

* *American Federationist*, April, 1913.

" is the necessity to overcome the dislike of the worker and to induce him to make the greater effort necessary under this system; but when all firms shall have adopted this system, the worker will have no choice; therefore, only that part of the bonus will continue to be paid which is necessary to replace muscular and nervous wear and tear of speeded up and more automatic work; that is, this bonus would be part of the cost of production and the laborer would get no higher payment for his increased productivity."*

Mr. Hobson concludes his criticism with the following remarks:

" Indeed, were the full rigor of scientific management to be applied throughout the staple industries, not only would the human costs of labor appear to be enhanced, but progress in the industrial arts itself would probably be damaged. For the whole strain of progress would be thrown upon the scientific manager and the consulting psychologist. The large assistance given to technical invention by the observation and experiments of intelligent workmen, the constant flow of suggestion for detailed improvements would cease. The elements of creative work still surviving in most routine labor would disappear. On the one hand, there would be small bodies of efficient taskmasters carefully administering the orders of expert managers; on the other, large masses of physically efficient but mentally inert executive machines. Though the productivity of existing industrial processes might be greatly increased by this economy, the future of industrial progress might be imperilled. For not only would the arts of invention and improvement be confined to the few, but the mechanization of the great mass of workmen would render them less capable of adapting their labor to any other method than that to which they had been drilled. Again, such automatism in the workers would react injuriously upon their character as consumers, damaging their capacity to get full human gain out of any higher remuneration that they might obtain. It would also injure them as citizens, disabling them from taking an intelligent part in the arts of political self-government. For industrial servitude is inimical to political liberty. It would become even more difficult than now for a majority of men, accustomed in their workday to mechanical obedience, to stand up in their capacity as citizens against their industrial rulers when, as often happens, upon critical occasions, political interests correspond with economic cleavages." †

Reduction of Cost of Living. A certain number of employers in order to improve the economic condition of their workers, endeavor to reduce the cost of living either by furnishing them with cheap rent, by building their own houses and making the rent at

---

* J. A. Hobson: *Sociological Review*, July, 1913.
† Ibid.

cost or below it, or by furnishing the workers with provisions, food, clothing, etc., at cost price or at a little above or below it. Of course, many of these schemes were introduced not with a view to benefiting the workers, but either because of necessity, as, for instance, in lonely districts where there were no houses or stores, or when the furnishing of houses and food products was made not to benefit the employes but for profit, and became a means of exploiting

Courtesy National Lamp Works.

Two-way Cafeteria.

their helplessness. These were the activities which led in a great many states and countries to the enactment of the " truck " acts, forbidding the employers to run " company stores " or pay their employes by checks or in the form of rent or food.

Cooperation in Administration. Capitalist industry is an aristocracy, an hierarchy. It is governed from the top by the employer, by the owner of the establishment without the consent of the governed. The old time capitalist was very jealous of his prerogatives and of his " vested interests and divine rights." One eminent coal baron stated that the coal mines and fields were given to him by Divine Providence and that he could brook no interference of anyone with his personal management of his divine responsibilities. " One of the most poignant paradoxes of the present situation in industry," says Prof. Felix Adler, " is the contradiction between the democracy outside of the factory and the absolute monarchy within the factory. Is it natural for men to be taught that so far

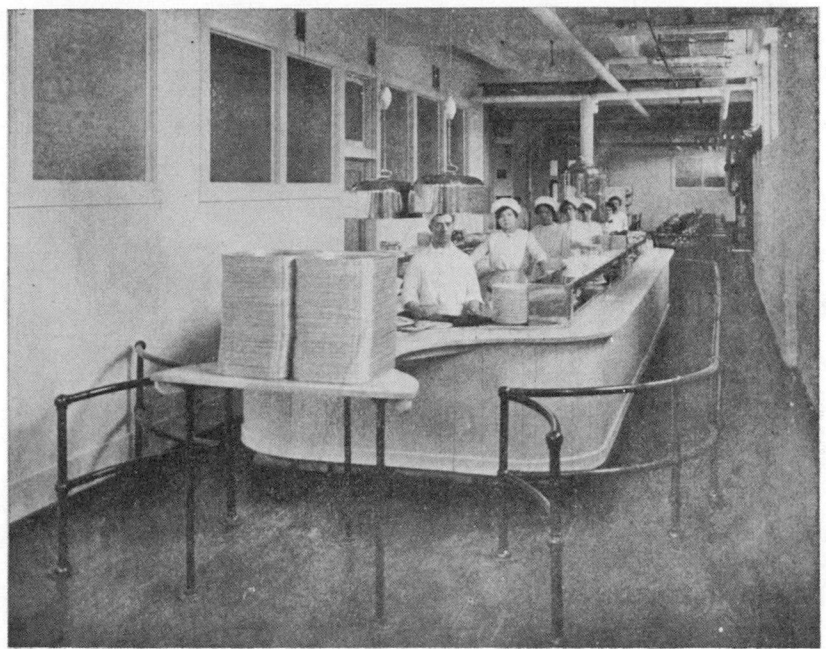

Courtesy National Lamp Works.

One-way Cafeteria.

as the government of the country is concerned, self respect demands their participation in the making of the laws which they are bound to obey, and, on the other hand to have it impressed upon them day by day in the factory that they are to take the orders of their superiors without any right on their part to assist in the making of the rules to which they are subordinated ? "

It is only with the growth of the labor movement that an increased tendency to democratization of industry and to the participation, at least partial, of the mass of workers in the management of industrial establishments has become apparent. While owners and employers have at last, though reluctantly, admitted the right of the state to interfere to some extent in the magagement of industrial establishments, they are still strenuously opposed to any admission of the right of the workers to any share in the government of the establishments in which they work. It is only here and there that intelligent and progressive employers seek to introduce some democratic system in their works, and so far as this has been successful, it may be considered a part of welfare work.

Many experiments have been tried in admitting the wage earners to some share in the management of industry. Some have been successful, while the results of others are admittedly doubtful. Some of the schemes remind their critics of the way in which small children are sometimes allowed to hold the ends of the reins while their father drives, with the illusion that they are really guiding the horse.

Among these experiments may be included suggestion systems and shop committees.

Suggestion Systems. The suggestion system has been adopted by many factories both large and small. It is an effort to utilize the practical ideas of employes in making the business more effective. In some establishments suggestions are solicited for every branch of the business; in others, only suggestions as to mechanical improvements or time-saving devices are desired. The Cadbury Cocoa Factory at Bournville receives suggestions from its employes in regard to (1) comfort, safety or health; (2) means of preventing waste of materials; (3) saving of time and expense; (4) improvements in machinery; (5) introduction of new goods or ideas; (6) existing defects; (7) athletic and other clubs and societies; and (8) anything not included in this list. Prizes ranging from five shillings to ten pounds are awarded at the end of the year for the best suggestions.

In the Karl Zeiss Optical Works at Jena the suggestions of employes have resulted in many improvements and inventions. From sixty to seventy suggestions are adopted each year. The Acme White Lead Works and the Bausch & Lomb Optical Company have employed a suggestion system for many years. The National Cash Register Company pays for suggestions in proportion to their value to the firm. It also gives educational trips as prizes to the authors of specially valuable suggestions. These trips are to Washington, New York or other commercial centers.

The Cleveland Hardware Company at one time put boxes in its factory, into which the employes were asked to drop any suggestions in regard to improvements in machinery, methods of work, economies, etc. At the end of six months a prize was to be given for the best suggestions. This scheme, however, had to be abandoned in favor of a promise to pay cash for all suggestions of value.

The Chandler & Taylor Company of Indianapolis abandoned

Courtesy National Cash Register Co.

Noon-hour Rest and Recreation.

their system of giving prizes for suggestions because the best men would not compete, considering a prize inadequate where a great saving was effected. This feeling prevails among the workers in many factories in regard to suggestion systems where small prizes or payments are made for suggestions which may result in saving the firm thousands of dollars through the year. The only fair plan to the worker is to pay him a percentage of the saving effected.

Shop Committees. Some of the large establishments have solicited the cooperation of their workers through committees of the men elected by them to represent their interests to the management. The National Cash Register Company conducts its whole business through a series of committees under the direction of the president, vice-president and general manager. Each department

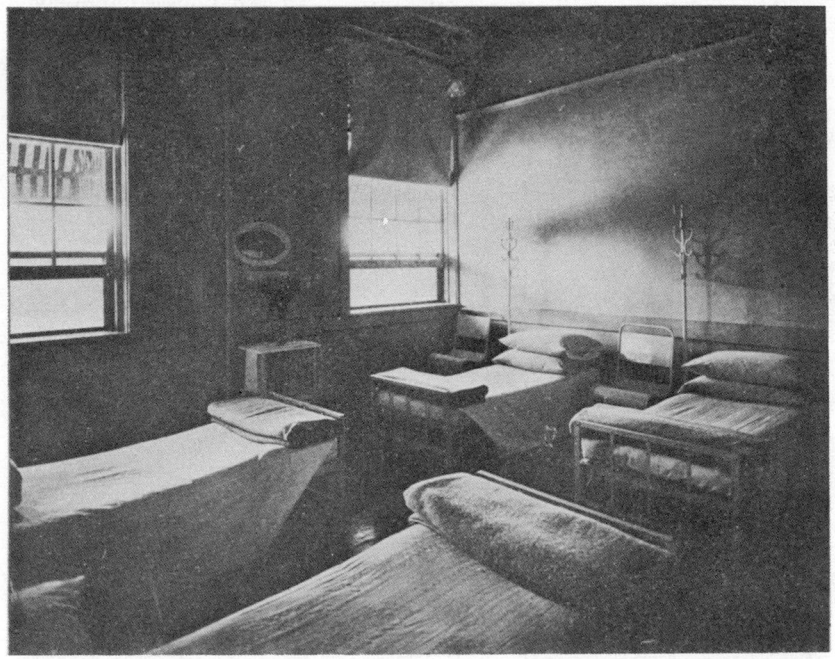

Courtesy National Lamp Works.

Rest Room.

in the works from the business department down elects a committee to administer the affairs of the department.

In the Karl Zeiss Works, the men elect annually a committee to represent them in their dealings with the board of managers; while a sub-committee of seven members acts as an executive committee for the larger body. All the transactions of the committees are posted in the work-rooms. These shop committees may, of course, be merely a decoration, and have no real authority or responsibility. On the other hand, they sometimes—as in the Zeiss Works—really assist in the administration, and are in fact a necessary part of the machinery of management. Another type of shop committee is the grievance or promotion committee which exists in some factories.

Special Provisions for Workers. *Accident and Sickness Insurance.* Sick and death benefit associations are maintained in many factories. Their organization, methods of payment, and regulations are more or less similar. Where these associations have grown up among the workers and where the employer does not contribute to the funds, these associations are naturally not to be considered a part of welfare work, although in many instances, they have been started at the instigation of the employer, who often furnishes a round sum of money to start the organization and contributes from time to time to a greater or lesser degree.

The membership in these associations is sometimes compulsory; that is, all workers entering the factory must belong to this benefit organization. In such cases, the weekly or monthly dues are deducted from the pay envelopes by the firm. Should an employe leave, he may or may not be entitled to the money he has deposited in this way. This form of benefit association is productive of a good deal of friction and bad feeling by reason of its compulsory character.

In the relief association of the Shredded Wheat Company, those whose weekly wages are less than $6.50 a week contribute two and one-half cents a week; those whose wages are more than $6.50 contribute five cents a week. Other relief associations charge a percentage of the wages received by their employes. The firm often acts as custodian and the money of the members is deducted from their pay envelopes. The usual benefit is $5.00 a week in case of sickness, and $100.00 to $200.00 in case of death. Benefits are paid for a certain length of time and most of the organizations have a stipulation that sick benefits shall not be paid for more than a definite number of weeks or months per year, the usual term being thirteen weeks.

In addition to the benefits provided by these associations, a number of firms pay additional sickness and accident benefits. The International Harvester Company have had a plan of accident insurance in effect since 1910. The workers do not contribute anything towards this insurance, a definite sum having been set aside for this purpose by the corporation. In case of death, three years' average wages are paid, but the amount cannot be less than $1500 or more than $4000. One-fourth of the wages during the first thirty days of disability are paid, and if the disability continues longer than thirty days, one-half wages are paid during that period; but not for more than two years after the accident. Special benefits are paid for the loss of hand, foot or eye.

Sick and accident benefits and death benefits are provided in

Courtesy Standard Sanitary Mfg. Co., Pittsburgh.

Swimming Pool for Employes of Pittsburgh Factory.

industrial establishments in Germany and England in accordance with the requirements of the national insurance legislation which has developed in both countries. In addition, however, to the legal payments, many establishments pay further benefits. The

Karl Zeiss Works at Jena and the Freese Company at Berlin have both placed a large sick fund in the hands of the workers for disbursement, the managers having no voice in its direction.

Old Age Pensions. Manufacturing establishments, both in England and on the continent, maintain pension schemes for their workers which give larger sums of money than those afforded by the national insurance acts. In the Zeiss Optical Works, every employe is legally assured a pension for infirmity or old age or for the benefit of his family in case of death, after five years of service. This pension is computed on the basis of a fixed minimum wage scale.

The United States Steel Corporation recently set aside twelve million dollars as a pension fund for superannuated employes. The Western Electric Company, the Westinghouse Air Brake Company, the International Harvester Company, Bausch & Lomb Optical Company, the Talbot Woolen Mills, and the Gorham Manufacturing Company all have pension schemes which, while varying in detail are similar in outline.

The Westinghouse Company retires all employes at the age of seventy years; while all who have been twenty years in the company's employ are pensioned. Employes between sixty-five and sixty-nine years old, who have worked twenty years for the company and are incapacitated, may be retired and pensioned. Men who have been twenty-five years in the employ of the company may be retired at the discretion of the managers. Men sixty years old who have been in the company's employ for forty years are retired on a pension, and those who are sixty-five years old, if they have been in the employ of the company for thirty years.

The International Harvester Company retires all male employes with pension after twenty years of service, on reaching sixty-five years of age. The Western Electric Company pensions employes who have worked for twenty years and are sixty years old. Any employe who has been with the company for thirty years may be retired at fifty-five.

The Talbot Woolen Mills give pensions after fifteen years of service, on reaching the age of seventy years. The amounts are reckoned at one per cent for every year of service of the wages received by the worker, determined by averaging his pay for the ten years preceding retirement. The Western Electric Company, however, pays one per cent for every year of service, reckoned on the basis of the highest ten years' average earnings. Most companies paying pensions to their retired workers stipulate that the pension shall not be less or more than a certain amount. The Talbot Woolen Mills pension employes after thirty-five years in the service at half pay. The Westinghouse Air Brake Company pays no pension of less than twenty dollars or more than seventy dollars a month. The minimum pension paid by the International Harvester Company is eighteen dollars a month, the maximum, one hundred dollars a month.

III

IMPROVEMENT OF THE PHYSICAL, INTELLECTUAL AND SOCIAL STATUS OF THE WORKERS.

Lessening the Dangers of Work. A most important function of employers' welfare work is the improvement of the physical condition of the workers by lessening the dangers of their work and by improving the working conditions in the industrial establishments in which they are employed. Of all the methods of lessening the dangers of work there is not one which is so beneficial to the health of the workers as shortening the hours of labor. The strenuous activity characteristic of all modern factory work inevitably causes great fatigue and, if continued for long periods, is inevitably followed by serious injuries to the health of the workers. Hence, from the very beginning of the factory era, the workers and their advocates have fought for a reduction of the hours of labor and for the introduction of a normal day's work.

While a shortening of the regular hours of labor in an industrial plant is not considered by many employers as a necessary part of their welfare work, those employers who have tried the experiment state that a shortening of the daily and weekly hours of labor has resulted in better workmanship and in an equal or increased output.

The Karl Zeiss Works at Jena initiated an eight-hour day in 1902 upon a vote of their employes. Freese & Company of Berlin have been working on the eight-hour basis for over ten years. J. Crosfield & Sons, soap manufacturers of Warrington, Lancashire, conduct their industry on the three shift system. Their hours are from 6 A.M. to 2 P.M. and from 2 P.M. to 10 P.M. and from 10 P.M. to 6 A.M. This reduction in hours from their former two shift system was accompanied by a temporary reduction in wages.

The Solvay Process Company of Syracuse, N. Y., changed to

the eight-hour shift several years ago with the very best of results for their workers and their product. The Carhart Manufacturing Company of Detroit, employing seven hundred women workers, mostly foreigners, reduced the hours of work from ten to eight hours and found that their eight-hour output exceeded their ten-hour one. Their workers, of course, are all paid by the piece. This experience has been repeated by many other factories in America where the change of hours has actually meant an increase in the amount produced. Some employers who have established a forty-eight hour week have found that their workers prefer to work a little longer five days in the week in order to have a Saturday half holiday. This arrangement of hours is generally known as the English week, since this custom is almost universal in England, where the Saturday half holiday is a national institution.

Pauses. In factories where the work is very monotonous, especially where girls or women are employed, it has been found beneficial to the workers to allow brief pauses during the morning and afternoon work periods. There are provisions in the labor codes of all states and countries for midday pauses. The duration of these pauses is from thirty to sixty minutes. In England the law provides that women and minors must not remain at their place of work or in the rooms where they work during the midday pause. In most continental countries the law provides for a one-hour midday pause and for an additional half hour pause divided into a fifteen-minute forenoon pause, taken usually at 10 A.M., and a fifteen-minute afternoon pause, taken usually at 4 P.M. A number of individual employers have adopted pauses somewhat longer than the ones required by law.

The Shredded Wheat Company of Niagara Falls allows its women workers twenty minutes each day, ten minutes in the morning and ten minutes in the afternoon, in which they must leave their work and can go to the rest room or library provided by the Company. The length of these rest periods is increased in some of the departments where the work is specially fatiguing.

The National Biscuit Company also gives two rest periods during the forenoon and afternoon, extending from fifteen to forty minutes, according to the character of the employe's work. The National Cash Register Company allows ten minutes morning and afternoon in which calisthenics are taught by a competent teacher. The Thomas Adams Company of Nottingham, a lace-making factory, allows a break at 10 A.M. and 4 P.M. for tea.

A writer in the *Iron Age* (May 8, 1913), says that

" In the newest German railroad shops arrangements have been made for all mechanics above a certain age to rest. A room has been furnished with couches and the men are allowed one hour a day at the expense of the Company, divided into twenty minute periods, in which they must rest."

Another means of decreasing the fatigue consequent on monotonous work is to rotate the occupations. The National Biscuit

Courtesy Pierce-Arrow Motor Car Co.

Bakery in Works: All Bread and Pastry Served to Employes is Baked Here.

Company changes its woman workers from one kind of work to another where the operations are particularly exacting. This system is said to have worked successfully. In many shops, a practical rotation of employment is worked out by the employes themselves. Where the work is unskilled in character, they change about among each other without receiving directions from the management. Over-specialization of work has sometimes resulted in serious labor conflicts, as, when in the glove industry, certain employers with a view to increasing the output, determined to have the stitching of fingers and thumbs of gloves done by different sets of workers instead of each girl performing the whole operation. The workers struck in this case for the right to keep some variety in their occupation. It was a relief for them to be able to change from stitching fingers to stitching thumbs and back again.

Vacations. The custom of allowing factory workers a holiday with pay is not at all general. In Germany, the Karl Zeiss Company and the Freese Company allow their workers, after a year's service, six days holiday with pay, and if desired, six additional days leave of absence without pay. In England a similar system has been instituted by the Cadbury Cocoa Company and Crosfield & Sons. The latter company grants this holiday only to punctual workers. Workers who have been late more than three times during a year, unless they belong to a shift beginning at 6 A.M., are disqualified from receiving this vacation.

In America, the Curtis Publishing Company in Philadelphia grants one week's holiday with full pay to all women factory workers. A number of department stores grant a vacation of one or two weeks to their women employees.

Improved Food and Diet. Under certain circumstances the provision of lunch rooms for employes becomes a necessity. Such is the case in establishments where food products are manufactured. To have the workers eating their lunches in the work rooms would not be conducive to cleanliness; and so in most food factories separate lunch rooms are provided as a matter of course. Separate lunch rooms are also a necessity in lead, paint, pottery, match factories, or other establishments where dangerous materials are handled. Where the workers come from a distance and where there are no places near at hand for them to lunch, some kind of restaurant or cafeteria or supplementary provision by the firm of hot drinks or light refreshments becomes necessary. On the other hand, where factories are situated in towns in which the workers have their homes nearby, lunch rooms within the factory are unnecessary. Lunch rooms are scarcely ever, for example, found in textile mills in the New England towns. As is customary in the textile trade, an hour and a half is usually allowed for the midday meal and the workers prefer to get dinner at their homes nearby.

The provision of lunch rooms for employes is one of the most popular branches of welfare work and is frequently undertaken in factories where no other welfare work is carried on. The most elementary method is simply to provide an empty room in the factory or to partition off a part of the work room and set up tables and benches where the workers can take their lunches which they have brought from home and eat them apart from their work. All kinds and grades of lunch rooms come between this and the elaborate dining rooms which provide a square meal with two or three courses for all employes free or at merely nominal sums.

The big industrial firms such as Friedrich Bayer & Company at Elberfeld, Freese & Company at Berlin, Krupp Bros., etc., all provide beautiful dining rooms where the workers can buy nourish-

Courtesy New York Telephone Co.

Operators' Dining Room.

ing food prepared in a scientific manner with wholesome materials, at cost or free to needy workers. In England, W. P. Hartley & Company in their jam factory at Aintree have a beautiful dining hall for their workers. At Port Sunlight in the Cadbury Cocoa Company similar provision is made. J. Crosfield & Sons provide a very substantial midday dinner with meat and vegetables for sixpence, pudding a penny extra.

The United Shoe Machinery Company at Beverly, Mass., has a separate restaurant for men and women workers where food

is sold at a low cost.   A similar plan is followed at the works of the
Thomas G. Plant Company at Boston, Mass.   The Shredded

Courtesy Pierce-Arrow Motor Car Co.

Dining Hall for Employes.

Wheat Company in their factory at Niagara Falls have a large
lunch room for their women employes.   The price of articles

on the menu is stated and each employe is allowed food to the
amount of fifteen cents free. The prices charged do not cover the
cost of the food.

The Pierce-Arrow Company maintains a dining room in connection with which is a bakery and butcher shop. A hot lunch is furnished for fifteen cents, consisting of meat or fish, potatoes, vegetable and pudding. The National Lamp Works maintains cafe-
terias and lunch rooms in eighteen factories where soups, sandwiches

Courtesy Royal Worcester Corset Co.

Dining Hall for Employes.

and hot and cold drinks prepared scientifically according to standard recipes are supplied.

On the other hand, some employers who have provided lunch
rooms and restaurants for their workers have had to abandon them
as they were not sufficiently used. This is the case with the National
Cash Register Company, where the workers preferred to go to their
homes for luncheon rather than use the company's restaurant.
The Pratt & Letchworth Company also started a dining room

which they were forced to abandon later as it was not used by the employes.

Many factories do not provide lunch or dinner, but allow the workers to make tea or coffee on the premises or provide hot drinks at cost to their employes in the noon hour. Some factory dining rooms in the large model establishments are really beautiful rooms, large, airy and charmingly decorated. The lunch room in the new building of the Curtis Publishing Company at Philadelphia, where women employes eat their lunch, has frescoes done by Maxfield Parrish. The dining room of the Lever Bros. Works at Port Sunlight looks more like the interior of a banqueting hall of the Middle Ages than an annex to a factory.

The following rules which the Shredded Wheat Company has issued to its kitchen management show the care which some employers take in the hygienic feeding of their employes:

" All fruits and vegetables to be served raw shall be washed in sterilized water. Under no circumstances—even for the first washing—shall water be utilized unless same has been sterilized."

" Sterilized water must be procured from the appliance located in the office of the janitor."

" Milk and cream shall be strained through a cheese cloth previous to its being placed in the special refrigerator."

" A sample weighing 100 grams shall be taken from every can of milk received daily, immediately upon its arrival, and same sent to the chief of the department."

" A second sample of 100 grams shall be taken from every can of milk, and same placed in a glass container with 25 grams of bichromate of potash, and the following days of the week a like sample must be placed in the container without the addition of bichromate of potash, and this composite be submitted at the end of the week to the chief of the department."

" Fresh meats delivered to the kitchen shall be carefully examined by the chief and an immediate report be made when same is not in a perfect state."

" Inspection of hams shall be made by partly splitting same and completely removing the bones so that the flesh is exposed."

" Discolorations, bruises, wounds or cuts inflicted previous to the slaughter of the animal shall be sufficient cause for rejection of all fresh or salt meats."

" The chef shall open and inspect upon arrival, all packages containing fresh fish. Should the package contain no ice and the flesh be otherwise than firm, and the eyes bright, the fish shall be declared unfit for use. The lack of sufficient ice pertains to the summer season only."

"Only fresh green cabbage—not any that has been kept in storage or in the cellar—shall be used to be served raw, and only during the period of the year when such can be obtained; cabbage kept in the cellar, or having the outside leaves partially dried or decomposed, shall be utilized only after thorough cooking."

"Canned fruit or vegetables shall be used only when the market does not offer sufficient variety of fresh articles."

"When making use of canned fruit or vegetables, the chef shall see that all cans are opened and not emptied until he has inspected the contents of each can."

"It is strictly forbidden to utilize cold storage eggs for the making of any article in which the eggs are not thoroughly cooked. Cold storage eggs must not be used in the making of sherbets, English creams, meringues or mayonaise."

In this country as well as abroad, a great many employers make an attempt to combat the use of alcohol by their employes. I was very much interested to find that one of the largest brewing concerns in the world, that of Shulteis, Berlin, discouraged the drinking of beer by their employes during meal time, and supplied them instead with tea and coffee free, a practice which has resulted in a decrease of more than fifty per cent in the consumption of alcoholic drinks. The same practice is followed in a great number of establishments in Germany.

In certain factories where specially dangerous materials are handled, the employers furnish the workers with special drinks which are considered as prophylactic against the action of poisons. Thus, the Pullman Company at Pullman, Illinois, encourages the drinking of milk; and several wagon loads of milk are sold daily to the employes in the lead branches of the establishment.

Improvement of Working Conditions. Industrial codes contain more or less detailed statements as to the working conditions required by law. These laws contain provisions for safety and prevention of accidents in factories, for the construction of industrial establishments, for fire protection and fire prevention, for light, ventilation, heating, washing and other sanitary comforts within the factory. The provisions of the law give the minimum requirements, but many employers go much further and provide their workers with more comforts than required by legislation, and seek to improve their working conditions far beyond the requirements of the statutes. In so far as these improvements represent a voluntary contribution on the part of the employers, they constitute real employers' welfare work.

Employers differ in the working conditions which they endeavor to improve. Some employers take pride in constructing model factories; others try to beautify the grounds and surroundings. Many employers make special provision for the absolute fire protection of their workers. Other employers introduce artificial ventilation, special methods of heating, improved lighting, etc. At present many employers are paying great attention to the safety of employes. Some large corporations spend great sums annually on

Courtesy Adler Bros., Rochester, N. Y.

Reading Room for Employes.

this form of welfare work. Thus, for instance, the United States Steel Corporation spent during 1912 the enormous sum of $1,068,253.02 for sanitation and welfare work of all sorts; while if we include the expenditures for relief of men injured and killed, for accident prevention, for the pension fund, and other expenditures for improving the condition of the workmen, the aggregate amount spent during 1912 reaches the enormous sum of $6,166,364.82.

Improved washing, dressing and bathing facilities are a part of the welfare work in many establishments. In some of the factories, model wash rooms and dressing rooms with lockers for each employe are splendidly located, with plenty of light and ventilation, and so arranged that employes are encouraged to be clean and to keep so. In some establishments not only are washrooms and dressing rooms provided, but the workmen are properly supervised in the use of these sanitary facilities.   Thus, at the Pullman Works in Pullman, Illinois, I found a splendid arrangement by which the washing of the hands of the employes during noon time was supervised by a

Courtesy New York Telephone Co.

Reading Room for Operators.

foreman and several assistants who saw that the workmen used the individual soap, basins and towels supplied to them, and inspected the hands of the employes when they were on their way to the lunch room.   This supervision is specially valuable for workers who handle poisonous materials.

The extent of the bathing facilities afforded by any concern is partly conditioned by the kind of work done.   Naturally, in large establishments producing food products on a large scale, the most scrupulous care must be observed. In factories where the materials handled are dangerous to health, such as white lead, match or chemical factories, it is necessary to have more extensive arrangements for bathing than in places where the materials are harmless. The

Courtesy Standard Sanitary Mfg. Co., Pittsburgh.

Plunge on Playground for Employes of a Large Steel Company.

elaborate bathing facilities provided in such cases are not a part of welfare work, but rather meet the demand of the public that food stuffs shall be produced in a cleanly manner, and that industries involving special danger to the health of the workers shall take special precautions.

In England and on the continent, factories which use dangerous chemicals, white lead and phosphorous, are required to install baths for their workers. In the United States, there are no special legal requirements made and many employers who should be leaders in providing adequate bathing facilities for workers in dangerous trades have not yet realized the necessity.

Apart from such industries, there are others where the bathing facilities provided may be considered as a part of the welfare work of the firm; that is to say, these additional arrangements are not necessitated by the character of the industry or by the legal requirements of the country, but are simply undertaken by the employer for the purpose of adding to the wellbeing and enjoyment of his workers.

Such are the arrangements at the Cadbury Cocoa Factory at Bournville, where there are large swimming baths for the men and women. Lever Bros., with their factory at Port Sunlight, provide free shower baths for the use of all their employes. At the factory of J. Crosfield & Sons, all the boys and girls are taught to swim when they have reached the age of sixteen years. The time lost and the cost of the swimming lessons are borne by the firm.

In Germany, the Krupp Company provides shower baths at their mines at Hanover, and shower and plunge baths for their workers in their factory at Essen. The Karl Zeiss Foundation built public swimming baths in the town of Jena where the works are situated, and all employes have the right to fifty-two baths a year at half price. Of course, on the continent the workers are accustomed to pay for baths, and bathing facilities such as are common in America are not found in working class homes abroad.

The Badische Analin and Soda Fabrik at Ludwigshafen has 529 shower baths. The workers in their color department where lead paints are manufactured are compelled to bathe once a day. In this country, the Solvay Chemical Works provides plain and mineral baths free for all its workers.

The provision of shower baths in large establishments is very common. The workers, however, do not always use them unless the company allows them time during working hours. This is done by the National Cash Register Company at Dayton, Ohio, which allows each employe twenty minutes twice a week during the summer on the company's time to take a plunge or shower bath. Pretty & Son, an English factory, allow their girls to bathe on the company's time during factory hours and charge one penny a bath. The Weston Electrical Instrument Company provides individual wash basins with soap, mirror and locker for each worker. It also has a swimming tank and shower baths. A similar arrangement is made by the Pierce-Arrow Company of Buffalo, New York.

Recreation. Another branch of welfare work which has developed quite extensively consists in the provisions made for rest and recreation of employes both during and after working hours. This type of welfare work usually starts in factories where many women workers are employed by providing rest rooms to be used during lunch hour or during brief pauses in the morning or afternoon. Sometimes this rest room is simply a corner of a work room partitioned off and provided with one or two comfortable chairs, a sofa and a few magazines. From this beginning, the idea has developed with many ramifications until it reaches its height in the great industrial plants which have built clubhouses with every facility for outdoor and indoor sports and games, great halls for entertainments and lectures, separate rooms within the factory building for music and dancing during the noon hour, separate rest rooms for men and women workers, and every provision for amusement, rest and change that ordinary mortals require.

The Friedrich Bayer Company at Leverkussen have a beautiful clubhouse for the use of all their workers, with restaurants, cafés, rooms for billiards, a lecture hall and theatre, and small rooms for meetings of committees and societies of workers. All the social life of the workers centers in this hall and the entertainments prepared by the various clubs take place there.

In the Karl Zeiss Works an opposite course is followed on principle. No workers' organizations of the employes for purposes of recreation and amusement have been formed except a football club and a singing society. For the rest, the workers (as was desired by the founder of the Stiftung) mingle in the social life of the town and develop their own pleasures according to their individual tastes.

In England, J. Crosfield & Sons have a recreation club with grounds for tennis, cricket, football, hockey and bowling. The dues for this club are a penny a week. The management has also developed an operatic society of the workers which produces comic operas. Every Saturday a dance is held at the works with a sixpenny admission fee. The proceeds of the dance go to local charities.

Similar clubs exist at the Cadbury Cocoa Works, Rowntree & Bros. at York, and at Lever Bros'. factory at Port Sunlight.

In America, most of the large industrial establishments provide

Tennis Courts for Use of Employes.

Courtesy Eastman Kodak Co.

rest rooms for their women workers and many of them provide some form of entertainment during part of the lunch hour. The United Shoe Machinery Company has separate rest and lounging rooms for the men and women workers, each furnished comfortably and having a piano and reading matter. A short distance outside of Beverly is a clubhouse, built and given to the workers by the management, which contains a theatre, auditorium, library and bowling alleys. In connection with the Employes' Athletic Association is a gun club and arrangements are made for football, cricket and other games. The affairs of the clubhouse are administered

Courtesy Utica Drop Forge and Tool Co.

Shooting Gallery (to left) and Bowling Alleys in Clubhouse for Employes.

by an athletic association and seventy-five per cent of its members must be employes.

The National Lamp Works provides rest rooms for its women workers in all of its eighteen factories. The National Cash Register Company has a club house similar to the one at the United Shoe Machinery Company, where all recreational and athletic activities of the employes center. In addition, there are within this factory rest rooms and sitting rooms for the women workers. In the Weston Electrical Instrument Company the men workers are not neglected, for in one wing of the factory a room has been fitted up as a recrea-

tion hall with a pianola, billiards and other games. Once a fort-
night entertainments are held at this hall. The J. Bancroft Company of Wilmington, Delaware, also provide recreation and smoking
rooms for the men workers. The International Harvester Company
has handsome clubhouses in connection with its works, which are
convenient centers for recreation.

While many of these provisions for rest and recreation are
enjoyed and utilized by the workers, in some cases they do not seem

Courtesy Utica Drop Forge and Tool Co.

Dance Hall, Clubhouse for Employes.

to be desired. The Pocasset Worsted Company near Providence,
R. I., built a handsome clubhouse at an expenditure of about
twenty thousand dollars, containing reading rooms, billiard rooms,
bowling alleys and a large auditorium; but the workers never used
the clubhouse in sufficient numbers to justify the expenditure.

Factories situated in large industrial centers do not find that
elaborate provisions for recreation or entertainments of their
workers meet with much response, since the workers usually prefer
to find their own amusement and recreation in the town; but where

the factory is situated in the country or in a small town in which there are only limited opportunities for rest and recreation, such undertakings are apt to prove more successful. Most employers state that it is necessary to get the workers to undertake the management of the clubs or recreation centers provided by the management, and that it is a mistake to furnish too much without requiring the workers to pay for their privileges or to undertake responsibilities in connection with them.

One of the first corporations to institute this form of welfare work was the United States Steel Company, which built a club near its works in Joliet at a cost of about $53,000. The management thought that the improved social and intellectual conditions resulting among the employes would not only promote their welfare, but advance the interests of the company. The clubhouse building has a gymnasium, tennis courts, showers and swimming pool, an auditorium, a library and a music room. The members pay $1.00 a year, which entitles them to all the benefits of the club. The management, however, admits that the membership of the club fluctuates. In 1893 the membership was 300, in 1895, 1200; in 1897, 500; in 1899, 650.*

The use of music and singing during working hours as a means of stimulating the workers has developed in several factories where the character of the work has made this possible. In many small dressmaking or millinery shops it has long been the custom for some one to read aloud during working hours; or the workers themselves burst into song. Henkel & Company in their works at Düsseldorf impress upon their forewomen the importance of singing because "it prevents the girls from talking, the girls thus stick to their work and more is done than without the singing."

The Care of Health. The improvement of the physical condition of the workers is one of the most important aspects of employers' welfare work. Most occupations have a certain element of danger in them and practically all industries demand good physique and health on the part of the employes. Good health is important not only to the workers, but to factory efficiency. Hence, all measures which tend to improve the health of the workers are of great benefit to the workers themselves, to the employers and to the industry.

In certain trades special dangers exist, either because of the

* Victor H. Olmstead: "Betterment of Industrial Conditions," Bulletin No. 31, Dept. of Labor, November, 1900.

dangerous machinery, hazardous processes or materials employed. Moreover, in many industrial establishments there are women and minors whose health needs care and who are specially susceptible to the dangers and hazards of trades.

The form of employers' welfare work which is usually installed for the purpose of improving the health of the workers consists in the provision of (a) rest and emergency rooms, (b) first aid

Medical Chest in a Factory.

facilities, (c) dispensaries and hospitals, (d) nursing staff, and (e) general medical care and supervision.

In every industrial establishment some suitable place should be provided where an employe feeling suddenly ill may rest. At present nearly every large industrial establishment has a special rest or emergency room, where employes who suddenly faint or become temporarily ill, are given first aid treatment. Some of these rooms are splendidly lighted, ventilated and cheerful, and are equipped with beds and all first aid facilities.

It is rather general to find some form of first aid equipment in the large American factories. The kind of equipment, its location and the methods of using it, differ very much. Sometimes the first aid equipment consists simply of a wooden box in which there is a miscellaneous collection of patent medicines, a roll of lint and some kind of disinfectant. The employes help themselves when injured as best they can. Sometimes the foreman of a department has charge

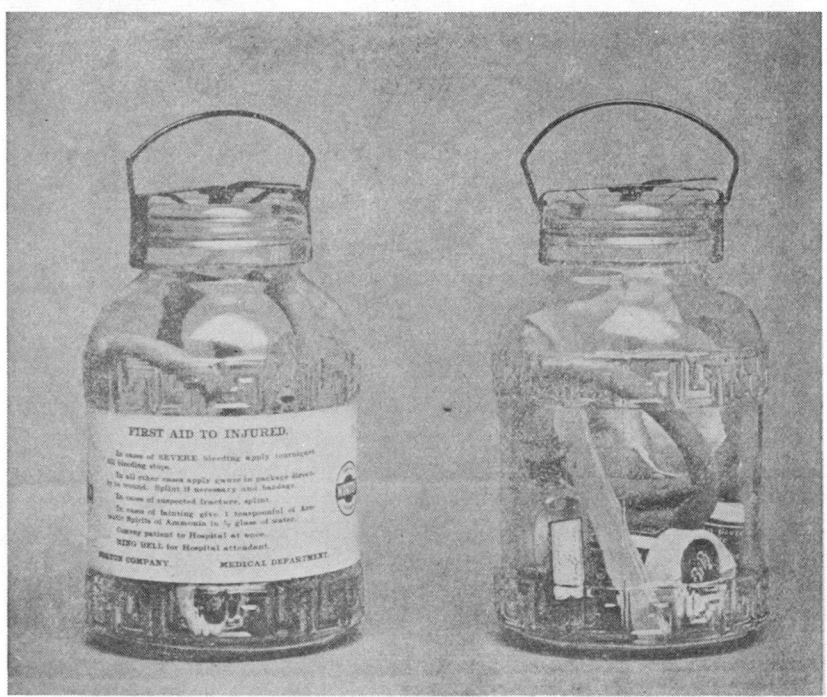

Courtesy Norton Company, Worcester, Mass.

First Aid Equipment.

of the outfit, and if he has been instructed in his duties and understands the necessity for antiseptic care, he may meet emergencies successfully. First aid equipment, however, should not be left to chance, and should contain not only standard articles needed for all cases of possible injuries occurring within the shop, but also such additional articles as may be necessary for the special kind of factory for which the equipment is intended, and competent persons should be appointed to handle the materials.

In factories where severe injuries, such as cuts, amputations, fractures and dislocations occur, special provision must be made for stopping the flow of blood and temporary splints provided for such emergencies. In factories where electric or traumatic shock, sudden collapse, gassing or acute intoxication of workers may occur, arrangements must be made for resuscitation by pulmotors or other means. The pulmotor has proved itself to be a reliable instrument in certain cases of asphyxiation, and is probably the best mechanical means for producing artificial respiration. Where no such instrument is available, some one connected with the establishment should be instructed in the ordinary methods of first aid and artificial respiration.

There are a number of standard outfits for first aid on the market, most of them more or less valuable. It is important, however, to bear in mind that it is hardly possible to devise a standard outfit to suit all establishments and locations, and that it is necessary to take into consideration the special conditions in each factory.

A number of American industrial plants have already made more or less adequate provision for dispensaries and hospitals connected with their establishments. In these dispensaries, sudden injuries as well as more or less chronic ailments of the workers in the factory are treated by one or more physicians attached to these establishments. The location and equipment of some of these dispensaries and clinics leave much to be desired, although in a number of plants they are above reproach.

Emergency hospitals with physicians in constant attendance are maintained by the General Electric Company, the Westinghouse Air Brake Company, the Westinghouse Electric Company, and many other industrial establishments. Physicians and medical assistants are often employed as a regular staff attached to the establishment. The Western Electric Company at Hawthorne, Ill., has an emergency hospital with physicians and nurses in constant attendance. The National Cash Register Company has a hygiene department of four rooms in charge of a physician and nurse, and assistants are in constant attendance. The Jeffrey Manufacturing Company at Columbus, O., has found that its emergency hospital with physicians and nurse in charge has saved a great deal of time which was formerly lost by its workers through slight injuries which became infected through lack of immediate antiseptic treatment.

In some of the large industrial plants abroad I found splendid provision made for medical care and treatment of employes.   Perhaps the most extensive work of this kind is carried on by the Friedrich Bayer Company at Elberfeld and Leverkussen.   Here they maintain not only first aid rooms, emergency rooms, clinics, dispensaries, regular hospitals and convalescent homes, but they have also provided tuberculosis sanatoria and homes for special treatment of delicate and defective workers and their offspring.

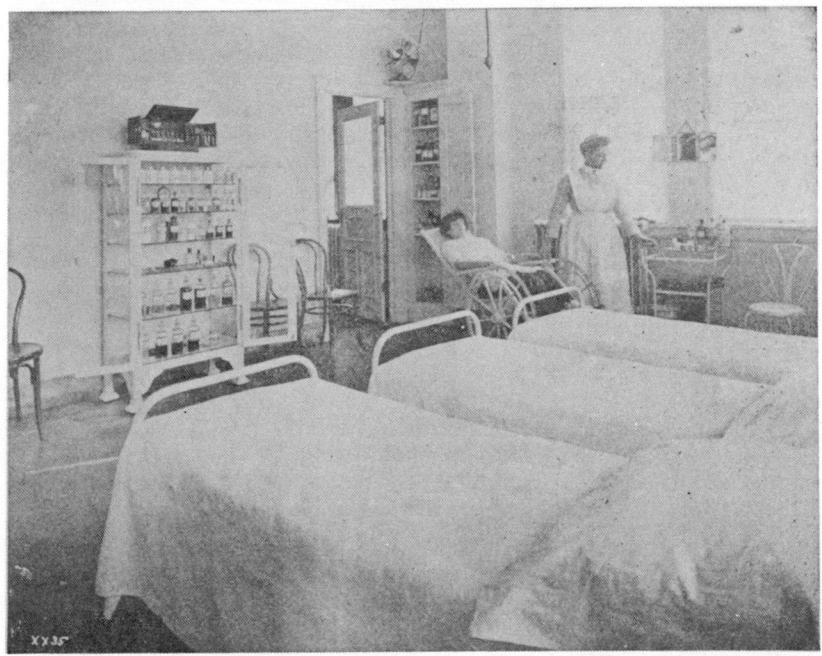

Courtesy Eastman Kodak Co.

Emergency Hospital Room for Employes.

A similar supervision of the health of the workers is undertaken by the Chatillon Company of France.   Dispensaries, clinics and free milk stations are maintained.   The Company also maintains a crêche for children from fifteen days to three years old, has a free midwife service, and maintains the necessary hospitals without charge.   The government tobacco works in Austria have splendid hospitals and clinics attached to each factory.   Male and female physicians are employed on full time and the health of the employes is minutely supervised.

The custom is developing in large factories of employing a nurse or a nursing staff who not only assist in the emergency room, first aid clinics and dispensaries, but also look after the health of the individual workers in the factory, visit absent workers in their homes and assist them in case of illness either of a worker or a member of his family.   Indeed, a new class of factory nurses is developing, whose work is extremely beneficial and is surely destined to extend its field.   In an article on " Factory Nursing," in the *Public Health Nurse Quarterly* for April, 1913, an experienced nurse says:

" The nurse in a mill will find herself called upon to care for burns and wounds of all sorts while the nurse in a " store " will have more cases of faintness, headache, indigestion, with occasional cuts and falls.   To render immediate assistance in all such emergencies, to give after care, at the shop in case the patient is able to go on working, at the home in more serious cases, is the primary work of most factory nurses.   Other curative work is also to be done, however, in the homes.   A list of absent employes may be given her, that she may ascertain if the absence is caused by illness either of the worker himself or in his family.   Employes may be asked to call for her advice in case of any illness among their families even though they are not kept at home by it themselves."
. . . " This service opens the door of opportunity for other and more important service of an educative type.   The care that a nurse gives soon makes her the friend of her patient.   As a friend she gains his confidence and can often persuade him to take advice which, coming from another, would fall on deaf ears.   Unhygienic living is at the bottom of many of the ills she finds."
. . . " With this great field of usefulness open to the factory nurse it must, however, be said that her best work can be done only under the best conditions.   An employer who wants no preventive suggestions from her, a foreman who believes that ' all this antiseptic stuff is nonsense and a cud of tobacco would be just as good a cure or better ' may render her work difficult or vain."

In some of the large establishments located in cities or towns, special arrangements are made either with physicians living in the neighborhood or with hospitals and dispensaries situated nearby for taking care of injured and diseased employes.

The care of the teeth of the workers is beginning to receive attention from employers who wish to be up to date in their welfare work.   Rowntree Bros., in their factory at York, England, employ a dentist to attend to the teeth of their workers.   Few American employers, however, have as yet introduced this innovation in welfare work.

Perhaps the most extensive provisions for first aid and rescue work are made by the United States Steel Corporation. All the companies of the Corporation have first aid and rescue crews made up of specially trained employes. It is purely voluntary, but before anyone is allowed to enter the work he must have a doctor's certificate showing that he is physically fit to undertake it. The system varies a little in each company, but the general plan is the same. The organization consists of a first aid crew of from four to six men

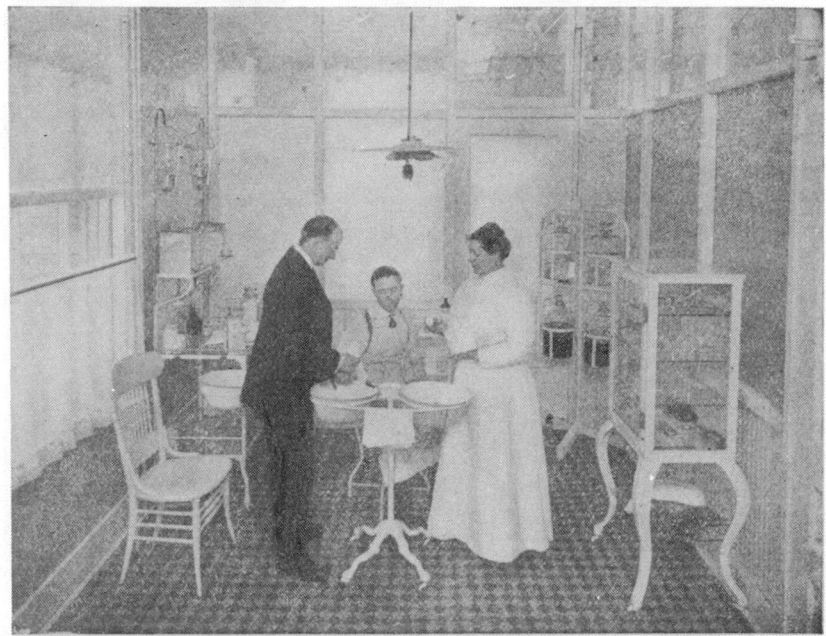

Coutesy National Cash Register Co., Dayton, O.

Emergency Hospital Room.

who are trained by the company's doctor. Instructions are given to them by the physician, and the training of the men for the work goes on continually. Rescue crews of from five to eight men are also assigned to each first aid crew. In some of the companies they have also a special rescue crew and a special operating room with the necessary sterilizing equipment, and an ample supply of drugs and medicines. They are also instructed in the use of flash lights, the life line, pulmotors and resuscitating packs.

The H. C. Frick Coke Company have a corps who are well trained and drilled in special rescue training stations.

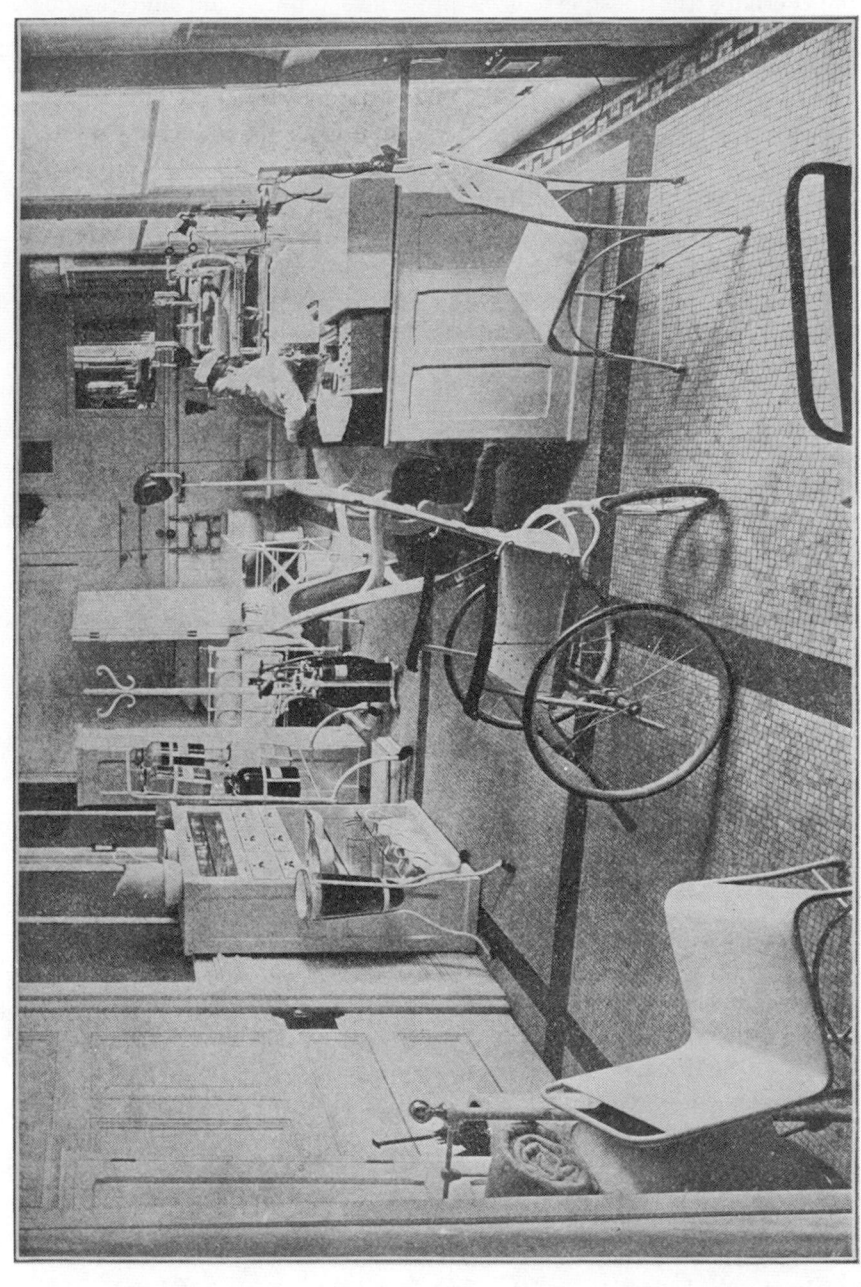

Government Printing Office Emergency Room, Washington, D. C.

Not many industrial establishments have as yet a complete system of medical supervision of their workers. By such a system is meant one that embraces the following features: (1) preliminary compulsory examination of all applicants and candidates for positions in the establishment, and rejection of all candidates below a certain standard of physique or having physical defects; (2) periodical, monthly or semi-annual physical examination of all employes within the establishment; (3) complete care of the health of the workers including prophylactic as well as curative treatment for all injuries and ills discovered while the persons are in the employ of the establishment.

It is evident that such a full medical supervision would be of the greatest benefit to the workers as well as to the establishments and there is no doubt that the tendency of modern industrial development is such that an extension of medical supervision of workers is bound to be accepted as a standard of industrial welfare work. The time is not distant when every large industrial establishment will consider the employment of a competent physician at full time for the medical supervision of their employes as necessary as the employment of a superintendent of production, or efficiency engineer.

At present some splendid examples of medical supervision are given by the Norton Company of Worcester, Mass., Sears, Roebuck & Company, the International Harvester Company, Swift & Company, and many other large American concerns.

Educational Work. Many employers rightly regard intellectual improvement as a great benefit to their working force. The workers begin to come into the factory at the age of from fourteen to sixteen, when their education has been very limited. The further development of these young workers as well as of those who are older is of great importance to the workers themselves as well as beneficial to the efficiency of the establishment. Many employers, therefore, have introduced continuation schools, apprenticeship education, corporation schools, libraries, etc.

Libraries. Industrial establishments situated in cities or towns where there are many advantages do not provide educational facilities for their workers, such as are provided by employers whose factories are in lonely districts in the country. Railroad machine shops, construction camps, and works carried on in connection with mining and engineering operations, are apt to have considerable libraries for their employes. Some corporations have traveling libraries which are sent about from one factory to another. The success of a factory library depends upon well chosen books, and its accessibility. It was found in one large establishment that sixty per cent of the users of books were the workers in the administration building where the library was kept. As a result, the library was divided up into sections which were exchanged between the different departments and buildings. The workers eagerly took advantage of this opportunity and the use of the library increased.

The Brown & Sharpe Manufacturing Company of Providence, R. I., maintain a library for their workers who are skilled machinists and mechanics. The library is in charge of the time keeping department, which all workers must pass at least once a day.

Branch stations of the public library are located in some factories, notably at the Deering Works in Chicago, the Sherwin-Williams Company of Cleveland and the Shredded Wheat Company of Niagara Falls. Other factories have had libraries at some time or other which became unnecessary when public libraries or Carnegie libraries were started.

Apprenticeship Schools. The matter of securing trained workers for skilled trades is a serious problem and one that has been discussed and investigated in all countries. In Germany, a system of continuation schools towards which the employer partly contributes, has largely taken the place of schools established by individual employers. At the same time, many large firms continue to have their own apprentice schools for purposes of technical education.

In America, where scarcely any provision is made for industrial education by the public school system, many corporations have established apprenticeship schools. The Westinghouse Electric Company support a night technical school with a four year course, which is followed by a two-year apprentice course of four hours per week with pay. The General Electric Company has four hundred trade and electrical apprentices who receive four years of training. The Western Electric Company's apprentices are required to attend school for one hour a day; the remainder of the time they spend in the factory. The Brown & Sharpe Company's apprentices must take a four-year course and attend a special school for two hours every day. They are paid for their shop work, eight, ten, twelve, and fourteen cents an hour, according to the year of their apprenticeship. The United Shoe Machinery Company have equipped a separate department as an industrial school. Their apprentices spend one week at school and one week in the shop.

The school, however, is a public school and the company has no authority over it, though it cooperates with it and furnishes the material for the boys working in the shop. The Ludlow Textile School trains apprentices in branches of the textile trade. The boys work five hours a day and are transferred to different machines or operations every month. They spend three hours a day in school and the course covers four years.

General Educational Activities. In skilled trades, the educational opportunities provided by employers take the form of technical

Courtesy United Shoe Machinery Co., Beverly, Mass.

Industrial School.

courses or apprenticeship schools. In unskilled trades or in trades where numbers of women are employed, educational activities are more general in type and are planned to afford relaxation and mental stimulus rather than any special skill or technical ability.

The Cadbury Cocoa Company of Bournville has evening classes for its women workers in cooking, sewing, millinery and music. J. Crosfield & Sons insist on all boy and girl workers between fourteen and seventeen years old attending their evening school for three nights a week during the winter. Prizes are given for attendance and proficiency in the subjects taught. The H. J. Heinz Company of Pittsburgh conducts drawing, sewing and cooking classes for its women employes.

The Friedrich Bayer Company with factories at Elberfeld and Leverkussen, Germany, have arts and crafts classes, garden schools, and domestic science classes of all kinds, chiefly for the children of their employes. The Solvay Process Company has several classes in dressmaking for the mothers and daughters of its workers. Cooking lessons, lessons in embroidering, dancing, housekeeping and sewing are all provided at very low prices. The National Cash Register Company in its employes' clubhouse at Rubicon conducts classes of all sorts. Especially successful are dancing and sewing classes for women workers.

HOUSING. The amount of money spent by a worker on rent is a much larger item in his budget than in the budget of a middle class or well-to-do family. The housing problem is one that affects the worker and his family very nearly, and the difficulty of obtaining cheap and suitable habitations is very great. Many employers have tried to meet this difficulty by providing homes for their workers in the neighborhood of the factory, or by building model villages or forming building and loan associations. This policy helps to attract workers to the neighborhood and also means a steadier working force, as a man who has a comfortable home at comparatively low rent is likely to think twice before he goes elsewhere. It is therefore advantageous for the employer to investigate the housing of his workers, especially when the factory is in the country or on the outskirts of a town.

On the other hand, the provision by factory owners of houses for their workers has often led to strained relations between the employer and his employes. In times of strikes, company-owned houses have become a weapon in the hands of the employer. Some employers are opposed to providing houses for their workers or for making any arrangements for their life outside of the factory. Instead, they prefer to establish building or loan associations and make it easy for their workers to acquire property and build their own houses if they desire to do so. This is the policy followed by the Karl Zeiss Works at Jena, the Joseph Fels Company near Philadelphia, and many other large corporations.

There are many model villages in existence which have been built entirely by employers for their workers, the houses planned, the grounds laid out, the roads made, trees and shrubbery planted, markets and stores established, and regulations for the government of the town laid down. Where the employes are consulted and allowed a voice in these undertakings, where they are permitted to purchase their own homes and to acquire an interest in the affairs of the town, these experiments have often been successful. On the other hand, there have been some disastrous failures, notably that of Pullman.

Another method followed is that which has been developed at Bournville where an estate of 609 acres was transferred to a trust.

Courtesy Joseph Bancroft & Sons Co., Wilmington, Del.

Ivy Road: Houses for Employes.

In the terms of the foundation certain stipulations were made. Each house was to have a garden and was to occupy no more than one-quarter of the area of land on which it was built. One-tenth of the land, exclusive of roads and gardens, was to be reserved for parks and recreation grounds. Many different types of houses have been built, and in 1911 there were 731 houses in the village. The houses are both small and large and many different plans have been used to suit the different tastes and requirements of the workers. Bungalows for single women were built. Many houses have bath-rooms and all of them have baths. Fruit trees and small fruit bushes were planted in all the gardens. The roads are wide and bordered with trees. Playgrounds have been reserved here and there through the village.

The only restriction made by the foundation is that alcoholic liquors cannot be sold except by the unanimous consent of the trustees. This foundation now is the property of the nation and is not in any way connected with the Cadbury Works. The fact that only forty-one per cent of the householders belong to the works shows the village has been as great a benefit to the workers of Birmingham as to the workers in the Cadbury factory.

Other model villages in England which are used largely by the working force are Easwick, a town built by Rowntree Bros., on the outskirts of York; Port Sunlight, a charming village belonging to Lever Bros.; and Aintree near Liverpool, which is the property of Hartley Bros.

In Germany, there are several large scale housing schemes developed by employers for their employes, the most notable probably being those of Messrs. Krupp and Friedrich Bayer at Leverkussen and Elberfeld. No less than twelve colonies have been developed in connection with the Krupp Works. Their first experiments in housing were hideous barracks of corrugated iron. The later ones, such as Alfredshof and Friedrichshof, are model villages as far as the architecture, planning and finishing of houses and grounds are concerned. The Bayer colonies are also attractive and comfortable.

There are a number of corporation villages in France. At Le Creusot Steel Mills there are approximately twelve hundred houses with gardens provided by the company, and the erection or purchase of houses is facilitated by building loans. The Menier Chocolate Factory at Noisiel-sur-Seine has built an attractive village with 312 semi-detached cottages, free schools, a restaurant and boarding house for single men and a public laundry and bathhouses. They also provide almshouses for old employes.

In America, company-owned houses have often resulted disastrously for both workers and employers during labor conflicts. Especially has this been true of the company owned houses in lonely districts in the neighborhood of mines. The wholesale evictions that take place in times of strikes have made the workers fight shy of such schemes. At the same time there are several housing schemes that have been very successful, notably Leclair, a town started for the employes of the Nelson Paint Works near St. Louis. At

Leclair, the land is sold to the workers outright with the right of preemption to the company if the owner leaves. The workers erect their own houses and pay for them gradually, and in case of leaving the employ of the firm, all money and interest is repaid after an agreed sum is deducted for rent. The utmost freedom is allowed to the workers in their planning and building, and the town is governed just as any other American town would be with the single exception that no saloons are permitted.

Vandergrift is a town for employes of the American Sheet Steel

Courtesy Joseph Bancroft & Sons Co., Wilmington, Del.

Boarding House for Employes.

Company in Pennsylvania. Eighty per cent of the workers own their own homes and much is left to their individual enterprise. Other model villages are at South Manchester in connection with the Cheney Silk Mills, and at Ludlow, Mass., and at Hopedale. In most of these American workers' colonies, the employer has simply made it possible for the workers to escape the operations of land speculators by buying the land and making building loans and arrangements for the erection of homes; in this way keeping rents and cost of homes down to a minimum. The only general regulation seems to be that prohibiting the sale of intoxicating liquors.

The policy of the Prussian State Mines towards the housing of their workers is to encourage the workers to build and own their own homes; but not to build houses for them. The government makes a present of from $185 to $225 to any workman proposing to build his own house and in addition lends him without interest enough to make up the cost.

CHAPTER VIII

AIR AND VENTILATION IN FACTORIES

I

CONFINED AIR

FOR a great many years physicians, sanitarians, and educators have sought to impress upon the public the importance of fresh air. For years they have tried to instil a wholesome fear of bad and impure air to which they ascribed all the ills that mankind is heir to. There was hardly a disease which they did not attribute to impure air or an epidemic that was not ascribed to the same cause.

The inevitable reaction was bound to come. Sanitarians began to ask questions. Doubt assailed experimenters, and scientists made profound studies. As is the case in all reactions, the pendulum seems to have swung too far in the other direction. Exaggerated statements of the effect of bad air have given rise to unwarranted sanitary nihilism, and former conceptions of the rôle of impure air are regarded as vagaries of sanitary science. However, scientific studies and investigations of the problem of air and ventilation have led to a readjustment of opinion, and at present the problem is not far from being solved.

The questions which must be considered are the following: Is there a difference between the air outside of inhabited rooms and workshops and the air within these rooms? What does this difference consist of? What is it due to? What effect have such differences upon the human body? How is a change of the air between the outside and inside to be brought about? What are the means and rate of such a change?

Confined Air. The atmosphere of the outside air is a mixture of gases, the principal constituents being nitrogen and oxygen. The composition of air is—nitrogen 79.02, oxygen 20.96, carbonic acid 0.03, and traces of other gases, such as argon, neon, xenon,

347

etc., the character and functions of which have not as yet been determined. This composition of air is about the same in the whole atmosphere surrounding the earth, the change in the air of different localities being slight and mainly consisting in variations in the percentage of oxygen and carbonic acid.

In building a house, a factory, or workshop, we inclose a space in which air is confined, and in which at the beginning the air is the same as the outside atmosphere. Soon, however, due to the various processes within the room, the air begins to change in its composition and becomes different from the air outside.

The processes which are going on within the closed room are each accompanied by changes influencing the condition and composition of the air within. These processes are due to the presence of human beings, to mechanical appliances and devices, machinery, friction, etc., and to the chemical processes of combustion, illumination, and industrial activity, all of which produce certain chemical and physical changes in the air.

The changes which are produced by the presence of human beings are the following: (1) a diminution in the percentage of oxygen, (2) an increase in the percentage of carbon dioxide, (3) an increase of volatile odoriferous organic products, (4) a possible increase in the number of bacteria and micro-organisms in the air, (5) an increase in the temperature, and (6) an increase in the relative humidity of the air in the room.

Combustion and illumination within the room or shop produce changes in the air according to the character and source of the combustion, the most important changes being the increase in temperature and humidity and the addition of certain gases, such as CO_2, CO, and others due to the processes of combustion and illumination. The physical and chemical processes going on within the shop add a large amount of dust from the processes and materials used, and sometimes gases and fumes, due to certain chemical processes, are produced.

All these additions to and changes in the normal consistency of the air are usually regarded as air impurities and have a greater or lesser effect upon the human beings within the confined air spaces.

Diminution of Oxygen. There is considerable diminution in the quantity of oxygen in confined spaces where persons are at work and where illumination and combustion are going on. The air which is inspired by persons contains nearly 21 per cent of oxygen; the air which is expired by persons contains only about

New York State Factory Commission.

Bleaching Furs with Ammonia.   The work is very irritating to throat and eyes and there is no duct in this room to carry off the fumes.

16 per cent of oxygen, a loss of 5 per cent of oxygen in every 300 cubic feet or more of air which is used by every person at every breath. The percentage of oxygen is also diminished by processes of illumination and combustion. All illuminants except electricity, and all direct combustion, consume a large percentage of oxygen in the air, varying with the character, kind, and intensity of the illumination and combustion. An ordinary gas-jet which consumes from 5 to 10 cubic feet of gas per hour consumes about 5 to 10 feet of oxygen. It is, therefore, evident that the number of gas-burners in a shop will cause a considerable diminution in the oxygen available.

Increase of CO_2. The air of inhabitable rooms also differs from normal air by considerable increase in the proportion of carbonic acid (CO_2) contained, such increase also being due to the presence of human beings, to illumination, combustion, etc.

	Nitrogen.	Oxygen.	CO_2.
Normal air......................	79.02	20.96	0.03
Expired air......................	79.02	16.03	4.4

There is therefore a large diminution in the percentage of oxygen and also a more than 100-fold increase of carbonic acid (CO_2). It has been calculated that every adult person adds to the air of the room hourly at least one cubic foot of carbonic acid (CO_2), depending upon the character of the work performed. A large amount of carbonic acid (CO_2) is also produced by processes of illumination, an ordinary gas-jet on the average producing about $2\frac{1}{2}$ to 5 feet of carbonic acid per hour; thus adding considerably to the carbonic acid (CO_2) contents of rooms in which illuminants are necessary.

As to the influence of the diminution of oxygen and increase of the carbonic acid (CO_2), the consensus of opinion is that under ordinary conditions this diminution has no special influence upon the health of the body and has no injurious effects. "The oxygen in the air must be reduced from 21 per cent to 15 per cent before any marked physical effect is manifest."[*] Indeed, it has been found that human beings become accustomed to air in which the proportion of oxygen is considerably decreased. A decrease down to 17 per cent is considered not at all injurious, and it is probable that an ordinary decrease of oxygen in inhabited rooms has no

[*] C.-E. A. Winslow: Scientific Basis for Ventilation Standards.

special bearing upon the problem of ventilation. This opinion as to the effect of diminution of oxygen and increase of carbonic acid (CO_2) has been well expressed by Haldane and Osborn in the report of the Departmental Committee on Ventilation of Factories and Workshops (Great Britain), as follows:

" Mere increase of carbonic acid and diminution of oxygen to the extent which actually occurs in the air of buildings has no direct influence upon the comfort or health of the persons present. The proportion of carbonic acid, even where ventilation is very bad, seldom rises beyond 50 volumes per 10,000; and it requires about six times as much to produce an immediate perceptible effect (increased depth and frequency of breathing). A similar remark applies to the oxygen percentage. Neither a diminution nor an increase of 2 or 3 per cent in the oxygen seems to produce any appreciable effect on a man. The living organism regulates its own consumption of oxygen, and in this respect differs entirely from a burning candle or fire, in the case of which the rate of consumption of oxygen rises and falls with the oxygen percentage in the air. A large fall in the oxygen percentage, or a corresponding diminution in the barometric pressure, produces the train of symptoms known to mountaineers as ' mountain sickness'; but the diminution requires to be a very considerable one. Some of the best-known health resorts are at altitudes where the diminution of pressure corresponds physiologically to a diminution by fully a fifth in the oxygen percentage. Further evidence showing that a moderate increase in carbonic acid and diminution of oxygen in the air is not in itself prejudicial to health is afforded by the fact that, apart from accidents, the life of a coal-miner is exceptionally healthy, although he breathes, when at work, air which contains a notable excess of carbonic acid and deficiency of oxygen owing to chemical changes in the coal. The importance of the carbonic acid in the air of a building arises solely from the fact that it is an index of conditions which are usually prejudicial to both health and comfort."*

The older hygienists considered carbonic acid a virulent poison, extremely dangerous to health, and ascribed all the ill effects of confined air to the presence of carbonic acid in ill-ventilated rooms. Later studies, however, showed that the rôle of carbonic acid was greatly overrated and that a very large increase in the contents of carbonic acid in the air of the room is needed before any perceptible effects are produced upon the human beings present. The increase which is considered as possibly dangerous varies from 4 to 10 per cent, and it is claimed by some that air even with 25

* Second Report of the Departmental Committee on Ventilation of Factories, Haldane and Osborn.

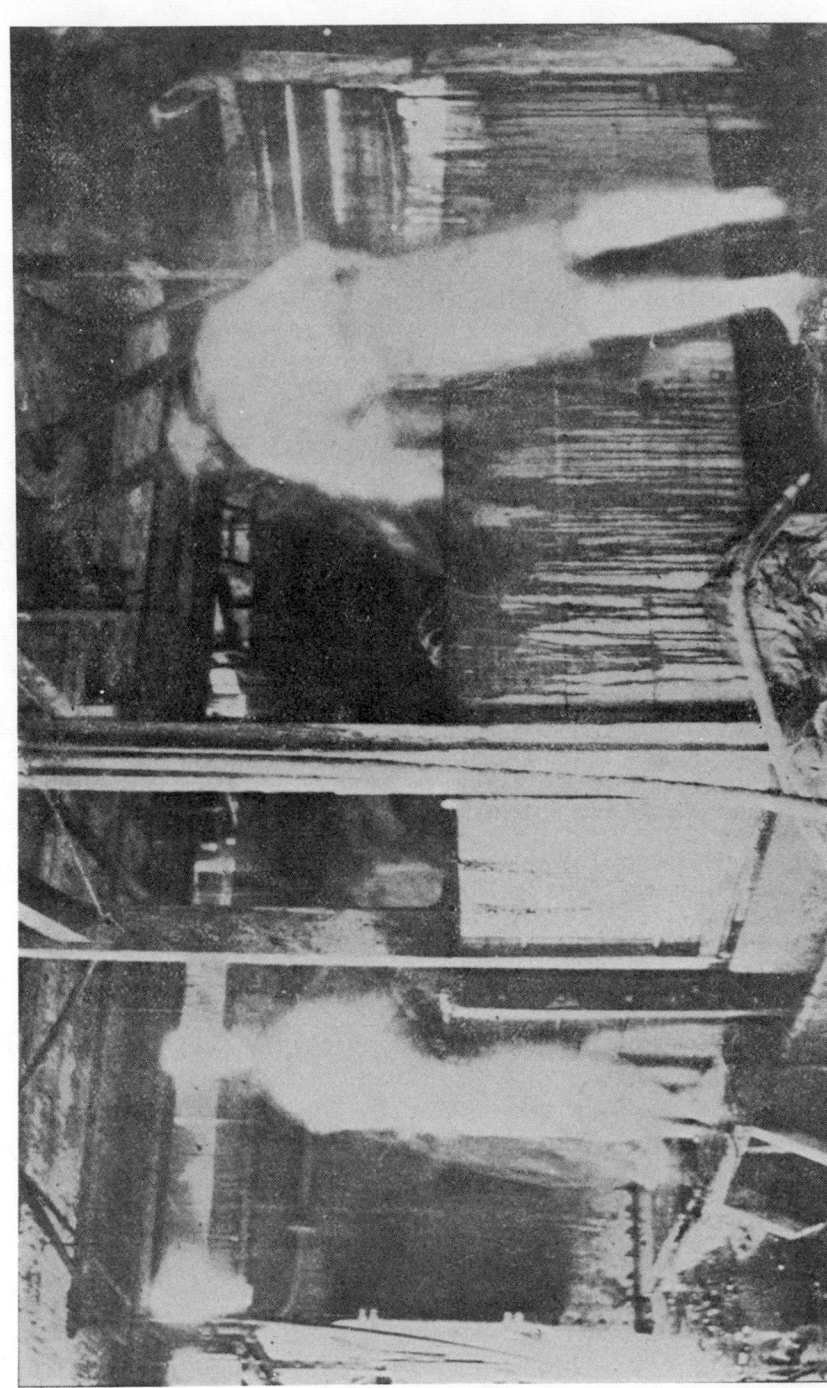

The Filter Bag Wash Room in a Sugar Refinery.

A photograph taken under difficulties. The room full of steam; excessive temperature; employes work naked except for a loin cloth.

New York State Factory Commission.

or 30 per cent of carbonic acid may be inhaled with impunity. Such a proportion of carbonic acid, however, is scarcely ever found in a closed room. Experiments have also shown that guinea pigs may live for half an hour in air consisting of 80 per cent of CO_2 and 20 per cent of oxygen. Only an increase of carbonic acid not often found in rooms produces frequent and labored breathing, discomfort and distress. According to Gärtner, one may work for hours in an atmosphere containing 1 per cent CO_2.

In all investigations of air in rooms and workshops, the proportion of CO_2 in the air has hardly ever exceeded 50 volumes per 10,000, and the usual percentage of carbonic acid, even in foul and ill-ventilated rooms with a number of burning gas-fixtures, ranges from 20 to 30 volumes per 10,000. The highest CO_2 contents found by the Departmental Committee were only from 0.32 per cent to 0.53 per cent in tailoring shops, 0.47 per cent in textile establishments, and 0.56 per cent to 0.57 per cent in cotton-spinning mills.

The following table taken from the reports of the Commissioner of Labor for 1908, 1909 and 1910, shows the temperature and humidity in New York factories.*

Industry.	Number of Workrooms with Temperature			Number with relative humidity over 70%.
	72 Deg. or Less.	72 Deg.- 79 Deg.	80 Deg. or Over.	
Printing shops.......	2	25	29	3
Clothing shops.......	9	23	7	6
Bakeries.............	1	20	15	7
Pearl button factories.	33	9	0	14
Cigar-making shops ..	8	4	5	7
Laundries...........	0	7	7	1
Miscellaneous........	6	5	0	1
Total.........	59	93	63	39

The importance of the presence of carbonic acid in the air is not because of its poisonous character in the proportion in which it is usually found in the air, but because, as a rule, it is found in proportion to the general contamination of the air of a room by human beings, and has been regarded therefore as a valuable index of the general impurities of the air in confined spaces. This importance

* " Factory Sanitation and Efficiency," by C.-E. A. Winslow, Smithsonian Report for 1911, page 615.

of carbonic acid (CO_2) as an indicator of the condition of the air and of air-change in inhabited rooms was emphasized by Pettenkoffer and his pupils, who were the first to indicate the importance of carbonic acid as such an index, and devised appliances for tests of the air for carbonic-acid contents.

The carbonic-acid contents of the air have also been made a basis for legal standards for ventilation in various countries and states.

Organic Matter. The presence of living beings in an inhabited room results in adding to the air of the room certain volatile odoriferous organic products, some due to emanations from the skin, from the clothes and bodies of persons, others due to the expired air from the lungs, to saliva and other products of coughing, sneezing, decayed teeth, etc. These products are often perceptible in crowded rooms, and result in the feeling of nausea and discomfort which one feels on entering such places. Scientists have sought to prove the existence of a specific " crowd poison " (anthropotoxin), which was claimed to exist in the air of inhabited rooms. Numerous experiments have been made to determine the presence and toxicity of this organic product, but later investigations have proved that the claim of the presence of such a " subtle and mysterious, poisonous, morbific matter or crowd poison is intangible." *

There is no doubt that the specific odors emanating from persons in rooms are unpleasant and may cause discomfort, but it has yet to be proved that these odors are injurious.

Infectious Bacteria. The air very often contains a number of micro-organisms, among which may be found some which are regarded as pathogenic, such as tubercle bacilli, and others. These pathogenic micro-organisms come from diseased persons through droplets, saliva and excretions from coughing, sneezing, etc. An infection from the presence of such bacteria may be possible, although the rôle of air in the transmission of infectious diseases is now regarded as negligible, except perhaps as far as tuberculosis is concerned. There is a tendency among scientists to disregard the danger of aerial infection, although it has been repeatedly shown that ill-ventilated rooms are apt to contain a larger number of bacteria per cubic foot of air than the air of well-ventilated rooms.

Dust, Gases and Fumes. Besides the impurities already considered which are found in the air of inhabited rooms and shops, there are also a large number of additional impurities found in

* Professor C.-E. A. Winslow: New Art of Ventilation, p. 1.

manufacturing establishments. These impurities consist of dust, gases and fumes which are products of illumination, combustion, and mechanical and chemical processes within the establishment. The quantity and character of these impurities, as well as their influences upon health, deserve special consideration, and will be treated in other chapters.

Temperature and Humidity. The most important physical changes in confined air of rooms and shops are the increase of the temperature and humidity of the air. These physical changes are at present considered of greater importance than the chemical changes alluded to before, and in the light of modern science the problem of ventilation, as Professor Lee well expresses it, " is not chemical but physical, not pulmonary but cutaneous."

The temperature and humidity of the outside air varies greatly, according to climate, season, altitude, etc., and human beings have the power within certain limits to adjust themselves to extremes in these environmental conditions if they are properly clothed, fed and exercised. A person may stand with impunity low temperature and low relative humidity of air, as has been proved by those who take arctic trips or live in the extreme north. The effects of a sojourn in extremely hot climates and the higher rate of humidity are more serious. Not every person can stand the effects of living in tropical climates, and all of us feel distress on humid, hot summer days, showing the serious effect of hot and moist air.

Air always contains a certain amount of moisture. The amount of moisture which a given volume of air contains at a given time depends upon the temperature of the air; the higher the temperature, the more moisture the air will absorb. Thus, at a temperature of 59° F., one cubic foot of air will absorb six grains of water. At a temperature of 86° F., the same volume of air will be able to absorb twelve grains or twice as much water. For every increase in the temperature of air there is an increase in its ability to absorb moisture. At 32° F., air can hold 1/60 of its weight of water-vapor; at 59° F., 1/80; at 86°, F. 1/40. Roughly, every 27° of F. of increase in temperature doubles the amount of water-vapor air can hold in proportion to its weight.

When air at a given temperature contains all the moisture it is capable of absorbing it is said to be saturated, and any excess of moisture is condensed and deposited upon surfaces, the air having reached what is called the " dew " point. *Absolute humidity* is the amount of water in a given volume of air. The air at a given temperature does not always contain all the moisture it may absorb. As a rule, it contains only part of the moisture. The relation of the amount of water contained in a given volume of air at a certain temperature to absolute saturation is called " relative humidity." Thus, a relative humidity of 60 per cent means that at a'given temperature the air holds but 60 per cent of the moisture which it is capable of absorbing at the same temperature. Temperature is measured by thermometers, in this country the Fahrenheit thermometer being used. It is graduated to 212°, of which 32° is the freezing-point, and 212° the boiling-point of water (at a certain barometric pressure).

The presence of persons in rooms affects the air of the room not only chemically but physically. The body absorbs oxygen, exhales carbonic acid (CO_2), and other products, and is also a living warm radiator at $98\frac{1}{2}°$ F., giving off heat from the skin of the whole body and moisture from the lungs and from the skin. Heat is given off by direct contact with objects, by transmission, by radiation to surrounding objects and by evaporation. Moisture is given off by exhalation from the lungs and by evaporation from the skin.

The amount of heat and moisture given off by a body differs very much, according to many factors, both external and internal, such as the temperature, climate, and humidity of the air outside, and the food, drink, amount of work and exercise, and metabolism of the body. The temperature and humidity of confined air are also increased by the friction of the machinery and other physical processes, and also by various chemical processes, especially combustion and illumination.

A large number of industrial establishments have an extraordinarily high temperature combined with a high relative humidity. Such is the case in textile mills, in dyeing establishments, in laundries, in bakeries, in refining of sugar and other products, in canning factories, in all places where food or other objects are boiled, steamed, etc., in meat-rendering and packing establishments, and in a very large number of factories too numerous to mention.

The temperature and high degree of moisture in the air of some establishments is especially excessive. Thus, I remember visiting a large sugar refinery'and coming to a part of the establishment where filter bags were washed, where the heat reached a temperature of 110°, and the steam in the room was so dense that it was impossible to see a few feet away. A photograph made of this room is shown in the illustration on page 352. The persons

Manufacture of Felt Hats.

The workmen are exposed to excessive heat and humidity.

Courtesy Wm. C. Hanson, U. S. Dept. Labor, Bulletin 127.

working in this room were entirely naked, and their distress was apparent. I was told that a great many of these workers are subject to colds and must frequently stop work, and the superintendent testified before the Factory Commission that a number of workers were carried out frequently in the summer in a fainting condition. The other illustration on page 363 is of the sausage department in a meat-packing establishment, where the temperature and humidity were also found to be exceedingly high.

The effects of working in air of high temperature and high humidity have been carefully studied by many investigators. Rubner, Wolpert, Flügge and his pupils, in Germany, were the first to call attention to the effects of working under such physical conditions, and ascribed most of the effects of bad air to the temperature and humidity of ill-ventilated rooms.

The physiological effect of high temperature and humidity, and their pathological influence, have been reported upon by Haldane, and lately commented upon by Professors Lee and Winslow.

The British Committee on Ventilation summarized its findings as follows in its second report:

" The conclusion is drawn that prolonged exposure to a hot, moist atmosphere would appear to be more injurious than exposure to an even higher wet bulb temperature for a short time, and that the views expressed entirely support the contention that humidification in any shape or form combined with a hot atmosphere causes bodily discomfort and injury to health."*

Haldane found that with the air temperature at 131° and the wet bulb at 88° the body temperature remained the same after two and one-quarter hours. With air temperature at 89° and wet bulb temperature also at 89° the body temperature rose nearly 3° in the same time, and with the air temperature at 94° and wet bulb temperature at 94° the body temperature rose 4° in two hours. With moderate hard work and a wet bulb temperature of 87° the body temperature rose 4° in one hour. He also found that at a temperature over a certain point, any considerable amount of moisture in the air which diminishes the radiation, tends to cause an accumulation of heat in the body.†

The report of Pembrey and Collis on the physiological condition of weavers working in humid atmospheres gives a detailed

* Second Report of Departmental Committee on Humidity and Ventilation in Cotton-Weaving Sheds.
† The temperature degrees referred to in this paragraph were degrees Fahrenheit.

account of their studies and the conclusions they reached. Their report is as follows:

"Our observations show that the influence of warm, moist atmosphere is to diminish the difference between the internal temperature of the body and that of the peripheral parts. The tendency is to establish a more uniform temperature of the body as a whole, and to throw a tax upon the powers of accommodation, which is indicated by the low blood-pressure, notwithstanding the rapid rate of the pulse. This is exactly the condition which would explain the discomfort and low state of health of which many of the weavers complain.

"During work, heat is produced by the contraction of the muscles, and a rise of internal temperature up to a certain optimum is an advantage to the worker. If, however, the air is hot and moist, the worker must send more blood to the skin to be cooled, and must sweat in order to prevent his temperature from rising too high. Hot, moist air is not favorable for the cooling of the blood or the evaporation of sweat. Muscular work, by creating the need for a greater and faster supply of blood to the muscles, increases the rate of the heart's action. If, at the same time, more blood must be sent to the skin to be cooled, then an extra amount of work must be done by the heart. The regulation of the distribution of the blood is effected by the nervous system. A warm skin diminishes the tone of the muscles, lowers the exchange of material in the body, and depresses the appetite; and the natural tendency is for the nervous system to become less active, and for muscular work to be diminished. In a weaving-shed, however, the machine sets the pace, and the worker must neglect the dictates of his sensations, which are the natural guardians of his health and wellbeing. He must strive as far as possible to accommodate himself to the adverse conditions of heat and moisture. Some workers can respond to the demand better than others, but all must have their powers of accommodation taxed when the temperature of the wet bulb rises much above 70° F. It is not surprising, therefore, that at the end of a day's work many of the weavers complain that they have no energy left, have no great desire for food, and need only drink and rest. The need of food for the production of heat in the body is diminished in a warm, moist atmosphere, but food is needed for supplying the energy for work, and for the growth of the body."*

The opinion of British experts is substantiated by American investigators. Lee, Winslow, Crowder, Benedict, Evans, Phelps, and others have studied the questions of effects of high temperatures and humidity and have also come to the conclusion that these

* Second Report of the Departmental Committee on Humidity and Ventilation in Cotton-Weaving Sheds, p. 24.

Courtesy Wm. C. Hanson, U. S. Dept. Labor, Bulletin 127.

Casting Yellow Brass.

When the molten metal is poured into the molds, fumes of zinc arise and are precipitated by the cool air of the room into fine gray powdered flakes. In the room shown, these are unavoidably inhaled by the workmen, who are thus exposed to the disease known as brass founders' ague.

physical aspects are much more important than the chemical composition of the air.

Professor C.-E. A. Winslow, who has made special studies of ventilation for schools and factories, is strongly convinced of the paramount importance of the physical conditions of the air, and has expressed himself as follows on the subject:

" It is quite clear that the principal thing which makes the air of confined spaces harmful, aside from the special problems presented by dust and fumes, is overheating, especially when combined with excessive moisture. Any temperature over 70° F. puts a strain upon the heat-regulating mechanism of the body, keeps the blood in the skin away from the vital organs, and produces far-reaching impairments of the efficiency of the nervous system, the digestive system, and the body as a whole. Changes in metabolism and blood-pressure, to which attention has recently been called by Dr. Gilman Thompson, are similar well-known physiological reactions to temperature change. This general effect of heat and humidity is familiar to every one who contrasts his own ability to do either brain work or muscular work in the dogs-day and in brisk autumn weather. It is established by the exhaustive studies of physiologists in Germany, in England, and in the United States, while the same studies have as yet failed to reveal any definite bad effects due to the chemical constituents of the air. Other atmospheric conditions are still in doubt. The best lower limit of temperature is uncertain. The action of hot, dry air is debatable. The physiological effect of odors in air has not been demonstrated. It is beyond question, however, that the workers in a factory where the temperature is over 70° are injured by a lowering of their vitality that may lead to tuberculosis and other serious diseases; and that they are working below their normal standard of efficiency, so that both they and their employer are the losers."

Professor F. C. Lee has the following to say on this subject.

" Of the two environmental conditions in question, the temperature and the humidity of the air, there exists a certain medium range of variation within which the human body is capable of performing its best work. Prolonged exposure to extremes of these conditions does not conduce to the continuance of a normal physiological state. The effects of exposure to the atmosphere of these situations are many and various. The bodily mechanism for resisting external heat is at once brought into action. The blood-vessels of the skin become dilated and charged with blood, the skin becomes heated, and the sweat-glands become active. From the skin there occurs a loss of bodily heat by radiation, conduction, convection, and the evaporation of perspiration. The loss of heat by these processes, amounting, according to Rubner, to 95.25 per cent of the total heat loss, may suffice for a time to keep the bodily temperature at its normal level. In proportion, however, as the temperature of the air approaches or surpasses that of the body, and the humidity of the air is sufficient to prevent the evaporation of sweat, loss of bodily heat by the customary channels becomes lessened. Without adequate means for eliminating the heat that is being constantly produced within, the internal temperature rises and a febrile condition results. Such a state is reached the sooner the more mechanical work is performed and the more heat is thereby produced. Its oncoming is favored also by a lack of movement in the air. With a continuance of the unfavorable environmental conditions, a simple rise of internal temperature may pass into a higher fever characteristic of simple heat prostration, or a moderately severe heat-stroke with a temperature up to 40.6° C. (105° F.), and finally into the hyperpyrexial or intense form of heat-stroke, in which the bodily temperature has been known to rise to the phenomenal height of 47.6° C. (117.8° F.). That the elevation of bodily temperature is the result of an elevation of external temperature and humidity combined has been well shown by various British authorities, whose information is drawn partly from laboratory experiments and partly from observations in mines and factories.

"When in a hot and humid atmosphere, the blood-vessels of the skin are dilated and overcharged with blood, the brain and spinal cord, among other organs, are rendered correspondingly anemic. This is sufficient of itself to account largely for the feeling of weariness, the indifference and apathy toward laboring, that are then present. The changed bodily sensations and the general bodily discomfort may also tend toward the same end. But if the stage of elevated bodily temperature be reached, the internal conditions are still more radically changed. A febrile state, especially when pronounced and long-continued, affords unusually good chemical conditions for the oncoming of fatigue. One of the striking metabolic accompaniments of the fevers that result from bacterial invasion of the living body is an increased excretion of nitrogen, which is derived, as is inferred from the work of various investigators, from an increased destruction of the proteins of the tissues, probably due largely to the direct action of the higher temperature upon them."

Summarizing the discussion of the character and effects of confined air, we may make the following resumé of the present state of opinion on the subject:

(1) That confined air in living-rooms and in workshops differs from normal air in the following respcets:

(a) Decrease in percentage of oxygen.

(b) Increase in percentage of carbonic acid (CO_2).

(c) Presence of certain volatile odoriferous organic products.

New York State Factory Commission.

Casing Room in a Sausage Factory. High Temperature and High Relative Humidity.

(d) Presence of micro-organisms and possible presence of infectious bacteria.

(e) Frequent addition of dust, gases and fumes.

(f) Higher rate of temperature.

(g) Increase in amount of moisture.

(2) That ordinary decrease of oxygen as found in inhabited rooms and shops probably does not exert any deleterious influence on the persons within them;

(3) That an increase in the contents of carbonic acid (CO_2) from 4 parts to 15 and up to 100 parts in 10,000 volumes is not dangerous to health.

(4) That it has not as yet been proven that the presence of organic matter in confined air has an important bearing upon the health of the persons therein, although a prolonged breathing of a large quantity of volatile malodorous products may be followed by nausea, loss of appetite and general malaise;

(5) That the presence of dust, gases and fumes is extremely dangerous in proportion to their kind, character and quantity and the conditions of bodily resistance of the workers;

(6) That while it is possible that tuberculosis and some other bacterial diseases may be due to aerial infection, the probability of such infection is not great;

(7) That the ill effects commonly ascribed to impure confined air of ill-ventilated rooms and shops are due not so much to the chemical impurities in the air, but to the physical properties such as increased temperature, higher rate of humidity and stagnation of the air surrounding the body;

(8) That an increase of the temperature of confined air in workshops above 70° F., and particularly an increase in the wet bulb reading of the thermometer above the same degree is probably injurious to health if maintained for too prolonged periods, and may cause fatigue, lassitude, decreased metabolism, anæmia and loss of resistance, predisposing the workers to acute and chronic diseases.

II

PRINCIPLES AND METHODS OF VENTILATION

THE chemical and physical changes in air confined in enclosed spaces increase in intensity, until a time comes when the air becomes so different from normal air that a further sojourn in such rooms

may be injurious.   If life and work are to go on within the rooms,
a change must be made in the air.   This change of air in a room
has been designated by the word *ventilation,* by which is meant a
substitution of outside air for that of inside air.   This definition,
however, is not complete nor entirely correct.   By ventilation is
meant not only a simple change but a certain kind and character
of change.   Ventilation means removal of air charged with chemical
impurities, dusts, gases and fumes, and the substitution for it of
other air which is normal in its chemical composition and also in its
physical condition.

Air is a gas.   As such, it has the properties of all gases; it diffuses
in space; it is subject to motion; it is subject to variations of temperature.   The specific gravity of air differs according to its temperature.   Volumes of air at a different temperature have a different
specific gravity and pressure.   The volumes of air which are at a
higher temperature and exert a lesser pressure, come in contact
with the volumes of air which are at a lower temperature and an
increased pressure.   A general movement of air, therefore, is constantly going on at different rates of velocity.   When the velocity
of air is great, the motion becomes noticeable and is called *wind.*
Due to the difference in temperature in different localities, there
is always a movement going on, so that through diffusion, through
the winds, through the differences in temperature, the air is constantly changing from place to place.

Spontaneous ventilation, which is caused by the described
properties of air, makes it possible for confined spaces to have a
certain air-change without special artificial provisions being made.
The porosity of materials of construction, the crevices and cracks
which are found in buildings, the openings which are made for various
purposes, all serve as means of air *diffusion.*   It is due to this fact
that ventilation, or the proper change of air in confined rooms,
has been so long neglected, because in ordinary rooms, especially of
flimsy construction, there has always been possible a certain change
of air which made a sojourn in them more or less comfortable.   Therefore, no special provisions were thought necessary for introducing
a definite quantity of air, or for the removal of impurities of the air
or change in its physical conditions.

As a matter of fact, spontaneous ventilation cannot be depended
upon.   It is neither constant nor uniform.   The rate of change
and the amount of air-change are variable.   While it may be sufficient for rooms in ill-constructed buildings, where there are few

persons and where no special impurities are added to the air, spontaneous ventilation cannot be relied upon in modern well-constructed
buildings, or in rooms where a large number of persons are con-
gregated, or where many mechanical and chemical processes are
being carried on.

The quantity of air needed in manufacturing establishments
depends upon a number of factors, such as the character of construction of a building, character, size and air space of the room,
number and character of the persons in the room, extent of illumination, combustion, and other physical and chemical processes
going on within the room, the kind and intensity of work which
is being performed, and a number of other factors.

The number of persons in a room is of importance because of
the impurities and changes in the physical conditions of the air
which are due to each additional person in the room. The age
as well as the sex of persons should be considered, for an adult
male worker needs more air than an adult woman, and more than
minors and children. More air is needed where gas or other artificial illumination (except electricity) is used, or where certain
mechanical or chemical processes are going on, or where either
dust, gases or fumes are added to the contents of the room. The
character of the work has also a bearing on the problem, because
an adult person at rest does not take in as much air and his rate of
metabolism is much less; while a person hard at work respires a
large quantity of air, adds more impurities to the air and produces more heat and moisture.

The quantity of air which a person needs depends on a number
of factors. Pettenkoffer and his pupils showed that the amount
of carbonic acid (CO_2) in the air goes hand in hand with organic
impurities from the presence of persons, and is an index of the
amount of the various impurities in the air. They have taught
that we should regard the air in a room in which human beings
are found as reaching a stage where it must be changed when its
contents of CO_2 exceed 2 volumes per 10,000 in excess of the normal
contents of CO_2 in the air of cities. Based upon this difference,
Pettenkoffer calculated that the average adult individual needs about
3000 cubic feet of air in an hour in order to keep the CO_2 contents
at 6 per 10,000 volumes. This standard, while coinciding with
the generally accepted opinion of the needed quantity of air, cannot,
however, be so well determined on the CO_2 contents because of the
possible presence of a larger quantity of CO_2, due to various chemical

processes, and because CO_2 is not always a reliable index of other impurities such as gases, dusts and increased temperature and humidity of rooms.

Standards have also been established for the size of rooms, for their height, and for the number of square feet and of cubic feet of space for each individual. Some of these standards have been legalized by industrial codes in various countries and states. Thus, we find statutes requiring 250 to 400 cubic feet of air-space for each individual, 10 or 12 feet for the height of rooms, and a minimum and maximum dry and wet bulb thermometer reading in workshops.

The State of Illinois gives several very interesting standards as to the air-space per employe needed according to the difference in the character of the rooms, as follows:

Every room or apartment of a factory, mercantile establishment, mill or workshop where a person is employed, must have 500 cubic feet of air-space per employe. Fresh air must be supplied so as not to cause injurious drops of temperature to fall below normal. Supply must not be taken from cellar or basement. Where lights do not consume oxygen 250 cubic feet is sufficient. Rooms with 200 cubic feet per employe and outside window and door area one-eighth of floor space do not require artificial ventilation, but must be properly aired before beginning work and at noon hour. Rooms with 500 to 2000 cubic feet per employe with outside window and doors one-eighth of floor space must have artificial ventilation when weather requires windows closed, supplying 1500 cubic feet of fresh air to each employee. Rooms with less than 500 cubic feet per employe, rooms without outside windows or doors, rooms with less than 2000 cubic feet per employe and outside windows and door area less than one-eighth of floor space, must have artificial ventilation, supplying 1800 cubic feet of fresh air per employe each working hour.

The size of the room, while having some bearing upon the length of time in which the air of the room may become uncomfortable, does not play an important role in ventilation, because the chemical and physical conditions of the air in the room do not depend upon the size of rooms but upon the rate of change and the velocity of air which comes in from the outside. A very small space where the rate of change is higher will have purer air than a large room in which the rate of change is lower.

A rate of change in the air of a room of about three times an hour is hardly perceptible to the ordinary senses of persons. A

New York State Factory Commission.

Beating-up Machines in a Hat Factory.

The workmen are constantly splashed with very hot water; the humidity is intense and there is no proper exhaust.

rate of change from four to five times an hour may not be perceptible, according to the weather, the clothing of persons and the
character of the work which they perform. Higher rates of a
change, however, especially when air comes through large openings,
are liable to be felt as draughts and may become harmful because
of rapid evaporation from the skin and of the catarrhs and colds
resulting therefrom. This is especially the case in winter-time
when the temperature of the incoming air is so much lower than the
air in the room.

It has been determined that about 3000 cubic feet of air are
necessary on the average for each individual per hour; also that
the air in a room may be changed from three to five times during
the hour without causing draughts and discomforts from them.
Based upon this, it has been calculated that an air-space between
700 and 1000 cubic feet of space per person will suffice to admit
the necessary amount of air into the room without causing draughts.

Spontaneous ventilation carried on by diffusion through difference of temperature, causing change of air through the porosity
of the various building materials, crevices and cracks in ill-constructed buildings, and other openings, is very seldom sufficient.

The porosity of walls, ceilings, floors and roofs differs very
much, according to the material which is used for construction
and according to the inner and outer decorations of these surfaces.
Although most materials are porous, the amount of air which can
penetrate the walls and floors constructed of such materials depends
upon their physical state. Damp walls and floors lose their porosity
and the ordinary calcimining, and to a still greater degree, papering
and painting with oil colors, may make them practically imper-
meable. Nor can much reliance be put upon ventilation through
imperfections, cracks, crevices, etc., which are only found in old
or ill-constructed buildings. We may safely conclude that the
ventilation which may be gained through porous materials and
imperfections in buildings is practically negligible.

Windows are usually regarded as a great aid to ventilation.
They are constructed however not primarily for ventilating purposes, but for light. When windows are ill-constructed there are
always spaces and imperfections around the sashes and frames
through which air may come in. In better construction this is
negligible. Closed windows can hardly be regarded as proper
means for ventilation, although in winter when the difference of
temperature between the outside air and the inside is great, the

pressure of the colder, heavier, outside air may be so great that a certain amount of air goes through them.

Windows, however, in order to serve for ventilating purposes

View of Forge and Hardening Departments, Showing Ventilating Plant.

Utica Drop Forge and Tool Co.

must be either partly or fully open. The opening of windows in the summer, when the temperature of the inside and the outside air is nearly equal, does not serve for ventilating purposes, because, in the absence of wind, very little change of air can take place through such openings when there is very little difference in the temperature of the inside and outside air. It is only when there is more that 5 or 10 degrees difference between the outside and inside temperature and when there is much movement of air that any considerable change of air can occur.

In winter, when the temperature is low, it is not always practicable to open the windows, because of the incoming cold air. Windows are therefore not good means of ventilation in either very cold or very warm weather. Only in temperate weather may a partial or full opening of the windows serve a good purpose. Doors serve to change the air, depending upon the frequency with which these doors are opened and where these doors open to. The amount of air which may be thus gained is difficult to determine.

In order to increase the rate of ventilation in rooms, it is the practice to make special openings for the purpose, such openings being called inlets or outlets, according to whether they are constructed for the incoming or for the letting out of air. These inlets or outlets, however, do not always serve the purpose for which they are constructed, as it is difficult to determine beforehand how the air will act, and the inlet at times works as an outlet and vice versa. As a rule, inlet openings are made in the lower part of a room for the cold air to come in at the bottom and distribute itself in the room; while outlet openings are made at the top for the warm air to be let out.

Openings for ventilation are made in walls, in ceilings, in floors, or in windows. There are a great many devices and appliances patented by inventors, for each of which special advantages are claimed. All these openings, of whatever nature, and in whatever part of the room they may be, serve at times for the purpose of letting out air from the room or letting in air from the outside into the room.

These openings are often made by cutting out a circular piece from the upper part of the window-pane, and inserting a piece of perforated sheet-metal. Another device is to raise the lower sash and insert in the opening a wooden board or perforated sheet-metal box or plate, so that the air may come in through this part as well as through the opening left between the lower and upper sashes. Window-panes are sometimes constructed on pivots, so as to swing and open when necessary. There are also a number of devices, consisting of boxes, tubes, elbows, etc., which are inserted either in the sash or in the wall under the sash of the window. Perforated

New York State Factory Commission.

First Process in Felt Hat-making: Excessive Humidity and Heat.

bricks with large openings outside and small openings inside are at times inserted in the wall, serving for ventilating purposes. Hollow beams may be inserted, with openings in the ceilings, so that the air from the outside may enter, or the air from the rooms may escape through these openings.

All these devices may serve a good purpose at times and may be the means of considerable exchange of air under favorable cir- cumstances and when properly arranged and maintained. No reliance, however, can be put upon them for ventilating crowded rooms, and it is impossible to calculate the rate of exchange through them and the amount of air which may be let in or let out. As an ancillary means of ventilation to ordinary window-ventilated rooms they may be valuable, but this is as much as can be conceded to them.

Better ventilation is gained by tubes, shafts and openings which are specially made for the purpose, or which, though made for other purposes, serve the same effect. Elevator-shafts, courts, vent- shafts, stairwells, and other vertical openings made throughout the building, often play an important rôle in ventilation, by the large amount of air which is circulated through them, aided by the forcible ascent and descent of the elevators, by the communication of the shafts with the external air at the bottom by intakes, and at the top by the opening to the external air.

Shafts in the form of tubes and ducts are specially constructed for ventilating purposes, with openings to each room and to the outside, and act as outlets for the confined air of the room, and at times may also serve for inlets of the outside air. Chimneys also serve the same purpose. The amount of air which goes through these chimneys and other openings depends very much upon external and internal conditions of temperature and many other factors.

The means of ventilation through the openings described may be adequate at certain times and for ordinary rooms, but it is doubt- ful whether they are sufficient for industrial establishments where a large number of employes are at work or where special impurities are produced.

In workshops where a large number of workers are employed, where there are not more than 250 to 400 cubic feet of space for each worker, and where considerable dust, deleterious gases and fumes are produced, no reliance can be placed upon ventilation through windows or through any of the other openings described.

The problem of ventilating crowded workshops, therefore, is

still to be solved. The large majority of workshops and factories are badly ventilated whenever there are no special artificial mechanical means used for ventilating purposes. Complaints of the bad ventilation of factories are universal and are found in all reports of factory inspectors of different countries and states.

No attention whatever is paid by those who construct factory buildings or by individual employers to the subject of ventilation. The opinion seems to prevail that a change of air in a room should come by itself without human aid or mechanical means, and that no special provisions need be made for ventilating industrial establishments. According to a table presented by the New York State Factory Commission in its investigation of 5124 shops, it appears that only 604 or 11.8 per cent were provided with some system of mechanical ventilation, and this was not always in good order or properly used. As the report of the Commission says, " The problem of ventilation in industrial establishments is very great and cannot be solved by additional opening of windows or even by special devices such as have been put in about 15.5 per cent of the shops investigated." *

The industries in which the worst conditions were found by the Commission were the chemical, textile, printing, tobacco, artificial flowers and feathers, and human hair trades. In these industries there is a very large amount of dust, and in some of them, as in printing, there is a certain percentage of lead-dust in the air.

III

MECHANICAL VENTILATION

By mechanical ventilation is understood a change of air in rooms brought about by mechanical means. Before discussing real mechanical means for ventilating purposes, attention must be drawn to two aids to ventilation which are sometimes resorted to in lieu of mechanical ventilation. These are wind and temperature.

Wind, or a strong movement of air, when passing about a house or building, may produce a change of air in a building by aspirating the air in passing over certain openings in the building. Notter and Firth define the aspirating action of wind as follows:

* Report of Director, Second Report of Factory Investigating Commission, vol. ii, p. 43 .

Courtesy Globe Ventilator Co., Troy, N. Y.

Factory of the Library Bureau at Ilion. Equipped with Globe Ventilators on a Saw Tooth Roof Construction.

" A moving body of air sets in motion all the air in its vicinity. It drives air before it, and, at the same time, causes a pressure-vacuum on either side of its own path, toward which all the air in the vicinity flows at angles more or less approaching a right angle. In this way a small current moving at a high velocity will

Base Fan Set in Top of Window.

set in motion a large body of air. The wind, therefore, blowing over the tops of chimneys, causes a current at right angles to itself up the chimney, and the unequal draught it furnishes is owing in part to the variations in the velocity of the wind. Advantage, therefore, can be taken of the aspirating power of the wind to cause a movement of air up a tube."

Based upon the aspirating power of the wind numerous devices have been patented in the form of cowls, and other ventilators, which are usually placed upon chimneys and openings on the roof, and are said to facilitate the aspirating power of the wind, and are so arranged that they may adjust themselves to the direction of the wind. A very popular device of this character used in this country is the Globe ventilator, shown in the illustration on page 375. The wind being variable, cannot, however, be wholly depended upon as a means for ventilation where such is necessary at all times.

Heat has been relied upon as a means of ventilation in many living-rooms, although it is not so applicable to workshops and factories. The ventilating qualities of open fireplaces are well known. With an ordinary fire ten to fifteen thousand cubic feet of air are drawn by a chimney in an hour in an ordinary medium-size room. According to Notter and Firth, the best type of open fireplace causes 2600 cubic feet of air to pass up a flue per pound of coal consumed, or a total of 18,000 cubic feet of air per hour. Chimneys, even when fireplaces are not needed, and other shafts and ducts which are carried vertically throughout the whole building, may serve as a means of ventilation through artificial heating by gas jets within these chimneys or shafts. The heating causes a rise of temperature, and the ascension of the air within the tubes thus causes an aspirating action and an exhaust of air from the rooms with which they are connected.

Mechanical ventilation is carried on by means of devices which (a) stir up the air within the room, (b) take out, aspirate, and exhaust the air from the room, (c) bring in, propel, shove in, air from the outside into the room, and (d) which combine one or two or all of the above methods.

A simple stirring up of the air of a room and setting it in motion, while neither removing the impurities from the air nor changing its physical condition much, serves, however, to break up the stagnation of air in ill-ventilated rooms and to increase the evaporation from the skin of the workers and also reduce the temperature. Hence, the action of electric or other fans within the room often reduces the temperature of the room and lowers its relative humidity, thereby increasing the comfort of the workers.

The three methods of mechanical ventilation are the vacuum, plenum, and combined methods. In the vacuum method air is exhausted or aspirated from the room; in the plenum, air is brought into the room from the outside; and in the combined method, air is taken out from the room and other air at the same time is brought into the room.

The vacuum system of ventilation consists in drawing the air from a room by forcible means and aspiration, without making any provisions whatever for a supply of fresh air to be brought into the room. Reliance is placed upon the fact that when air is withdrawn from a room other air must necessarily enter, on the principle of nature abhorring a vacuum. The supply of air is usually supposed to come in through the windows, doors, transoms, and other openings, and also through the porosity of the walls and the cracks, crevices and imperfections in the building construc-

Courtesy American Blower Co., Detroit.

Exhauster in Connection with System of Hoods and Piping for the Removal of Dust from Emery Wheels.

tion. It is evident that such a system of ventilation has a great disadvantage in not being able to make provision for a supply of fresh air; and sometimes it may happen that the air which comes in may not come from proper or clean sources. Neither can the quantity of air and the rate of change of ventilation be very well calculated, nor is it possible to modify or temper the incoming air.

There are two types of the vacuum system of ventilation: the general and local. By general vacuum ventilation is meant that which withdraws the air from the room by means of fans through openings in the wall or window, without any tubes or ducts whatever. The fan is placed in an opening in the window or in the wall, and by its motion is made to withdraw the air from the room. The advantage of this method is the low initial cost and the comparatively low cost of maintenance. It is especially valuable in laundries, foundries, and all such plants, where there is much heat and where a lot of steam, gases, fumes, etc., are generated. The local system of vacuum ventilation is especially adapted to the exhaust of dust, gases and fumes at the place of production. This method needs hoods and ducts and will be discussed in a later chapter.

In the plenum system of ventilation, air is forcibly driven and propelled into the room by means of fans. While by this method it is possible to choose the source of the air as well as to modify its quantity and quality, there is no provision made for the removal of the bad air from the room, which is simply diluted and mixed with the fesh air from the outside.

The best system of ventilation is that which combines the two methods; which simultaneously exhausts or removes the air from the room, and replenishes it with a fresh supply from the outside.

The selection of the appropriate method of ventilation depends very much upon individual circumstances in each industrial establishment, on the power at hand, the number of persons in the establishment, the character of production, and a number of other factors.

The exhaust system is the simplest; but it is used chiefly either in places where local exhaust is necessary for dust, gases and fumes, or in large rooms which are not occupied by too many persons. The plenum system is usually installed in establishments where a large supply of air must be introduced from some remote source and where provision must be made for the modification of the incoming air either by cleaning, filtering or washing, or by tempering and humidifying.

The motive power for all fans may be the same which is used for the driving of the other machinery within the building, or may be separate from the general motive power of the factory. The fans may be driven by belts or may have their individual motors. A large number and variety of fans are used for ventilating purposes. They may be divided into two principal types: the propeller type and the centrifugal fan. They are also called low-pressure and high-pressure fans. The propeller fan is the one which acts upon the principle of the ship-screw propeller turning the blades of the fan on its axis, thereby either removing air from the room or introducing air into the room, according to the shape of the blades.

The propeller fan, of which " Blackman's air propeller " is an accepted and popular type, is used in places where there is low resistance, and where some provision is made against draughts caused by the blowing fan. This type of fan usually needs no special ducts, as the provision of ducts increases the resistance, and the low-pressure fan does not work well with an increased resistance of air.

Courtesy American Blower Co., Detroit.

Exhausting in Room.

Centrifugal fans are used where there is considerable resistance to be overcome either for taking out or introducing air. They are usually run at a high velocity and speed and are used either for local exhaust of dust from grinding-wheels or machines by which considerable dust is created, or when narrow tubes and ducts must be installed and run for long distances, or where there is considerable resistance to the air which is introduced. In this type of fan the air-inlet is in the center of the fan, which is usually enclosed in a box or " housed."

There is a variety of fans of both kinds, a large number of patents having been issued to different concerns, each claiming their production the best. Some of the illustrations show the type of fan most popular in this country, although there are many others perthaps equally good. Without going into technical descriptions of the fans, ducts, and parts of the ventilating mechanism, it is necessary to say that the installation of a mechanical ventilating plant is a highly technical problem in each separate shop and must be solved on the spot, taking all the individual factors into consideration. It is therefore

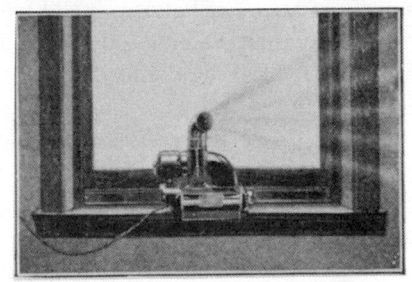

Courtesy American Blower Co., Detroit.

"Sirocco" Fan Blowing into Room.

necessary in each and every case to employ a mechanical and ventilating expert to install a proper system of ventilation according to the exact needs and wants of each plant.

It must, however, be noted that as a rule, the ventilating plants which are found by inspectors in industrial establishments act in a very faulty manner, because either their installation has not been properly done or because of faulty calculations of the diameters of the ducts in the process of their construction.   The total area and diameter of the ducts must be calculated in relation to the strength and velocity of the fans and to the work to be performed. As a rule, ducts are too narrow and the high resistance of air there-fore increases the difficulty of the work of the fans and results either in too high a cost of ventilation or in an inadequate supply of air.

Courtesy American Blower Co., Detroit.

Double Inlet "Sirocco" Fan.   Full Housed, Right Hand Top Horizontal Discharge.   Pulley Drive.   Inlet Side.

The long distances which ducts are run and the bends, some of them at right angle, contribute largely to the nullification of the efficiency of the ventilating system.

"The Sirocco fan (see illustrations) is a centrifugal fan comprised of a wheel constructed with numerous thin, elongated blades arranged in drum form.   These blades are extended in an axial direction, so as to enclose within them a relatively large and unob-structed intake-chamber, and in transverse section arranged, relatively to the axis and direction of rotation, to carry the fluid with them rotatively and discharge it tangentially. The fan has sixty-four blades. This multiplicity of blades reduces the space for resulting eddy currents to a minimum, and, the blades being very narrow, there is no opportunity for a great difference in velocity due to their radial depth. Further, the blades being concave, with the inner edge practically perpendicular to the direction of the flow into the space between the blades, the outer edge presents a very much narrower space than the inner edge, resulting in the velocity of the air being increased as it passes between the blades, instead of being reduced as in the old steel-plate type. This fan also per‹ mits the use of a very large air-inlet."

Courtesy American Blower Co., Detroit.
Steel Pressure Blower in Foundry.

In the vacuum methods of ventilation which are used for dust extraction special dust-separators, usually of the " cyclone " type, are provided where the dust is extracted, settled and collected, so that the air which is afterwards let out is free from dust. The ducts lead to the roof where the cyclone dust-separators are placed, although a downward direction of the ducts is also used when the dust-collection is done in the basement or cellar. At times, the dust, if of a combustible kind, may be directed into the furnace and utilized for heating purposes.

In the plenum system of ventilation the incoming air cannot always be admitted without being purified and modified in temperature and humidity. With present mechanical progress it is possible at not too high a cost to modify the temperature of the incoming air, to regulate its humidity, and purify it by filtering and washing.

There are objections against a combination of heating and ventilating plants, especially against the method of hot-air supply by furnaces, the objections being that the air supplied is usually too hot, sometimes burnt, often contains much dust and other impurities. It is claimed, therefore, that it is best to separate the heating and ventilating plants and have a separate system for each purpose.

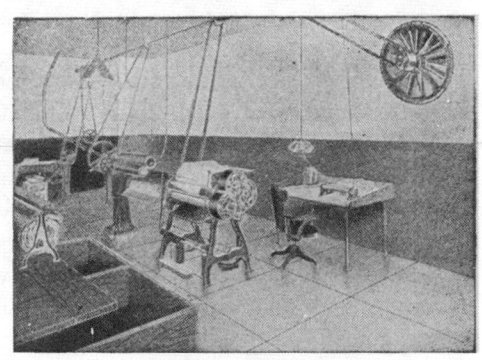

Courtesy American Blower Co., Detroit.

Disk Fan in Laundry.

The methods of modifying the temperature of the air coming in through ducts differ. There are devices to cool the air as well as to heat it. In raising the temperature of the incoming air, care must be taken not to raise it too high. In winter the air must come in above a temperature of 60° F., and in summer it should be as cool as possible.

There are a number of devices for the cleaning of air by filtering or washing. The filtering media are meshed materials intended to catch the dust particles in the air. The filtering process increases the resistance to the inflow of air, this resistance increasing with the closeness of the meshes of the filtering material.

Courtesy American Blower Co., Detroit.

Disk Fan in Engine Room.

The washing of air is accomplished by having the air pass horizontally through a closed chamber which the water enters in the form of raindrops, sprays, or a water-curtain. The water comes through perforations, or through a number of sprinklers, which form sprays and bring the air and water into intimate contact

and clean the air of all suspended matter.   Besides cleaning the air,
this process of washing also cools it.   The same water may be recir-
culated and used over again.

There are a number of patent air-washers, all of them more
or less efficient, according to their method of use.   It has been
found that the water coming from the air-washers after washing a
large volume of street air, has the appearance of sewage, and does
not differ very much from it in composition.

[Artificial humidification of air is claimed to be necessary in
certain textile processes, although this necessity is denied by some.
The humidification is accomplished by sprays and special steam
humidifiers.

The art of industrial mechanical ventilation is as yet in its
infancy, owing to the fact that comparatively few of the factories
in the country deem it necessary to install mechanical ventilating
plants.   As the legal standards of ventilation increase, and industrial
efficiency comes into wider practice, there is no doubt that most,
if not all, of the larger industrial establishments in the country
will be compelled to install efficient mechanical ventilating plants,
and by that time the science and art of the mechanical ventilating
engineer will be ready for practice.

IV

EXAMINATION AND TESTING OF AIR

Legal and other standards for ventilation prescribed in industrial
codes, and the frequent investigations of air conditions in industrial
establishments, make necessary a standardization of methods of
testing air.   The tests usually made are those for temperature,
humidity, CO_2 contents, for presence of dust, bacteria, and deleterious gases, poisons, etc.

The temperature is tested by the ordinary thermometer, the
Fahrenheit instrument being used in this country.   Special thermo-
graphs are often used for automatic recording of the temperature
of rooms, in order to have a complete record of the variations in
the temperature in the room during a certain period or at all times.

The relative humidity of the air of a room is measured by a number of instruments called hygrometers, psychrophores, etc.   The
instruments which are based upon the hygroscopic qualities of air
are not very accurate, and practically the only instrument used for

testing the humidity of a room is the sling thermometer. The instrument consists of two Fahrenheit thermometers fastened to an aluminum back, one of which extends beyond the aluminum case for two inches. Around the bulb of this thermometer is fastened a thin piece of silk cloth which when ready for use is soaked in distilled water. This is called the wet-bulb thermometer. A handle is fastened to the upper end of the aluminum by means of which the psychrometer is swung when making a test. A copper case is made to surround the instrument as a protection to the thermometer when not in use.

The test for humidity is made by dipping the wet bulb in water and swinging the instrument several times, to prevent the formation of a saturated area around the bulb. Care must be taken not to wet the dry bulb.*

The instrument of which an illustration is given on this page was the one used by Professors Winslow and Baskerville. It is long, measuring about 16 inches. In using this instrument I have often found that one or the other thermometer easily breaks, and therefore the use of the instrument becomes costly. A similar instrument which I saw being used by

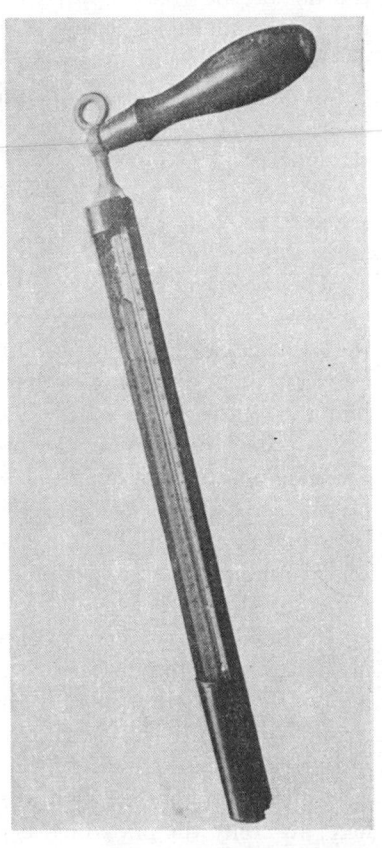

Tycos.

Sling Psychrometer.

the Illinois Factory Inspection Department is much shorter, being about 4 or 5 inches long, and is said to do the same work without being put out of order so often.

Dr. J. W. Schereschewsky, of the United States Public Health Service, uses the same dry- and wet-bulb thermometer fixed in a portable box, in which are enclosed dry batteries working a small motor

* Winslow and Baskerville: Report on School Ventilation.

operating a blower upon the wet bulb, obviating the necessity of swinging the instrument. This box, however, is rather heavy, and is not convenient for carrying around.

The wet-bulb thermometer is constructed on the theory that as the air in the room approaches the wet bulb it absorbs from the wet bulb sufficient moisture to raise its humidity to saturation point, at the same time it loses sufficient heat to cool it down to the temperature of the wet bulb. Hence, the quantity of heat lost by the air will be equal to the quantity of heat necessary to convert into steam a quantity of water sufficient to saturate that air. From this we get an equation establishing a relation between the difference of temperature of the wet and dry bulbs and the proportion of humidity in the air.*

The relative humidity of the air is calculated according to Glaisher's table, which gives the grains of moisture in the air and the percentage of relative humidity according to the difference between the dry- and wet-bulb thermometer. The following humidity table, which was established by the Departmental Committee on Humidity and Ventilation in Cotton-Weaving Sheds, gives the limits of temperature and the maximum limits of humidity in the atmosphere permitted in cotton-cloth factories during the introduction of humidity by artificial means, and shows also the relative humidity based upon the difference between the dry- and wet-bulb thermometers. (See next page.)

Carbonic Acid. Pettenkoffer and his followers insisted so much upon the great importance of the CO_2 contents in the air that for many years the CO_2 test of air was the one most frequently used. A whole literature has been created on the subject and many ingenious tests have been devised for the examination of air for CO_2. Of the large number of tests which are used, only a few may be mentioned here, and only the one which is ordinarily used in this country will be described in greater detail.

Pettenkoffer's Test. Barium hydrate mixed with carbonic acid produces, besides water, an insoluble salt—barium carbonate. If we then mix a known amount of barium hydrate in solution with a known amount of air, part of the barium hydrate will go to form the barium carbonate with the carbonic acid in the air and part will be left undissolved. We can then calculate the difference in the amount of the barium hydrate in the solution before its mixture with the air and after, which difference will indicate the amount

---

* Departmental Committee on Humidity and Ventilation, p. 30.

HUMIDITY TABLE

LIMITS OF TEMPERATURE AND MAXIMUM LIMITS OF HUMIDITY OF ATMOSPHERE
PERMITTED IN COTTON-CLOTH FACTORIES DURING THE INTRODUCTION OF
HUMIDITY BY ARTIFICIAL MEANS

Grains of Vapor Per Cubic Foot of Air.	Readings of Thermometers, in Degrees Fahrenheit.		Percentage of Humidity (Saturation = 100).
	Dry Bulb.	Wet Bulb.	
3.5	50	48	86
3.6	51	49	86
3.8	52	50	86
3.9	53	51	86
4.1	54	52	86
4.2	55	53	87
4.4	56	54	87
4.5	57	55	87
4.7	58	56	87
4.9	59	57	88
5.1	60	58	88
5.2	61	59	88
5.4	62	60	88
5.6	63	61	88
5.8	64	62	88
6.0	65	63	88
6.2	66	64	88
6.4	67	65	88
6.6	68	66	88
6.9	69	67	88
7.1	70	68	88
7.1	71	68.5	85.5
7.1	72	69	84
7.4	73	70	84
7.4	74	70.5	81.5
7.65	75	71.5	81.5
7.7	76	72	79
8.0	77	73	79
8.0	78	73.5	77
8.25 (etc.)	79 (etc.)	74.5 (etc.)	77.5 (etc.)

of carbonic acid in the examined air. The amount of barium hydrate is determined by a standard solution of oxalic acid. The tests must be made at a temperature of 32° F. and barometric pressure from 30 inches of mercury, or corrections must be made as to this temperature and barometric pressure. The test is very complicated, and requires special apparatus and great skill.

Wolpert's Test. In this test a solution of carbonate of soda colored red by phenolphthalein is used to mix with a given volume of air to be examined.   When mixed with the examined air, part of the carbonate of soda unites with the carbonic acid and forms bicarbonate of soda, thus lessening the alkalinity and also the red color of the solution.   The more carbonic acid in the examined air the quicker the disappearance of the red color.   The apparatus is furnished with a scale so that the approximate amount of carbonic acid is determined.

Lunge-Zeckendorf Test.   A very small portable and convenient apparatus is that which bears the name of Lunge-Zeckendorf, and which is very widely used in Germany and Switzerland.   Professor Roth of Zurich tells me that he has made thousands of tests in factories with this instrument and, as a rule, found it accurate and very convenient.

This test is based upon the same principle as that of Wolpert's: the discoloration of an alkaline solution colored by phenolphthalein by carbonic acid in air.   The instrument consists of a jar in which is inserted a glass tube attached by a rubber pipe to a rubber bulb of a standard capacity.   The jar or flask is filled with a normal solution of one-tenth per cent of bicarbonate of soda colored with phenolphthalein.   The test is based upon the fact that with every pressing of the rubber bulb air is introduced from the outside and the CO_2 in the air when in a sufficient quantity lessens the alkalinity of the solution and discolors the phenolphthalein.   The greater the contents of the CO_2 in the air the less times it is necessary to press the bulb in order to discolor the contents.   The capacity of the bulb, etc., is so arranged that with a four-per-ten-thousand volumes of CO_2 contents in the air it is necessary to press the bulb 35 times. It takes only 27 times to discolor the solution with a five-per-ten-thousand CO_2 contents, 21 with a six-per-ten-thousand CO_2 contents, 17 with a seven-per-ten-thousand CO_2 contents, 13 with an eight-per-ten-thousand CO_2 contents, 10 with a nine-per-ten-thousand, CO_2 contents, and only 9 pressings of the bulb for a one to a thousand, etc.   This test has the disadvantage that it is only applicable where there is considerable CO_2 contents in the air.

The Peterson and Palmquist Test.   This test has been used for some time by the Labor Department of New York State, and was also employed by Professors Winslow and Baskerville in their investigations of ventilation in the public schools of New York City. The instrument (see illustration on next page) has been modified somewhat by Professors Winslow and Baskerville, and consists of the following parts:

A 25 cc. pipette, graduated on its lower branch, is divided at the top at right angles into three branches. One is the air-intake, another leads to the KOH reservoir, and the third, which is a continuation of the pipette stem, opens into the horizontal gauge at the top of the instrument. Each branch may be opened or closed by stop-cocks. The gauge or tube holding the meniscus of red kerosene is bent up at both ends and provided with stop-cocks. As stated

Front View   Back View
Courtesy Profs. Winslow and Baskerville.

Peterson-Palmquist Apparatus Used by Profs. C.-E. A. Winslow and Ch. Baskerville.

above, one branch of the pipette opens into one end of the gauge below the stop-cock. Similarly, at the other end there enters a tube from a closed vessel which acts as an equalizing chamber. The pipette, equalizing vessel, and KOH reservoir are immersed in the water held in a glass jar. Into this runs a glass tube through which air is forced by means of a rubber bulb connected with it at the upper end. The lower branch of the pipette runs down the center of a 1-inch glass tube connected with the water-jar and communicates with the mercury reservoir by means of rubber tubing.

A stop-cock and a pressure screw are in this circuit. The whole apparatus is mounted on a wooden stand.

N. B.—50 per cent KOH (Potassium Hydroxide) is used.

The instrument is used as follows:

Assuming that all stop-cocks are closed, except the one on the branch from the meniscus tube to the equalizing chamber, open that one on the meniscus tube which is near the tube leading to the equalizing chamber. Next open the corresponding cock on the other end. The meniscus may now be moved to any desired position on the scale by simply tipping the apparatus. Close both stop-cocks. Open the air-intake. Lower the mercury reservoir slowly until the top of the mercury column is at zero. Close the stop-cock which regulates the flow of mercury. Close the air-intake. Open the stop-cock on the vertical branch of the pipette. Force air through the water by means of the rubber bulb until the meniscus comes to rest. Record the reading. Close the stop-cock on the vertical branch of the pipette. Open the stop-cock to the KOH reservoir. Open the cock from the mercury reservoir and allow the pipette to fill. Let the mercury flow back into its reservoir until the level of the KOH is at the point shown on the KOH reservoir. Close the stop-cock from the mercury reservoir. Close the stop-cock to the KOH reservoir. Open the stop-cock on the vertical branch of the pipette. Bubble air through the water until the meniscus comes to rest. By means of the pressure-screw force the mercury up into the pipette until the meniscus is at its former reading. Read the level of the mercury on the lower branch of the pipette. The result is the number of parts of CO_2 per 10,000.

The following precautions must be taken while using this instrument:

(1) Never close the stop-cock on the tube leading from the equalizing chamber to the meniscus tube.

(2) Always open the stop-cock on the meniscus tube, which is near the tube leading from the equalizing chamber *before* opening the corresponding one on the other side.

(3) Never leave the stop-cock controlling the flow of mercury and the one in the vertical branch of the pipette open at the same time.

(4) Care should always be taken when the stop-cock to the KOH reservoir is open, not to force the mercury over into the KOH or suck the KOH over into the mercury.

(5) The operator should take care not to breathe into the air-intake or allow others to do so.

Courtesy Profs. Winslow and Baskerville.

Wallace and Tiernan Pump Used by Professors C.-E. A. Winslow and Ch. Baskerville in Collecting Samples for Enumeration of Dust and Bacteria in the Air of Schools.

CHAPTER IX

INDUSTRIAL DUSTS AND DUSTY TRADES

I

DUST AND ITS EFFECT ON HEALTH

Extent and Character of Industrial Dusts. Dust consists of fine particles of matter. It is ubiquitous. There is no air which is free from it. There is no place where it is not present.

Ordinary air counts its dust particles by the thousands and hundreds of thousands per cubic foot. At the fifty-seventh story in the air outside of the Woolworth Building, 27,000 dust particles were counted in a cubic foot; at the thirtieth story, 70,000; at the tenth story, 85,000; and at the street level 221,000. Even on the top of the Rigi, Aitken counted dust particles from 210 to over 2000 per cubic centimeter. On the Eiffel Tower the number varied from 226 to 104,000 per cubic centimeter. Nor is the air over the sea free from particles of dust. Mr. E. D. Friedlander found 2000 to 4000 particles per cubic centimeter in the air over some parts of the Western Atlantic; 280 to 2125 per cubic centimeter over the Pacific Ocean; and 875 to 2500 over the Mediterranean.*

The extent of dust is still greater in the air of rooms. Aitken found 275,000 particles of dust in a meeting-room at Edinburgh, and 3,000,000 to 3,500,000 some time after the meeting was over. In another room he found as many as 5,420,000 particles.†

Dust in air comes from the pulverized particles of matter, from various materials and processes. Numerous as are the particles of dust in outside air, and in the air of ordinary rooms, they are still more numerous in the air of factories and workshops. During the processes of industry, clouds of dust, invisible and visible, are given off and fill the air of the establishment.

* R. C. Macfie: Air and Health, p. 164.
† Ibid.

Hesse, Arens, Rogers, and others have made determinations of dust particles in industrial establishments, and have found the contents are very large. According to Hesse, a person working ten hours a day would inhale the following amounts of dust in grams.*

Horse-hair Works........0.05 grams per day; 15 grams per year (300 days).
Saw Mills..............0.09 grams per day; 27 grams per year.
Wool Mills.............0.10 grams per day; 30 grams per year.
Flour Mills.............0.12 grams per day; 36 grams per year.
Iron Foundries.........0.14 grams per day; 42 grams per year.
Snuff-tobacco Works.....0.36 grams per day; 108 grams per year.
Cement Works..........1.12 grams per day; 336 grams per year.

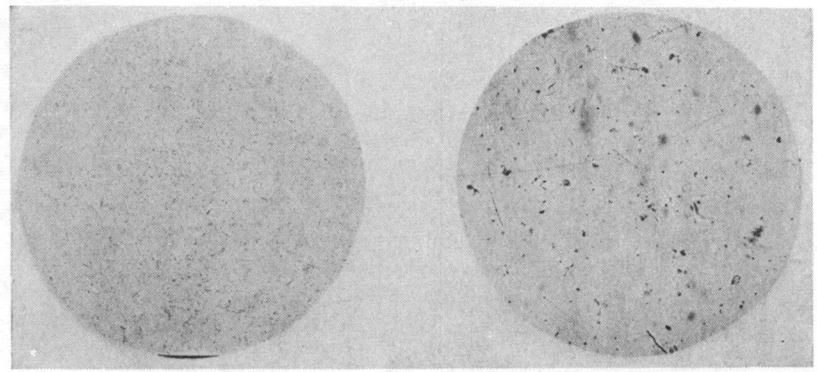

Courtesy Profs. Winslow and Baskerville.

Lighter Particles Floating on Surface.   Heavier Particles Settling to Bottom.

Dust Particles as Seen Under the Microscope.   50 times natural size.

According to Arens, there were in cement-making works 130 milligrams of dust in one cubic meter of air when work was not being done, and 244 milligrams during work. He also found 175 milligrams of dust in one cubic meter of the air in a felt-shoe factory.†

Rogers found on an analysis of samples of air, secured in shops where skirts are made, 70 grams of dust per million litres of air; and as much in pearl-button factories. Samples of air secured in a brass foundry showed 75.2 grams per million litres of air.‡

These figures, gathered from analyses by scientists, are interesting in showing the amount of dust in the air of industrial establishments and the extent of dust production in factories and workshops. But to one who goes through factories in different industries

* Rambousek: " Luftverunreinigung und Ventilation," p. 103.
† Ibid.
‡ Report of New York State Department of Labor.

day by day, these figures are unnecessary, as one cannot help but see in almost every industrial establishment clouds of dust in which the workers are employed, and which are produced by the materials and processes of the industry. In cotton and other textile mills, in carding-rooms and preparing-rooms, in the sorting and manufacturing of shoddy, rags, and similar waste products, in the manufacture of all kinds of clothing, in the milling of flour, in the grinding of stones, in the production of minerals, in the polishing and buffing of metals, etc., no count of dust particles is needed to convince every observer of the large amount found in the air of the workshops, which is inhaled hourly and daily by the workers. In coal,

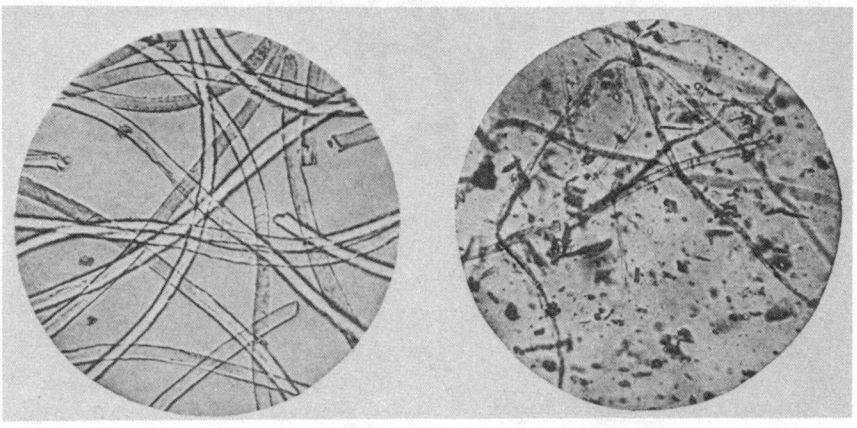

Silk.   Hemp.

metal and mineral mining, in the manufacture of carborundum, graphite, carbide, and other materials, the dust in the air where workers are employed is so thick that one is hardly able to see through the mists and clouds of the rising and floating dust particles.

Dust is classified by its sources, by its physical qualities, shape, size, etc., and by its chemical characteristics.

As to the sources, dust is classified in four large groups—metal, mineral, vegetable, and animal.

Dust varies in size and shape, from the finest, which has very penetrating qualities, to the coarsest; and from dust which is smooth and has all its edges rounded, to dust which has very sharp edges.

Chemically, dust is divided into organic and inorganic, soluble and insoluble.

Hoffman gives a rough classification of forty-two industries according to the sources of their dusts.* These groups, of course, do not embrace all dusty industries. They are as follows:

Group 1: *Exposure to metallic dust:*
(1) Grinders
(2) Polishers.
(3) Tool- and instrument-makers.
(4) Jewelers.
(5) Gold-leaf manufacture.
(6) Brass-workers.
(7) Printers.
(8) Compositors.
(9) Pressmen.
(10) Engravers.

Group 2: *Exposure to mineral dust:*
(11) Stone-workers.
(12) Marble-workers.
(13) Glass-blowers.
(14) Glass-cutters.
(15) Diamond-cutters.
(16) Potters.
(17) Cement-workers.
(18) Plasterers.
(19) Paper-hangers.
(20) Molders.
(21) Core-makers.
(22) Lithographers.

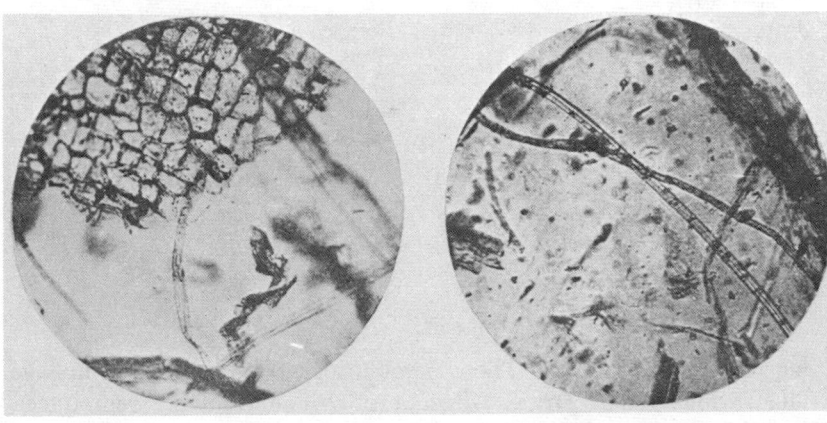

Jute   Flax

Group 3: *Exposure to vegetable fiber dust:*
(23) Cotton-ginning.
(24) Cotton textile manufacture.
(25) Spinners.
(26) Weavers.
(27) Hosiery- and knitting-mills.
(28) Lace-making.
(29) Flax and linen manufacture.
(30) Hemp and cordage manu- facture.
(31) Manufacture of jute and jute goods.
(32) Paper manufacture.
(33) Cabinet-makers.
(34) Wood-turners and carvers.

* United States Department of Labor, Bulletin No. 79. Mortality from Consumption in Dusty Trades.

Group 4: Exposure to animal and mixed fiber dust:

(35) Furriers and taxidermists.

(36) Hatters.

(37) Silk manufacture.

(38) Woolen and worsted manufacture.

(39) Carpet and rug manufacture.

(40) Shoddy manufacture.

(41) Rag industry.

(42) Upholstery and hair-mattress-makers.

To these may be added, in the metal group, miners of and workers in metals; to the mineral group may be added coal-miners, coal-heavers, stokers, carborundum, graphite, carbide, and other workers; and a number of others to these and other groups.

The size, shape and appearance of the dust particles differ accord-

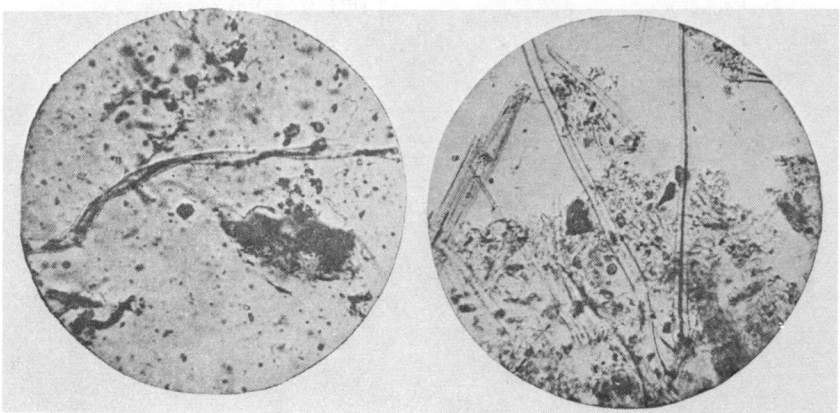

Cotton.   Wheat Dust.

ing to their sources. The microphotographs presented in the illustrations are by Dr. F. Migerka of Vienna and are reproduced from his book on " The Kinds of Dust in Industrial Establishments," published by the Museum of Industrial Hygiene in Vienna.

Effect of Industrial Dusts upon Workers. The baneful effects of industrial dust and its relations to occupational disease was recognized even before Ramazzini. From Ramazzini to the present day all authorities agree that prolonged inhalations of large quantities of dust or continuous sojourn in a dusty atmosphere is harmful to health and causes certain diseases.

" Few, indeed," says Arlidge, " are the occupations in which dust is not given off. In none can it be absolutely harmless. Its disabling action is very slow, but is ever progressive, and until it has already worked its baneful results upon the smaller bronchial tubes and air-cells, and caused difficulty of breathing with coughing and spitting, it is let pass as a matter of indifference and inconvenience of the trade."* Arlidge shows how bronchitis, asthma, and tubercular and fibroid consumption are due to dust inhalations, and concludes that persons predisposed to respiratory diseases and phthisis ought not to engage in dusty occupations.

Sir Thomas Oliver begins his article on dust in his " Diseases of Occupation " with the following sentences: " Dust is the enemy of the workman.   Much ill health and many of the industrial diseases are caused by the inhalation of dust or by the work-people swallowing it along with their food."   In another place† he says, " Were it not for dust, fumes or gas, there would be little or no disease due to occupation, except such as might be caused by infection, by breathing of air poisoned by the emanations of fellow-workers, and exposure to cold after working in overheated rooms."

Professor W. Gilman Thompson says: " Although dust of every kind is a menace to health, it is in its relationship to tuberculosis that dust in general produces the greatest harm."

Indeed, the general consensus of opinion of all authorities on industrial hygiene seems to be unanimous in the recognition of the harmful effect of dust upon the human organism.

Physiological Defences of the Body.   The body is equipped with physiological defensive organs that render harmless ordinary invasion of mechanical, chemical or bacterial foes. It is only when the foes attacking the body are too numerous and their attack unduly prolonged, or when the body, for some reason or other, is bereft of its normal physiological defensive properties, that pathological conditions ensue.

The physiological defences of the body against the effects of inhalation of dust and other solid impurities in the air consist in the mucous lining of the respiratory passages: the nose, mouth, throat, and bronchi, and in the hairs which are abundant in the nasal passages.   These hairs catch, sift, and expel a large quantity of the dust which is inhaled through the nose.   The dust coming in through the respiratory passages adheres to the mucous membrane, and by the action of the ciliated epithelia, with which this mucous membrane is lined, the dust particles adhering to the moist membrane are removed.   If the dust accumulates in larger quan-

---

* J. T. Arlidge: " Hygiene, Diseases and Mortality of Occupations," p. 244.
† Sir Thomas Oliver: " Dangerous Trades."

tities, its irritant effects upon the nerves in the delicate mucous
membrane cause coughing and sneezing, by which a large amount
of the dust with mucous fluid is discharged.

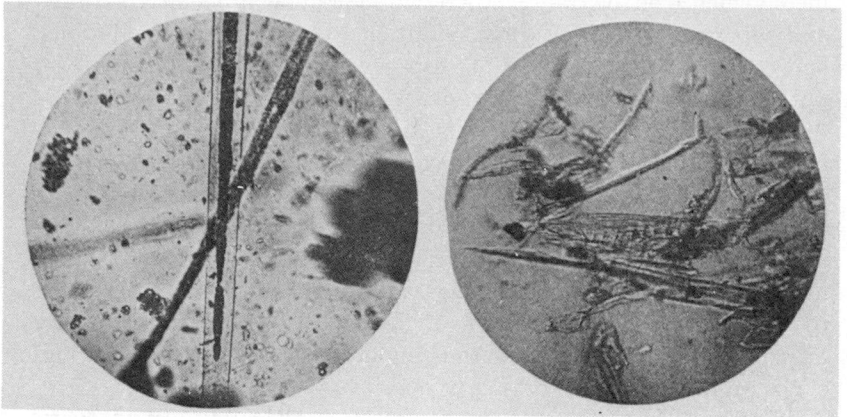

Felt.   Woodworking Machine.

Dr. Gfrörer, in a study of the absorption of lead-dust through
the respiratory passages, found that more than 50 per cent of the
dust inhaled was caught in the nasal passages.   The mouth showed
a maximum of only 15 per cent of the dust inhaled.   The lungs,

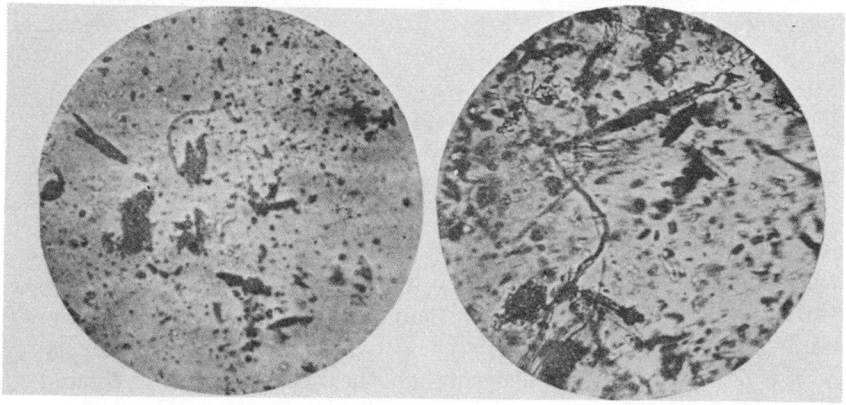

Bonemeal.   Horsehair.

when inhalation is through nasal passages, get about 38 per cent
of the dust.   When inhalation is not through the nose, the lungs
absorb about 80 per cent.*

* Dr. Gfrörer: Inaugural Dissertation: " Orientierende Versuche über quantitative Staub-
absorption durch den Menschen aus staubreicher Luft," Wurzburg, 1912, p. 22.

When the upper respiratory passages are intact and in normal condition, even the finest dust does not ordinarily pass very far into these passages. Heim and Hébert show in their study of the hygiene of the plaster of Paris industry that in the case of rabbits and dogs but few particles of that fine dust pass beyond the vocal chords. Below the larynx, the moisture of the air-passages forms a trap for dust, which, by ciliary action is then removed.*

Dr. Collis says that dust must pass through the upper air-passages, escape entanglement in the bronchi, and finally reach the alveoli of the lungs before it reaches a situation whence it can be carried into the substance of the lungs. In ordinary breathing, aeration of the blood is carried on by diffusion of the gas between the residual air of the alveoli and the inspired air, and dust particles can hardly be carried to the alveoli by such diffusion.†

As long, therefore, as the mucous membrane of the upper respiratory passages is healthy, not much harm can be done by ordinary dust inhalation, even in dusty factories and workshops; but if the dust inhalation is continued for a long period, and if the dust comes in very large quantities, or if, because of catarrhs, colds, or other disease, the respiratory passages become diseased, and thereby denuded of their healthy mucous membrane, then, the defensive qualities of the body being absent, the attacking force of the dust becomes injurious and dangerous to health by producing certain diseases.

It is well known that a great many workers, especially those engaged in dusty trades, very often suffer from diseases of the upper respiratory passages.

Dr. Otto Glogau,‡ on examining a number of workers in a jute-rope mill and in artificial flower and feather shops, came to the conclusion, " that the upper respiratory tract is undoubtedly damaged by the dust that contains minute particles of feathers, fur and cordage material; that the nose was entirely filled with dust, while in others only the septum or the turbinates were affected. In 119 of the 155 workers examined, particles of working material were found in the nose; in 91 cases such particles were lodged in the throat. When minute particles of dust irritate the nasal mucous lining for any length of time, the respiratory organs within the nose, the so-called turbinates, are damaged. The turbinates consist of spongy tissue;

* Quoted by E. L. Collis: " Effects of Dust in Producing Diseases of the Lungs." A Lecture before the 17th International Congress of Medicine, London, 1913, p. 21.
† Ibid.
‡ Report to the New York State Factory Commission, Second Report, vol. ii, p. 537.

their function is to filtrate, warm and moisten the air. The pathological changes of the turbinates brought about by the irritation of the workshop dust consist of hyperthrophies or degenerative

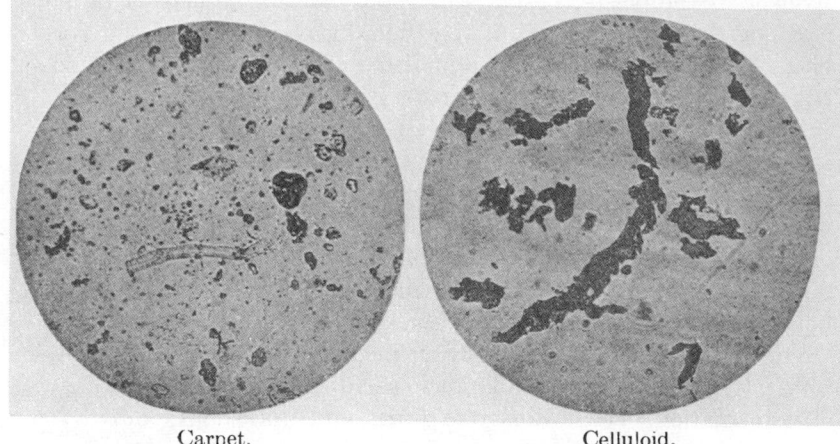

Carpet.   Celluloid.

processes with either the formation of polypi or complete atrophy. By any of these conditions the function of the turbinates is interfered with and the breathing space within the nose is reduced to a minimum. A chronic inflammation of the mucuous lining of the

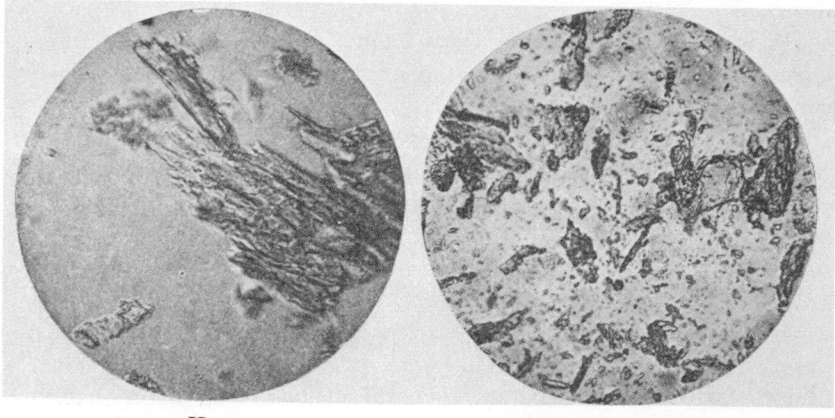

Horn.   Mother of Pearl.

nose, rhinitis, was noticed in 128 cases, and a chronic inflammation of the mucous lining of the throat, pharyngitis, was detected in 115 cases."

Workers are also subject to frequent colds, because of excessive heat and the sudden changes from high to low temperatures which are followed by bronchial catarrh. Diseases of the respiratory passages, so frequent among workers, break down the defensive physiological forces of the body and render the workmen a prey to the effects of industrial dust.

Arnold experimented on animals by placing them in atmospheres filled with smoke, ultramarine, and sandstone dust. Smoke, which is pure coal dust, was found to reach the lung easily, and was found not only in the bronchi but also in the alveoli and lung-cells. The same was true of ultramarine and fine sandstone dust.*

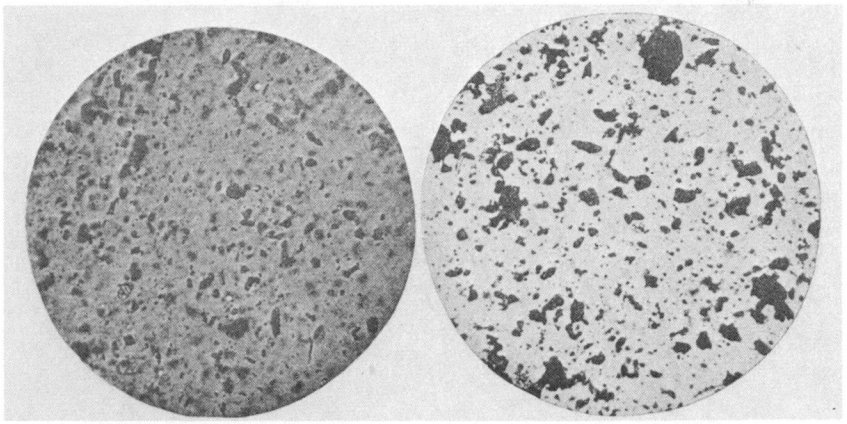

Lead.   Cast-iron Polishing.

Anyone who has visited the museums of safety in European capitals, or the anatomical museums and exhibitions in this country, may see for himself the effect of dust-inhalation upon the lungs of the workers. There he will see before him specimens of the coal-miner's lung, black with coal dust, the lungs of the stone-cutter, and of other workers, showing distinctly the amount of the dust lodged within the parynchema of the lung, which dust remains there until death.

Not all dusts have the same effects, nor are all dusts equally harmful. The effect of dusts depends upon the size, shape and mechanical action of their particles, upon their chemical character and their toxicity.

Outside of poisonous dusts, those containing silica are said to

* Dr. Ascher: " Dammer's Handbuch der Arbeiter Wohlfahrt," p. 410.

be the most harmful. Dust particles of large size with sharp and cutting edges are harmful because of the scratches and wounds which they make in the delicate mucous lining of the respiratory membranes, thereby opening the way for infectious bacteria. Dusts of metallic or mineral origin have different effects than dusts of organic, vegetable, or animal origin. Dust may act as a mechanical irritant and thus produce harmful effects, especially dust of emery, glass, granite, gritstone, etc.

The chemical character of dust has an important bearing upon its influence and effect. Certain dusts which are soluble and non-toxic may be innocuous; other dusts may either act as irritants or

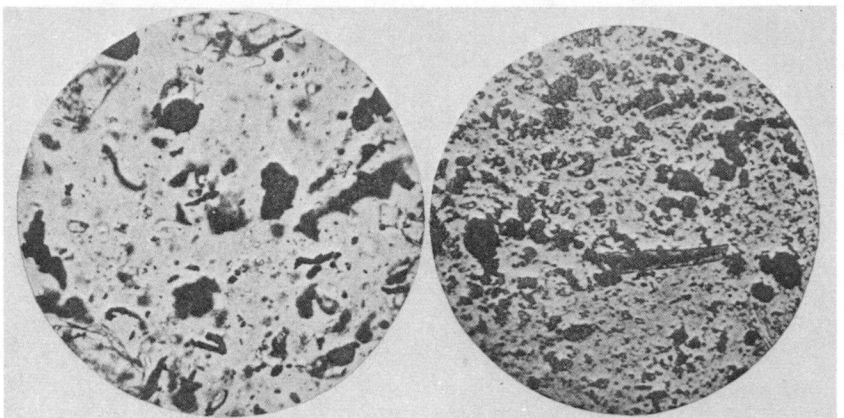

Needle Polishing.   Brass Polishing.

may injure the body by their toxic character. A great many dusts come from poisonous materials. Reference has been made to the large inhalation of dust in lead trades and in all dangerous trades where poisonous materials are employed. These poisonous dusts may be either absorbed, and exert toxic influences upon the whole organism through the blood, or they may act locally, as for instance chrome dust which produces chrome sores; paraffine, coal-tar, and other dusts, which produce various skin lesions, from plain inflammations to deadly cancers.

Investigations by Dr. Collis seem to indicate that a large proportion of silica is the most important factor in the injurious effects of dust, especially in causing pulmonary tuberculosis. Dr. Collis' conclusions on the effects of dust and its relation to disease are the following: Inhalation of all forms of dust is accompanied by diminished power of chest expansion. Diminished power of chest expansion, so produced, is accompanied by high blood-pressure. Animal dusts, apart from the presence in them of pathogenic micro-organisms,

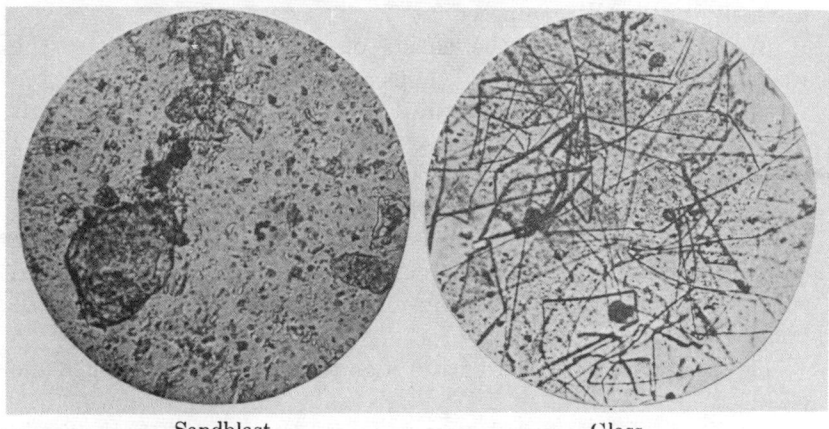

Sandblast.   Glass.

when inhaled produce less effects than do vegetable and mineral dusts. Vegetable dusts when inhaled tend to produce a type of chest affection best described as asthmatic. Of mineral dusts, those composed of calcium salts are least injurious; inhalation of

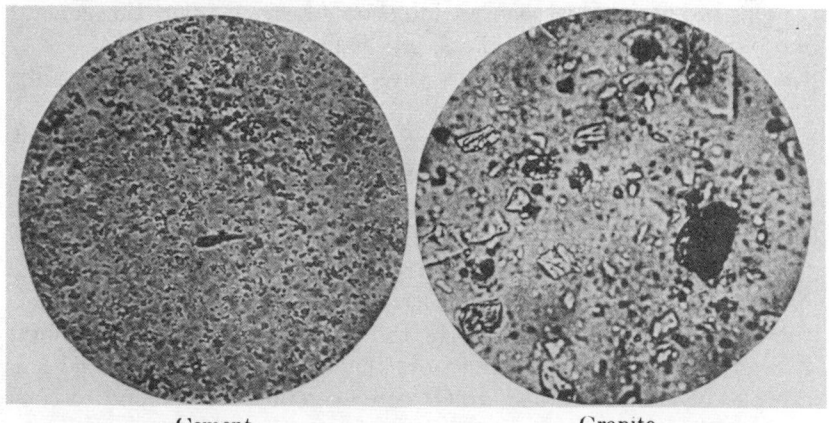

Cement.   Granite.

mineral dusts which do not contain free silica tends to produce irritation of the upper air-passages and respiratory diseases other than phthisis; inhalation of mineral dusts which contain free silica is associated with an excess of phthisis, an excess which bears a direct relation to the amount of free silica present. In general, dusts appear to be more injurious as their chemical composition differs from that of the human body or from the elements of which the body is normally composed.*

We may summarize the effects of industrial dusts upon the workmen in factories and workshops as follows:

(1) Dust acts as a mechanical obstruction as well as irritant in the upper respiratory passages.

(2) Dust may cut and wound the delicate mucous membrane lining the organs of the upper respiratory passages.

(3) Dust may carry infectious germs into the respiratory tract.

(4) Dust may carry infectious germs to the lacerations and wounds caused by it, or to any openings or wounds on the skin or the body of the worker.

(5) Dust acts as a direct irritant to the skin, to the eyes, to the ears.

(6) Dust of a toxic character may be carried into the body by the digestive system, by the lymphatic vessels, and by the blood.

(7) Inhalation of dust may give rise to fibroid changes in lungs and to fibroid phthisis.

(8) Dust in the lungs is a predisposing cause to pulmonary tuberculosis.

(9) Industrial dust has an important bearing upon the general morbidity of industrial workers, especially from tuberculosis.

(10) Industrial dust has a direct bearing upon the mortality rate of the industrial population.

Dust and Disease. Before proceeding with a brief discussion of the relation of dust to disease, mention must be made of the dangers of industrial dusts in so far as fires and explosions are concerned. Certain dusts, such as cotton, flour, etc., may cause explosions and fires. Only recently there occurred in the Husted Mill in Buffalo, New York, an explosion which cost a number of lives and which was found to have been due to the explosion of dust. Although it was difficult to determine how the explosion came about, the samples of grain and dust which were examined were found to contain highly explosive properties.

Reference has already been made to the action of dust as a mechanical irritant, as an obstruction to the respiratory passages, and as a means of lacerating the delicate mucous membrane of the

* E. L. Collis: " Effects of Dust in Producing Diseases of the Lungs." A Lecture before the 17th International Congress of Medicine, London, 1913.

nose and throat, and also of its possible action in carrying infectious germs to the respiratory tract, infecting wounds, etc.

The action of dust upon the skin is either mechanical or chemical, toxic or infectious, depending upon the source and kind of dust. The skin of the body comes in close contact with various kinds of industrial dust, which penetrate the clothes. The face and hands are especially exposed to its action. Dust clogs up pores, it acts as a chronic irritant and, if it has poisonous qualities, it may be absorbed through the skin. This is especially the case with dusts such as lead and arsenic, and with specially irritant stuffs like aniline dyes, coal-tar dyes, etc., etc.

Dust may carry infectious germs to open wounds or sores and

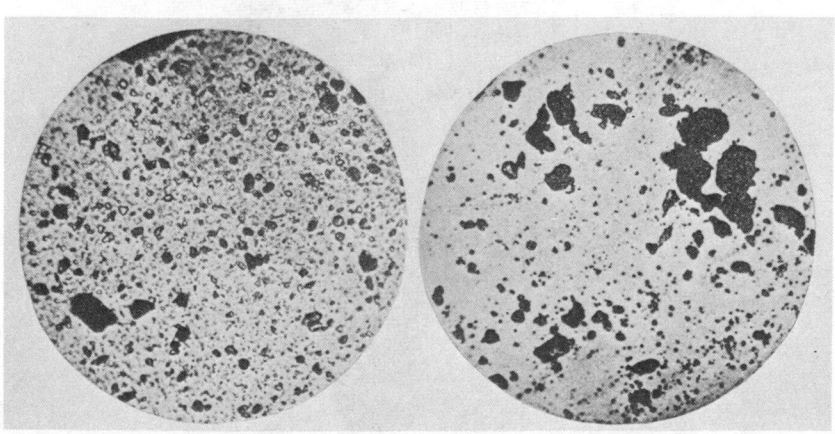

Sandstone.   Limestone.

cause inflammations, furunculosis, and other infections. Acute erythematus irritations are caused by certain coal-tar products, such as aniline dyes; these, as well as other irritant materials, cause acute dermatitis, chronic eczema, and various other inflammations of the skin, acute or chronic.

Workers have special names for the skin affections due to industrial dusts. Thus, there is the " cement-workers' itch," the " bakers' itch," and other skin diseases affecting flax and other spinners, furriers, painters, tobacco-workers, etc. Polishers, grinders and metal-workers suffer from a form of acne, while bleach-workers, and those who work in soda works or with calcium carbide, suffer from a special disease of swelling of the palms and hyper-

New York State Factory Commission.

Interior of Machine Room of Cordage Factory.

dyrosis, or excessive sweating of the inflamed surfaces which shed drops of sweat.

Prolonged exposure to certain kinds of dust leads at times to more serious affections, such as cancer. Paraffin-workers' and chimney-sweeps' cancer are well-known forms, due to industrial dusts. Cancer is also frequent in other dusty trades.

The eye affections which are due to industrial dusts are either wounds directly caused by large particles of dust entering the eye, or chronic irritation brought about by the finer dusts. Thousands of workers are injured by particles of dust lodging in the eyes and also through amateur attempts of their fellow-workers to extract these particles. Their unskillful handling often results in injuring the delicate eye-membrane. Chronic irritation of the eye by mechanically or chemically irritant dusts is seen in the various affections of the eye, such as conjunctivitis, blepharitis, and ulcerations of the cornea.

More important than the effects of dust upon the skin, eyes, and upper respiratory passages is the direct effect of prolonged exposure to industrial dusts on the lung-tissue itself. The two diseases which are caused by dust-inhalation are fibroid and tubercular phthisis, although the lesser affections, such as bronchitis, acute and chronic, emphysema, and asthma have also been proven to be due to action of dusts. Indeed, bronchitis is usually a forerunner of more serious lung affections, as are all the catarrhs of the respiratory passages. Only after a chronic inflammation of these passages can the dust gain access to the lung-tissue and produce more serious affections, either in fibrosis of the lung or in tubercular affection.

The chronic irritation of all dusts, and especially of certain kinds of dusts, causes infiltration and inflammation of the connective tissue of the cells of the lung, the dust particles become encapsulated, and part of the lung-tissue undergoes what is called fibroid changes. The cells of the lung lose their elasticity and various symptoms and pathological changes result from this fibrosis.

The fibroid changes in the lungs caused by dusts are called by the general name " pneumokoniosis," and the resulting diseases are designated according to the source of the dust; thus, " anthracosis," coal-miner's lung; " siderosis," the lungs of metal-grinders, etc.; " chalicosis," of the stone-workers, etc. Lung diseases of workers are also known as " potter's rot," " coal-miner's phthisis," " stone-cutter's rot," " furrier's asthma," etc.

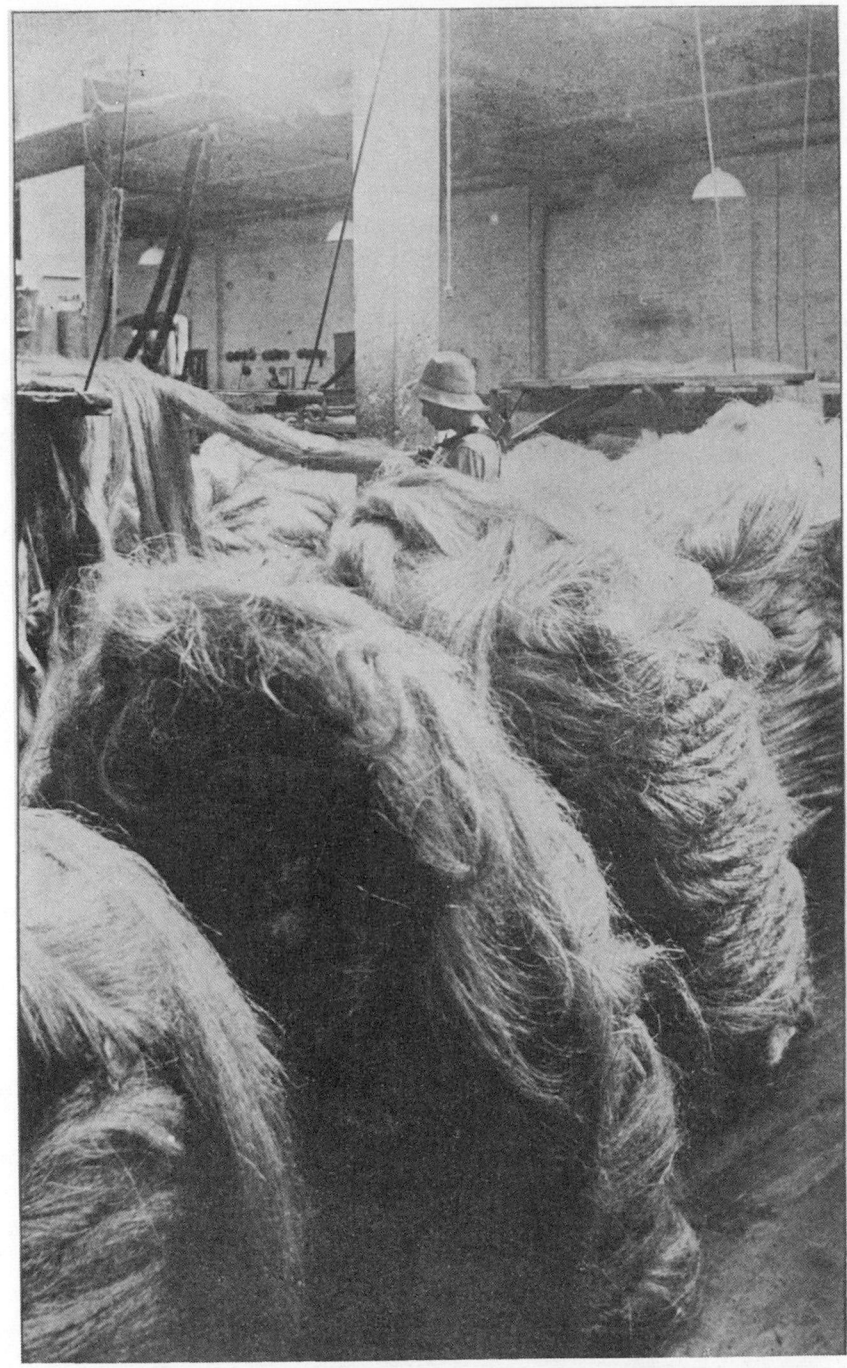

New York State Factory Commission.

Girl Worker in a Preparing Room of a Cordage Factory. A very Dusty
Occupation.

Fibroid phthisis usually comes on very slowly and its symptoms are at first masked, but with the progress of the disease they become more marked and last for a great many years, unless the disease becomes complicated with a tubercular affection. Coughs, shortness of breath, diminution of chest expansion, difficulty of breathing, fatigue on exertion, anaemia, and general weakness of the body usually go hand in hand with the development of fibrosis of the lungs, although the worker, while decreasing in his industrial efficiency, may go on with his work for a great many years. If he leaves his work, the disease may be arrested and the worker recover from his affection. Not all cases of fibroid phthisis remain uncomplicated or present the same pathological picture. Many of them become affected with tuberculosis; some of them suffer from emphysema; and many of them drop out from their industry and take up other less dusty trades.

The relation of dust-inhalation to tuberculosis of the lungs of workers is well known. Workers suffering from chronic inflammations of the upper respiratory passages, from chronic bronchitis, and from impairment of the action of the lungs through dust-inhalations fall ready prey to the effects of the tubercular bacilli which are so ubiquitous and may be found in every industrial plant, due to dry sputum and excretions from tuberculous workers. Such workers have not the necessary resistance to withstand the attack of tubercular germs and tuberculous phthisis easily develops and counts its victims by the thousands and tens of thousands. The role of pulmonary phthisis in general morbidity and mortality of workers has been abundantly proven by statistical data gained from the census reports of the Registrar General of England, and from the careful statistics of the sick-benefit societies and state insurance of Germany and other countries.

The classic table of John Tatham has been cited many times and gives a graphic view of the relation of dusty trades to consumption.* That table is as follows:

* Oliver: " Dangerous Trades," p. 135.

| Occupation. | Comparative Mortality Figures (All Causes). | Mortality Figures. | |
		Phthisis.	Diseases of the Respiratory Organs.
Agriculturist....................	602	106	115
Pottery: Earthenware Manufacture....	1706	333	668
Cutler........................	1516	382	518
File-maker	1810	402	423
Glass-maker	1487	295	445
Copper-worker.................	1381	294	406
Iron and Steel Manufacture.........	1301	195	450
Stone Quarries.................	1176	269	307
Brass-worker..................	1088	279	273
Chimney-sweep.................	1311	260	291
Lead-worker...................	1783	148	397
Cotton Manufacture.............	1141	202	338

Sommerfeld's statistics also show the following changes in the pulmonary phthisis rate between workers in occupations without dust and workers in occupations with various kinds of dust.*

Occupation.	Number of Deaths Due to Phthisis Per Thousand.	Percentage of Deaths Due to Phthisis Per Thousand.
Occupations without Dust.............	381.0	2.39
Mortality in Dusty Trades............	480.0	5.42
Metallic Dusts......................	470.6	5.84
Mineral Dusts......................	403.4	4.42
Organic Dusts......................	537.04	5.64

Hoffman, in his statistics, based upon the experience of an industrial-insurance company, has shown the following mortality rate due to consumption, according to ages, in the various groups of dusty trades.†

| Occupation. | Percentage of Deaths Due to Consumption in Each Age Group. | | |
	25 to 34	35 to 44.	45 to 54.
Occupations with Exposure to Metallic Dusts	57.2	42.4	23.4
Mineral Dusts........................	47.6	36.3	27.9
Vegetable Fibre Dusts.................	53.9	43.0	23.3
Animal and Mixed Fibre Dusts...........	53.3	48.3	25.3

* Sommerfeld: " Die Schwindsucht der Arbeiter."
† " Mortality from Consumption in Dusty Trades," Bulletin, Bureau of Labor, No. 79, p. 857.

II

DUSTY TRADES

Attempts at classifying the dusty trades have been made according to source, character, kind and toxicity of the dust. To one, however, who daily visits all kinds of industrial establishments it seems that no classification is possible, that there are no dusty trades, for the reason that all trades are dusty. If the trade itself has no special dust, the establishment where the trade is housed has some dusty process or condition in some part of the establishment. One often goes through a factory finding all conditions safe and sanitary until he reaches the boiler-room, where half a dozen men are shovelling soft coal into the boilers and raising clouds of dust, part of which is disseminated to other parts of the building. In an inspection of a sugar refinery, where one would not usually expect to find much dust, one suddenly enters a room where the air is full of charcoal dust, where working hours are from eight to twelve per day, and where the dust is so thick that one cannot see two to three feet away. It is this ubiquity of dust in industry that makes a classification of the dusty trades so difficult.

Metal Trades. All metals are used in industry. Iron, copper, zinc, lead, tin are used either in their pure state or as compounds, alloys, salts, etc. A number of trades are designated according to the principal metal used—thus, iron-workers, brass-workers, tin-smiths, lead-workers, etc. A greater number of trades, however, are designated by the character and kind of work performed, no matter what metal is used. Thus, we have miners, smelters, refiners, foundrymen, grinders, polishers, buffers, and makers of all kinds of objects, utensils, tools, and appliances of various kinds of metals, each designated by the work they are doing.

Most metal workers are exposed to the action of metal dust, depending upon the character of the work performed. After a statistical study of the mortality of workers in metal trades, Hoffman came to the conclusion " that the injurious effects of exposure to metal dusts are reflected in (1) a comparatively small proportion of persons of advanced years in industry, (2) a high general death rate, and (3) a very high specific rate from consumption and other respiratory diseases."*

* Mortality from Consumption in Dusty Trades, U. S. Dept. Labor, Bulletin No. 79, p. 681.

Foundries are places where iron or other metals are melted and cast in cores and forms of all kinds. Mineral dust is produced during

Courtesy Wm. C. Hanson, U. S. Dept. Labor, Bulletin 127.

Polishing Shoes in a Shoe Factory.

The well-equipped hood and exhaust system furnishes practically ideal protection.

the formation and baking of the cores, metal dust in the grinding off of the rough edges of cast articles, and a mixture of mineral and metal dust in the sand-blasting processes, by which the rough edges and parts of cast articles are polished off.

The greatest amount of dust occurs in the sand-blasting process, which is carried on in some nook or corner of the factory, and is at times not separated from other processes. I have seen sand-blasting done in an iron foundry in the middle of the establishment, with no protection whatever to the rest of the place. The dust which was raised spread all through the room in which the sand-blasting was done and to adjacent rooms. The only protection the worker had was a rough helmet, poorly devised, and which allowed dust to come in.

Sand-blasting as it is done in the open air, as shown in the illustration on page 419, is less harmful, although it raises no less dust and the worker needs the protection of special clothes and respirators.

In Belgium and Germany I saw sand-blasting processes carried on in special separate rooms which were well ventilated and supplied with air-exhaust. The worker was not allowed to go into the room, but carried on the process from the outside of the room, manipulating the tools through openings in the glass doors.

The process of sand-blasting is only an occasional one, and foundry workers are compelled to do it only for a short time on certain days of the week. Foundry workers say that if they were compelled to do sand-blasting every day of the week they could not live for more than a year. The great morbidity of foundry workers which has been reported by the New York State Factory Commission was due also to the other unhealthy conditions prevalent in foundries, such as exposure to extreme heat, and sudden change from heat to cold. The foundry workers demanded and received in New York State special legislation guarding them against dust, heat, etc.

In the processes of grinding, polishing, and buffing metal objects and articles, abundant dust, partly metallic and partly mineral, is given off. Metal-grinding is proverbially an unhealthy occupation, and all writers on the subject have by figures, facts, and statistics endeavored to prove the high mortality and great morbidity of workers in this trade.

Greenhow, Hall, Roepke, and a host of others have shown that the average age of steel-grinders was only twenty-nine years, that the mortality from pulmonary phthisis was 345 out of a thousand, that 458 grinders in a thousand died between the ages of forty-five and fifty-five, etc. The same is true of metal-polishers. A writer says: "Metal-polishers who have reached the age of forty often look like old men. There can hardly be found a trade more deleterious to health. Among the harmful conditions may be mentioned the amount of dust which gets into the lungs of the workmen; such dust is composed of metal, minerals, and cotton fiber."* Polishing of metals on a lathe, which turns at times at the rate of 2500 revolutions per minute, raises a cloud of dust, and "has wrecked many constitutions."

In some establishments the work of grinding and polishing has become a comparatively harmless process, thanks to modern dust-removal devices. I shall never forget the spectacle presented by one of the largest grinding- and polishing-rooms I have seen here or abroad; viz., the polishing-room of a cutlery establishment at Solingen, near Düsseldorf, Germany, an establishment several centuries old. In spite of the fact that nearly 800 workers were at work at the different benches, grinding and polishing knives, forks, etc., there was hardly any dust in the room, so well was each table and each polishing- and buffing-wheel and lathe protected with local exhausts.

Dr. Roepke of Solingen cites the difference in the sickness and death rates of the workers in Solingen before the introduction of local exhausts and strict state supervision and after such introduction. According to Roepke and Moritz, who examined 1250 grinders, they found 9.04 per cent suffering from diseases of the lungs and 48.1 per cent suffering from diseases of the pharynx and larynx. They also found no grinder over forty-five years who was healthy. The latest reports of Dr. Roepke are that there is a remarkable improvement in the mortality and morbidity of Solingen workers, due to rigorous state supervision and to the introduction of dust-removal appliances.

There is considerable metal dust generated in the brass, copper, and lead industries, and these dusts are more dangerous because of their poisonous character. The number of industries and industrial establishments in which dust of a poisonous character is evolved is very great. This subject will be discussed in the next chapter.

Mineral Trades. The industries in which dusts are abundant are very numerous. Mineral dust is found not only in trades where minerals are being worked with, but also in other trades; for instance, wherever grinding and polishing of metals is done upon mineral stones, lathes, etc. Quarrymen, cutters and workers with all kinds

* G. Willetts, quoted by Hoffman: Bulletin No. 79, U. S. Department of Labor.

of stone, glass-workers, glass-cutters, diamond-cutters and polishers, potters, cement-workers, plasterers, marble-workers, carborundum, graphite, emery, calcium carbide, and many other workers are all exposed to mineral dust.

The general effect of inhalation of mineral dust is about the same as that of the inhalation of metal and other dusts, and Hoffman found after a statistical study of a representative number of

N. Y. State Factory Commission.

Workers in a Factory where the Skins from Hares and Rabbits are Scraped off for Supplying Felt for Hats. The skins are "canotted" or treated with a solution of nitrate of mercury. Workers subject to dust inhalation and to mercurial poison.

employments necessitating exposure to mineral dust that the "health-injurious effects of such exposure revealed themselves in the high general death rate, especially at the age of thirty-five or over, and with a correspondingly high specific death rate from consumption and from other respiratory diseases at ages between 35 and over, by which time the dust inhaled began to show its effect."*

In a report by Dr. Sidney Barwise, Medical Officer of Derbyshire, the statement is made that the death rate from phthisis among

* "Mortality from Consumption in Dusty Trades," Bulletin No. 79, p. 726.

gritstone-workers is twenty times greater than in the same social class employed in agriculture, and seventeen times greater than in other workers; that the death rate from phthisis of workers employed in limestone is twice as great as that of other workers; that the rate among coal-miners is about the same as among those engaged in agriculture, and less than the average of other workers; that the death rate from phthisis among gritstone-workers is so high that it accounts for the death rate of the general population on the gritstone areas being above the average of England and Wales; that among gritstone-workers 45 per cent of all the deaths of workers above fifteen years of age are from phthisis, while 12 per cent of the limestone-workers and 7.4 per cent of coal-miners die from this cause.* It seems, therefore, that phthisis is more frequent among these workers with a large amount of silica than among the Sheffield workers suffering from " grinder's rot," or those who suffer from " stone-cutter's phthisis," and other workers exposed to ordinary mineral dust. The analysis of the gritstone worked by these men has shown 96.4 per cent of silica.

In a table given by Dr. Collis in his paper read before the International Congress of Medicine at London, 1913, detailed data are given as to the frequency of tuberculosis among workers in different dusty mineral trades, and the figures show that danger from phthisis is in proportion to the silica contents of the mineral dust.

Other workers subject to a great deal of mineral dust are the glass, diamond, pottery, cement-workers, plasterers, house-wreckers, core-makers, lithographers, etc.

In potteries the dust evolved is excessive in certain parts of the establishment. In modern cement mills the process is nearly automatic, and very little dust is allowed to escape. Much dust is inhaled by all workers on emery-wheels and on carborundum, alundum, and other materials used for grinding purposes. Painters who have to sandpaper and sandrub walls must very often inhale large quantities of mineral dusts, as well as lead-paint dust.

The dustiest establishments I have seen are the carborundum, graphite, calcium carbide, and alundum works at Niagara Falls, New York. These huge electro-thermal establishments, working as they do with mineral substances, cannot be compared with any other factories; for while other establishments may be dusty at certain times and places, these large works are dusty everywhere

* Report on the Prevalence of Phthisis among Quarry-Workers and Miners, Derbyshire County Council.

and at all the times. The crude minerals are brought in cars to the factory and shovelled by men working without any protection whatever, taken to the electric furnaces, and there subjected to a high degree of electric heat, which transforms them into the new substances, which then have to be cut, broken up or pulverized. In all processes from the first to the last, clouds of dust are evolved which there seems to be no way of preventing and which is constantly inhaled by the workers, of whom there are from several hundreds to several thousands in each establishment.

Investigations made by the New York State Factory Commission into the conditions in these establishments showed that a large number of workers were tuberculous, and that pneumonia was very prevalent among them. At the time of the investigation by the Commission, very little was being done by the employers to remove or prevent the dust or to protect the workers against the consequence of dust-exposure and inhalation.

Vegetable Dusts. The factories in which large amounts of vegetable dusts may be found are numerous. The industries containing such dust are many. Vegetable dust is found in cotton, hemp, jute, flax, textile mills, in establishments where wood is being worked with and wooden objects manufactured, in the large industry of making and manufacturing cotton clothing, in tobacco manufacture, in the making of buttons from vegetable ivory, and in many other similar trades.

In the cotton industry, much dust is produced during the ginning, preparing and carding processes, and in lesser quantities during the other stages of manufacture. The same is true in hemp, jute, flax, and other mills. The illustration on page 408, is from a large cordage mill at Auburn, New York, and shows a woman worker surrounded by hemp material raising clouds of dust. Hundreds of bales of hemp were being opened in the same establishment, prepared and carded without any provision for ventilation whatever, and only after the visit of the Commission and the consequent publicity given to working conditions in this factory was a ventilating plant installed, which mitigated the former dusty conditions.

In the large industry at Rochester, New York, of making buttons from vegetable ivory I found the dust in the factories excessive, although in some of the better class of establishments attempts have been made to remedy the evil. Hoffman came to the conclusion that " exposure to vegetable-fiber dust is decidedly injurious to health, and that the mortality from consumption among employes in this field of occupations is very much higher at all ages than would be expected."

One fact especially must be emphasized in relation to vegetable dusts—that in industries in which such dust is evolved there is a specially large proportion of women and minors at work. This is notably the case in textile mills and in tobacco factories, where a large number of young children and females are at work, especially

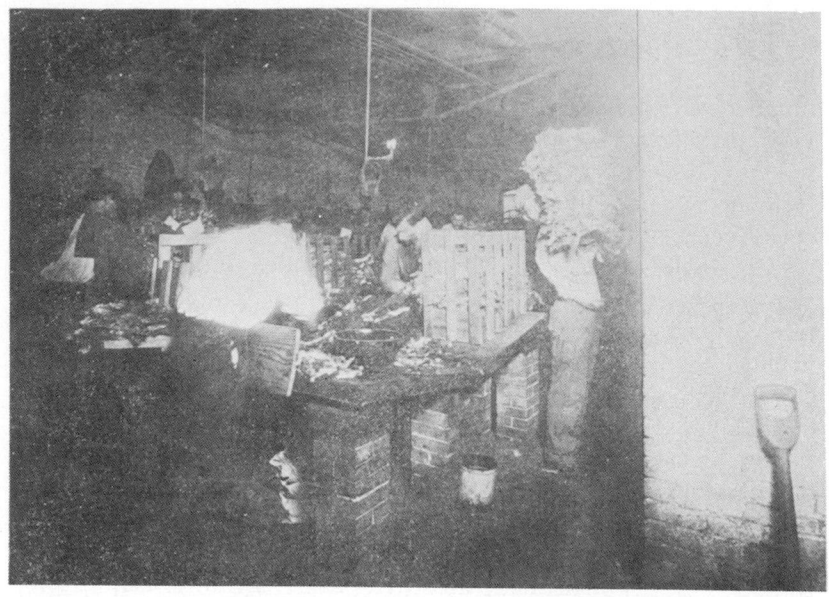

N. Y. State Factory Commission.

Workers Carrying Skins Treated with Nitrate of Mercury. They are subject to the dust, as well as to action of mercurial poison.

in states where the legal working age is very low and where state supervision is perfunctory.

Animal Dust. There are a number of industries in which there is much animal dust present, and the exposure to this dust has been found no less dangerous than exposure to other kinds of dusts. Such industries are the manufacture of silk and wool, rags and shoddy, boots and shoes, human hair, feathers, mattresses, etc., etc.

In silk, wool, rag, and shoddy mills the carding, preparing and sorting rooms are full of dust, while the other parts of the establishment are not entirely free from it. In the manufacture of hair, feathers, mattresses, etc., large amounts of dust are given off, covering the whole body of the worker and causing him to inhale large

Pullman Car Co.

Sand-blasting Exterior of Car.   Worker wears respirator.

amounts of these materials.   Most of these animal dusts are very irritating.   Some dusts, such as those from shoddy, may cause a special train of symptoms called " shoddy fever," while the inhalation of other animal dusts may cause many ills and injuries to various parts of the body, as already noted.

The handling of animal objects in manufacture and inhaling of dusts from these objects often causes disease by the presence of infectious bacteria. This is notably the case with "wool-sorter's disease," and "anthrax," which occurs among those working on animal hides and skins.

In the shoe industry there is considerable dust in various processes, as has been described in detail in Dr. William C. Hanson's "Dangers to Workers from Dusts and Fumes, and Methods of Protection," United States Department of Labor, Bulletin No. 127. According to Dr. Hanson, the most dusty processes in the making-department of boot and shoe factories are trimming, shaving, scouring, polishing, finishing and cleaning parts of the shoe. The dust generated includes leather, fine lint, fiber, bristles, dry blacking, sand, emery, and carborundum.

Fur-workers are exposed to irritating dust from skins of all kinds of animals, and often suffer from "furrier's asthma." Furriers also show a very large percentage of tuberculosis. In an examination of a limited number (100) of furriers in New York City, I found that 6 per cent of them suffered from pulmonary tuberculosis, over 30 per cent from chronic bronchitis; and 13 per cent from asthma and emphysema. Furriers are also subject to acute and chronic inflammatory conditions of the skin of the hands, due, it is said, to the irritant action of the dyes used on furs.

III

PREVENTION AND PROTECTION

Much of the dust produced in industry is not necessary, and a great many of the injurious effects of dust may be prevented. The enormous waste of human life in industry due to dust is a problem the solution of which is not difficult, if proper spirit is shown by employers, if adequate provisions are made by manufacturers, if these provisions are properly supervised by the state authorities, and if the workers are educated in the methods of prevention and know how to protect themselves against the baneful effects of dust inhalation.

Industrial efficiency demands the prevention of dust. Industrial economy is based upon the prevention of dust and its utilization

whenever possible.   Industrial hygiene teaches that there is ample
provision for the protection of workers in dusty occupations.

There are four principal methods of prevention of dust and protection of workers in dusty trades:

(1) Prevention of the formation of dust;

(2) Isolation of the dusty process;

(3) Removal of dust at its point of origin;

(4) Personal protection of the worker.

Prevention of Dust-formation.   There are two methods by
which the formation of dust may be prevented.   The first is the
wet method;   the second is the automatic and closed-machinery
method.

Wet processes in industry are as old as industry itself.   They
are employed in a great many trades and industrial establishments
and there is no reason why they should not be employed in a great
many more.   Wherever material is broken up, ground, milled,
polished, powdered, comminuted, or worked over in whatsoever
manner, there dust can be prevented from forming by the simple
addition of water, oil, or other appropriate liquid.   The water-spout
over a grinding-wheel is an example of the wet process of grinding;   the mixing of lead-dust with oil has greatly obviated dust-formation in lead factories;   glass-cutting and polishing by the wet
process has removed a great many dangers.   In a general way,
it should be the cardinal principle of industry, wherever possible,
to adapt this method which prevents the formation of dust and
thereby protects the worker.

The second method by which dust-formation is prevented is
the adoption of closed automatic devices.   A great many industrial
processes are at present so constructed as to present a consecutive
automatic series of processes, which are automatically performed,
in closed chambers, or drums, necessitating human supervision
only.   These automatic processes are especially useful in industries
where grinding, powdering, sifting, and mixing of special valuable
stuffs is done, and where the open process would result in economic loss.

An illustration of automatic processes is presented in the modern
flour-mill.   The milling of flour, which formerly was so dusty and
involved a great loss of valuable material, is at present almost wholly
automatic, from grinding to sifting, polishing, and filtering, throughout all the processes from one drum or hopper to another, until
the final stage when the flour is sent to be packed into barrels or

sacks. As a result of the automatic process, the flour-mill is at present a comparatively dustless establishment.

The same may be said of modern cement works which use automatic processes, closed vessels, and cylinders, so that a comparatively small amount of dust is formed. A dusty operation and, at the same time, a very dangerous one to health, is that of packing bleach powder in bleach chambers. A description of the process and its dangers will be given in the next chapter. As at present carried

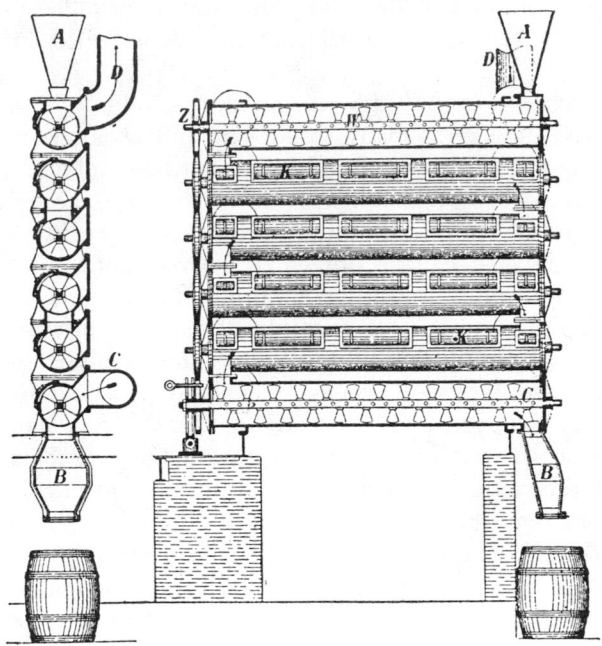

Automatic Process of Manufacturing Chloride of Lime.
From "Gewerbliche Vergiftungen," by Dr. J. Rambausek.

on in the United States, the powdered dry lime is spread and impregnated with chlorine gas in the bleach chambers, which the workers are obliged to enter in order to rake it up, and shovel it through chutes into packing barrels. The illustration on this page shows how this process of bleach-packing has been revolutionized in an industrial establishment which I saw at Brussels, where the whole process of getting the lime into the hoppers, the impregnating of the lime with chlorine gas, the mixing of the powder with the gas, and the final packing of the lime into barrels, is all done in her-metically-closed automatic machinery, which prevents the forma-tion of all dust and protects the worker from its injurious effects.

As I have said in another place, " If an infinitesimal part of the ingenuity, intelligence and thought which has been and is at the present time devoted to the improvement of machinery, the inven-tion of mechanical devices, and discovery of chemical secrets were devoted to inventions for the protection of the worker and for the preservation of his life and health, the danger from industrial dust, disease and accidents would become altogether negligible."* I have no doubt that automatic machinery can be invented which would make a great many of the dusty trades dustless ones, and which would make the pursuit of industry a healthy exercise and a blessing instead of a danger and a curse.

Dust can also be prevented by using tight and closed vessels. Especially is this the case in the transportation and packing of dusty materials. The common method of shovelling such materials into boxes, barrels or sacks, or throwing them from heights into these receptacles is more than ludicrous. I remember inspecting a large biscuit factory where all the latest modern automatic devices were employed, but where in one place I came upon half a dozen workers standing under a big spout, through which thousands of pounds of flour came down in an uninterrupted current, filling up and tying sacks of flour, while the whole room was full of flour-dust, presenting a waste of material as well as danger to the health of the workers. I wonder if they knew in this factory that it is possible to fill barrels and sacks automatically by closed and adjustable fillers attached to the place where the powdered material comes from, and also to the barrel or sack to be filled.

Isolation and Separation of Dusty Processes. Wherever the formation of dust cannot be prevented, or where dust is formed only by one special process or in one special part or room of an industrial establishment, there is no need to fill all the rooms and the whole establishment with dust. The dusty process or the dusty room may and should be entirely isolated and separated from other processes and other parts of the building by dust-tight walls, par-titions and doors. This is an important method of prophylaxis in view of the fact that there are so many industrial establishments where dust is formed only in part of the building, or is only con-

---

* Report of the Director on Chemical Trades, New York State Factory Commission, Second Report, p. 481.

fined to one process.   Thus, for instance, in textile mills the preparing- and carding-room is the most dusty place, and there is no reason why it should not be entirely separated and isolated from other parts of the building, and the dust kept there and not let fill the other parts which are ordinarily free from dust.   This is also true of a great many other establishments where similar conditions prevail.

In a lead factory in Germany, which I inspected, the whole process of manufacture of lead carbonate was conducted by the wet process,

Danneberge and Quand, Berlin.

Local Exhaust of Dye Dust in a Paper Factory.

and there was no dust in the entire building.   A small amount of dry lead was also manufactured in this establishment.   This part of the process was carried on in an entirely separate building, and thus the lead-dust could do no harm to the workers in the other buildings.

Instead of separating the dusty process from the workers it is sometimes possible to separate the workers from the dusty process by glass partitions through which their work is carried on.   This is accomplished by enclosing the dusty process in one room, placing the workers outside of the room, and making openings in the glass partitions through which, by means of long-handled ladles or rakes, the workers mix and stir the dusty materials. The dust rising in the room is kept within it and the glass partitions prevent dust inhalation.

Removal of Dust. All industrial dusts may, can, and should be removed. The removal should be accomplished at the point of origin by a system of local exhaust-ventilation. The proper installation of an efficient system of local exhaust-ventilation for dust-removal is an important and very complicated engineering problem. The

A. Kündig, Zürich.

Local Dust Exhaust in a Carding Shop.   Textile Mill.

solution of this problem, with the theoretical calculations and practical mechanical installations, should be given into the hands of competent scientifically trained industrial ventilating engineers. It is to be regretted that as yet there is no very large contingent of such engineers in this country, although there are already a number of companies which make local dust-extraction their specialty. Abroad, this branch of engineering is greatly developed and there are thousands of engineers in this specialty, and a large number of firms confine their work to the installation and maintenance of dust-removing apparata.

A brief discussion will suffice to illustrate the methods of this important work. The factors to be considered are: (1) kind, character, value, and specific gravity of the dust to be removed; (2) the hoods; (3) the branch pipes and ducts; (4) the main pipe or duct; (5) the fans; (6) the motive power; (7) the disposal of the dust.

In all systems of dust-removal the size of the particles and the specific gravity of the dust must be known in order to determine the power necessary for its removal. It is also necessary to know whether the dust is constant or intermittent and whether it is produced in large or small quantities. The value of the dust is also of importance, in order to determine whether the dust should be collected and utilized, or otherwise disposed of. Some dusts are extremely valuable, and must be collected immediately at the point of origin; other dusts may be collected at the distal end of the dust-removal system.

The collection of the dust at its point of origin is not always a simple matter. Machines and processes are of such great variety that it is not always possible to adjust the primary collection apparatus of the dust-removal system. For the ordinary dusty processes or machines, hoods are constructed of wood or sheet metal, usually of the latter. The hood encloses or boxes-in the point where the dust originates, and the dust is then drawn into this hood through systems of pipes by fans operated by motive power. The proper construction and adjustment of the hoods is a science by itself. It is desirable that their construction shall not be too costly or too cumbrous; but it is necessary at the same time to have them envelope all dust-producing apparata and come in close contact with all places where dust originates. Wherever possible, dust-producing machines or processes should be entirely enclosed. With smaller machines this is not difficult. Thus, in grinding-machines it is a comparatively easy matter to enclose them and leave only a small part of the grinding-wheel exposed. This can also be done with other polishing- and buffing-wheels. It is more difficult with carding-machines in textile mills and with other machines of a large size.

Wherever the dust-producing machine or process is either so big that its enclosure would be too costly, too cumbersome, or otherwise impossible, or where the nature of the process is such that its hooding or enveloping is inconvenient or impossible, other means may be used for the first step in the local dust-removal. Thus, in rolls and calenders where dust is only produced at a certain point, it may not be necessary to enclose the whole roll or calender with a hood; but a suction pipe may be attached to the place on the outside of the rolls where the dust is being produced. In rag-sorting, wool-sorting, shoddy-sorting, etc., it is often possible to place the materials upon a wire-mesh grating under which the exhaust system works, and thus draws in the dust, without any special hood or cover.

In factories manufacturing drugs, colors and dyes, notably in the Beyer Chemical Works at Leverkussen, Germany, and in many other chemical factories in this country, I have seen girls weighing and mixing colors and chemicals sitting before a glass-covered table partitioned off for each worker, there being an opening into a pipe at the distal end of the table through which air is exhausted. Attempts have also been made to protect workers in front of dusty machines by having a powerful blast of air blown against the dust-forming part of the machine, thus directing the dust into the exhaust system.

The shape of the hood also depends upon whether the exhaust is upward or downward. It must always be shaped so that the refuse and dust is thrown directly to a point where it may be caught by the highest velocity of the air.

The branch ducts or pipes, usually made of sheet metal, which are attached to the hoods and conduct the dust into the main exhaust dust-pipe, are of importance as to construction, maintenance, size, diameter, internal surface, etc., etc. Pipes of large diameter and size are costly but present less friction and need less motive power for the exhaust of air and dust through them. Branch ducts should not be too small, however, because they then unduly increase the resistance and the cost of the motive power and impair efficiency of the exhaust system. Pipes should not be too long, for increase in length increases the resistance too and also the road by which the dust travels. It is best that pipes should be straight, without bends or angles, for nothing increases the resistance for air as such bends and angles. If bends are necessary, they should be not more than at angles between thirty and forty-five degrees.

The inner surface of the duct should be smooth, so that the dust will not adhere to the sides and surfaces and clog up the pipe. At certain intervals traps and handholes should be made in the pipes. The traps are made to catch the heavier dust which at times is not exhausted; while the handholes, which are covered, are for the purpose of permitting the cleaning of the pipes

Engineers have a rule that " the sum of the area of the branch

Courtesy Wm. C. Hanson   U. S. Dept. Labor, Bulletin 127

Sand-blasting Castings in Open Shed.

The helmet shown does not prevent the inhalation of fine steel, iron and brass dust.

pipes must not be greater than the area of the main pipe." Wherever installations are made for a local exhaust system, the probable additions to the machines which may be needed to be exhausted should be taken into consideration. It often happens in a machine-shop that only twenty or twenty-five machines are provided for with branch exhaust pipes, and the main pipe is constructed with a view to carry the amount of dust exhausted through these twenty-five branch pipes. When, however, ten, fifteen, or more, new machines are added, and each provided with branch pipes, the main pipe gets overloaded and the whole efficiency of the ventilating system is in peril. The size and length of the branch pipes, as well as of the main pipe, is an engineering problem which must be considered with every case.

The following rules as to the installation of pipes, etc., by proper ventilating exhausts are of interest:

" Never attach a branch at right angles to the main. Two branches should never enter the main directly opposite one another; also avoid the use of Y-branches, as the two currents in conflict retard the flow, sometimes causing the pipes to clog.

Elbows should have a radius in the throat twice the diameter of the pipe. For example, a 6-inch pipe should have a radius of 12 inches in the throat. There is no advantage in making the radius more than twice the diameter. A right-angle elbow in a 6-inch pipe offers as much resistance as a straight pipe of the same diameter 44 feet long. With a radius of half the diameter, it is equal to a straight pipe 15 feet long. With a radius of one diameter, it is equal to a straight pipe $5\frac{1}{2}$ feet long. With a radius of two diameters, it is equal to a straight pipe $2\frac{1}{4}$ feet long. By making the radius more than twice, the resistance begins to increase again until at six diameters it is equal to a straight pipe 3 feet long. This is due to the greater distance the air is under compression on one side of the pipe while making the turn.

Friction of the air traveling through the pipes is another and very essential point for consideration, and it must be determined in order to know the minimum speed at which the fan can be run. Careful experiments have shown that a length of round pipe from 62 to 72 times its diameter will produce friction equivalent to the velocity head, the shorter length applying to small pipes, because of the relatively greater resistance the roughness of the surface presents per unit of volume. In actual practice, it is customary to allow about 40 diameters, to compensate for branch tees, reducers, dents, etc. The refuse carried along by the air also increases the resistance somewhat." *

* F. R. Still: " Removal of Refuse and Waste by Fans and Blowers." Read at Semi-Annual Meeting, 1912, American Society of Heating and Ventilating Engineers.

The type of fan which is used for exhausting dust differs according to the work to be done. Only in comparatively small establishments with large pipes and with not too great amounts of dust may the propeller type of fan be used. As a rule, the resistance is too great for this type of fan and centrifugal fans are used almost exclusively. The type and size are of great importance, as is also the velocity of the revolutions of the fan. These matters must be calculated according to many factors which vary with each establishment.

If a series of exhaust pipes are connected with one fan, it is of great importance that the strength and velocity of the air-exhaust should be equal in all pipes; as it sometimes happens when the velocity is too great in one series or branch of pipes that the others will be left with an insufficient power to draw off all the dust.

There are a number of more or less ingenious methods of testing the velocity of the flow of air in the pipes, these devices ranging from anemometers to a simple smoke test. This latter is accomplished by burning paper and noticing the force of the drawing-in of the smoke from the burning paper into the opening of the pipe.

The motive power used for driving fans may be taken from the general motive power of the factory. Some manufacturers prefer to install special motors for the ventilating exhaust system, in order to determine the horse-power needed and the amount of power used up during a certain time, so as to be able to calculate the cost of the running of the ventilating system.

The method of disposal of the dust gathered through an exhaust ventilating system depends largely upon the character of the dust. Dust which may be utilized for burning purposes, such as wood dust, may be sent direct through the exhaust system into the furnaces. Dust may also be wetted and sprayed. When a factory is situated in isolated localities the dust may be sent through tall chimneys; while in thickly inhabited places the dust must be separated by various devices constructed for this purpose and then subjected to treatment, collected, and otherwise disposed of. Most separators use centrifugal force. The " cyclone " separator is an efficient means for collecting dust, and is used in a great number of industrial establishments.

It is sometimes necessary to have local removal of dust by portable apparatus without the installation of hoods, pipes, fans, etc. This is notably the case in cleaning type-cases in printing places, in removing dust from places for which it is difficult to provide a permanent local exhaust and in freeing machinery from accumulated dust. The cleaning of such dusty places by blowers, or by dry rags, brushes, and feather dusters is very harmful to health. There are at present a number of portable vacuum cleaning apparata, with instruments fitted for every special kind of cleaning.

Wherever an efficient local exhaust system of ventilation is installed, some means should also be provided for the incoming of a large amount of air; otherwise the exhaust of the air through the ventilating pipes will encounter a great deal of resistance, especially when the doors and windows of the room are tightly closed.

It is also necessary in every large plant where there is a system of exhaust ventilation to appoint an inspector or supervisor, so that the whole plant, the hoods, pipes, fans, blowers, and dust-separators, etc., should be frequently inspected and defects speedily remedied.

Protection of Workers. In spite of all the methods of preventing the formation of dust, of the separation of the dusty processes from the workers, and the best methods of local exhaust ventilation, there will be a certain amount of industrial dust, which is very difficult to prevent or remove. Whether there are any general preventive measures adopted or not, the workers should always be protected as much as possible against the action of dust.

The protection of workers against dust may be accomplished by the following measures: (1) cleanliness of the shop; (2) proper clothing; (3) facilities for washing and bathing; (4) respirators; (5) change of work; (6) medical examination; (7) medical supervision; (8) education.

It is unnecessary to dwell here upon the necessity for proper removal of dust and dirt from shops and factories and for an efficient system of cleaning of the walls, ceilings, floors, and other surfaces within the shop. This matter has already been referred to in previous chapters. Much depends upon the proper construction of the factories; still much more upon proper supervision by owners. In every large industrial establishment special persons should be designated for cleaning purposes. In all shops where a great deal of dust is deposited upon walls, girders, and other surfaces, this dust should be removed by the wet process, by the hose, if possible, or by portable vacuum cleaners. There is no sense in providing a local exhaust system of ventilation in an industrial plant for removing the dust from the machines and dusty processes, and at the same time leaving inches of dust upon girders, walls, floors, etc.

Workers in all dusty trades and processes should not wear their clothing which they bring from home, but should be provided by the owners of the establishment with clothing specially appropriate for their work. Different workers require some variation in the material and in the kind of the clothing worn. Wherever dry dust in abundance is produced, a smooth tight-meshed cotton cloth should be used for overalls. At times it is advantageous to have the surfaces treated with some material which makes them smooth and easily wiped off, so that the dust does not adhere, or if it does adhere, it can easily be washed off from the clothing. Overalls and clothing to be worn in dusty places should be well-fitting and cover the whole body. Attention must be paid especially to the head-covering, as the dust which falls upon the hair and head is difficult to clean. Tight-fitting caps are often worn by men and women, and one who takes one of these caps and shakes it may readily see the amount of dust which accumulates upon it during a day's work.

New York State Factory Commission.

Packer of Bleach or Chloride of Lime.

Wears several thicknesses of moistened white flannel over his mouth and draws breath only through this.

Wherever the dust is of an irritating character, gloves should be provided by the employer and worn by the employe. The mere provision of gloves does not always mean that they are being worn by the workers. The gloves which are usually provided are too large and fit so badly that workers are loth to wear them. They also claim that the wearing of gloves interferes much with their dexterity and the amount of work they can do. Owners should especially insist that gloves be worn in all dusty processes where dust is of a poisonous or irritating character.   A great many industries have their own peculiar uniforms and clothing which their workers habitually wear, and which were found by them after years of experience and practice to be the best fitted for the purpose. Thus, we find special uniforms worn by foundry workers, by chimney-sweeps, and many other groups of workers.   Reference has been made in a previous chapter to the necessity of wearing special-fitting shoes and boots in foundries.   This is also necessary in other trades where it is important to prevent dust from penetrating to the skin of the workers.

The necessity for providing washing facilities in all factories and workshops is especially patent in factories where much dust is produced, particularly dust of an irritating and poisonous character.   Mention has already been made of the need of proper wash-basins, supplied with warm water, of a supply of soap and towels, and also of the necessity for providing bathing facilities either in the form of shower-baths or tub-baths in such factories.

More necessary even than the provision of fixtures for washing and bathing is an intelligent supervision of the washing and bathing arrangements.   I have already more than once referred to the excellent practice of one large company in granting their employes from five to ten minutes extra time at the noon hour for washing up purposes, in providing a separate wash-room with a large number of wash-basins supplied with hot and cold water, soap, towels, and locker-rooms; and arranging for one or two of the foremen to supervise the washing arrangements and stand at the door of the wash-room to examine the hands of all those who are through with their ablutions, thus assuring a proper performance of this most necessary function.   Washing and bathing are good means of preventing many skin and other diseases which are due to irritation and penetration of dust particles.

The problem of preventing dust from entering the nose and mouth is a most difficult one.   There are trades and processes in which it seems to be impossible in the present state of science to prevent a large quantity of dust from being inhaled through the nose and mouth.   There are processes, like sandpapering walls and sand-blasting, in which it has been impossible to invent an adequate method of removing the dust and preventing the workers from inhaling it. In such, and similar cases, it is absolutely necessary for the worker to wear some kind of apparatus which, while permitting him to freely inspire and expire, would at the same time catch, filter, and make harmless the dust in which he works.

The number of respirators which have been devised for this purpose cannot be counted. Every one who studies the subject and every manager and foreman in a shop has his own invention. As a result, there are hundreds of different kinds of respirators, whose inventors insist that theirs is the best on the market. I have seen in the Charlottenburg Museum of Safety, in Berlin, all kinds of respirators, some of them as light as feathers, others weighing from twenty to thirty pounds.

Besides respirators, head-gears and oxygen-helmets are frequently used. Some of these arrangements look like divers' uniforms, and all of them are heavy, unsightly, and uncomfortable.

Workers, as a rule, strenuously object to the wearing of respirators. Their objections are that these respirators are unsightly, that they are uncomfortable, that they become instruments of torture, that they interfere with work, and especially that they interfere with comfortable breathing. One who sees a worker with a respirator cannot blame him for objecting to wearing it. All respirators are uncomfortable, because they obstruct expiration and inspiration, increase the amount of heat and moisture around the nose and mouth, dim eyeglasses, heat the surfaces around the nose, mouth, and chin, chafe the skin by the bands with which they are fastened, prevent the workers from speaking, giving orders, or answering the foremen, and generally are an unnatural and abnormal method of wearing what the workers call a " muzzle."

In some trades the workers cannot do without some kind of respirator, and at times they improvise their own, which they claim are better than those given to them by the employers. Thus, the bleach-workers (see page 432) usually wear when they go into the bleach chambers a " muzzle " of six or seven folds of flannel, through which they inspire, leaving expiration free. The bleach-workers claim that it takes a long time for a man to become habituated to the wearing of a muzzle and to be able to expire properly through the nose, while inspiring through the mouth. These muzzles are only worn from ten to fifteen minutes when within the bleach chambers. It is doubtful whether such muzzles could be worn for longer periods. In sand-blasting and sandpapering of painted surfaces at the Pullman Works in Illinois, all workers are compelled to use respirators, as per illustration, this order being very strict. I was told that a foreman who was found working without his respirator had been discharged.

The principal part of a respirator is the filtering material, which is designed to catch the dust and prevent it from being inhaled. Such filtering material is usually made of tight-meshed cotton, or other material; and the smaller the meshes are the better the respirator is for the purpose of catching dust, but the more difficult for breathing purposes. There are as yet very few respirators on the market which are free from all objections.

Cover's automatic rubber respirator is claimed to have excellent advantages for use in dusty trades, especially where poisonous gases and dusts are produced. It is provided with a closed and protected automatic ventilating valve which operates under all conditions, thus securing proper ventilation of the respirator and preventing breathing over and over again of the inhaled air. The filtering material and its arrangement in the respirator should be such that the air will be purified while passing through it. A fine damp sponge or a wet silk cloth are among the best known filtering materials for separating impurities from the air, and when these two valuable filtering materials are combined in their action, as they are in Cover's combination filter, it is claimed that it is  a difficult matter for smoke, fumes, and gases to pass the silk cloth in contact with the wet sponge. The respirator is simple and is small in size. Some workers object to the irritation of the skin by the rubber adhering to the face and the metallic click of the valve.

Change of Work. The human body has remarkable powers of recuperation and of self-protection. Only when the action of harmful influences is constant and very prolonged does the body succumb to them. Whenever there are trades or processes in which very much dust is produced, and which cannot be prevented for one or more reasons, it should be the cardinal principle of intelligent employers to make frequent changes in the work of their employes, to give them frequent rest periods, to take the workers away from the dusty trades for some time in the free air, so that the action of the dust is not too constant and the body can have a chance to readjust itself and recover from the injurious influences.

Physical Examination. The reason why so many workers succumb to the injurious effects of dust in the dusty trades, and why the percentage of fibroid and tubercular phthisis is so great, is because a number of workers enter these trades with a physical constitution already undermined by disease or bad habits, and are unfit to withstand the harmful influences in dusty trades. No one but robust, physically fit, and perfectly healthy persons should be allowed to take up any dangerous trade.

In order to prevent the influx of weak persons into dusty trades it is necessary to provide for a preliminary medical examination in all dusty establishments. Industrial efficiency is not an engineering problem alone; it is also a medical problem. The industrial establishment is badly equipped if it only consists of the technical engineer, mechanic, and superintendent. The human factor in an industrial establishment is of far greater importance than the machinery and the mechanical devices within the establishment. More important even than the testing of all machinery coming into the factory by the engineer and technical expert is the compulsory examination of all the human machines by properly qualified medical practitioners. A rigid physical examination of all employes should be a *sine qua non* in every industrial establishment. Only by such examination would the weak and physically unfit, the human derelicts, be excluded from industrial life. Only by such a practice would work in dusty trades become less dangerous and deadly, and the percentage of disease, especially of tuberculosis and occupational mortality, be reduced.

Physical examination of workers before entering the establishment is not sufficient. It is only the first step. The human machine as well as the mechanical engine needs not only to be tested when it comes into the establishment, but should be subjected to periodical tests and examinations. For this, a medical supervision of industry is necessary.

The time is surely not distant when every factory and workshop, no matter how large or small, will count among its superintendents not only mechanically and technically trained men, but also educated physicians. Workers, especially in dusty trades, should be subjected to periodical examinations every three months at least, if not oftener, their condition of health carefully noted, all the symptoms of incipient disease marked, and preventive measures taken to remove them from work which seems to be injurious, and to treat the initial symptoms in order to prevent further inroads of disease.

Medical supervision should not limit itself only to the preliminary and periodical medical examination of the employe, but should go further.   It should be properly equipped for acting in an educational capacity, for supervising not only the worker's health but also his habits, his mode of nutrition, his clothing, and for preventing the influences of improper home surroundings.   Medical supervision should also take over the function of educating the worker in the dangers of his trade, of instructing him in the risks of his occupation, and of teaching him all modes and methods of prevention.

CHAPTER X

INDUSTRIAL POISONS, GASES AND FUMES

THE risks of industrial life and the hazards of occupations described in the previous chapters are only a part of the dangers of trades. The accidents and the injuries arising from faulty construction, defective light and illumination, poor sanitation and ventilation, improper safeguarding of machinery and industrial dusts are, at least in the majority of cases, not inherent to all industry. There are many occupations, however, which have their specific dangers which at present seem to be unavoidable. These dangers cause injuries and lesions which are embraced under the general name of occupational diseases.

By occupational diseases are meant such groups of symptoms and pathological changes in the body as are due more or less directly to the occupation in which the worker is engaged.

Some of the occupational diseases and their causes are outside of the scope of this work. Among the diseases which will not be discussed are those caused by extreme variations in air pressure, such as *caisson* disease; those caused by over-fatigue, such as neuritis, " telegrapher's cramp," " shoemaker's spasm," etc.; those caused by specific infectious bacteria in industry, such as anthrax of the wool-sorters and hair-, bristle-, hide- and skin-workers; ankylostomiasis of miners and tunnel-workers; tetanus occurring among jute and other workers; glanders of those who attend horses, etc.; and many other industrial diseases. Only a limited number of occupational diseases and but a few of the dangerous trades will be discussed in this chapter.

I

THE POISONS, GASES AND FUMES AND THEIR EFFECTS

Extent of Dangers. Certain industries, trades and industrial establishments employ materials or processes which evolve toxic elements either in the form of dust or in the form of gases and fumes.

The industries and trades in which some dangerous elements are present are numerous. Poisonous materials are employed, or deleterious gases and fumes are evolved in most of the chemical trades, in the majority of the metal industries, in the textile industry and in many other trades.

The extent of occupational diseases cannot be determined for the reason that statistical data are very incomplete and that compulsory reporting of industrial poisoning and occupational diseases has only been recently enacted in a few states.

The First National Conference on Industrial Diseases held in Chicago in 1910 attempted to estimate the probable extent of industrial diseases in the United States. The estimate was that there were in 1910 approximately 13,400,000 cases of sickness due to industrial diseases, with a total of 284,750,000 days of sickness and a loss in wages of $366,107,145.*

In the memorial of this conference, the paucity of data on the subject of mortality and morbidity from occupational diseases is deplored and comparison is made with the better statistical data to be found in other countries, especially in Germany. Reference is also made in the memorial to the striking death rate from pulmonary tuberculosis among certain workers in the United States. The figures of the United States Census for 1908 are quoted which show that the proportion of deaths from tuberculosis of the lungs, among workers between the ages of 25 to 34, was, for printers and compositors 49.2 per cent, glass-workers 40.5 per cent, hatters 56.9 per cent, lead-workers, 52.2 per cent, marble- and stone-workers 41.1 per cent, and textile-workers 39.8 per cent.†

Without a system of state sickness insurance and with faulty methods of occupational designations and statistics, it is impossible to even guess at the extent of occupational diseases due to industrial poisons, gases and fumes in American industries. There is one group, however, the so-called chemical industries, from which some figures may be obtained. The range of the chemical industry is very wide and includes among its manufactures the making of acids, alkalies, drugs, dyes and related compounds. It also includes technically the smelting and refining of metals, manufacture of coke, glass, cement, rubber, glucose, chemical pulp fibre, fermented and distilled liquors, starch and sugar, finishing of textiles, tanning of leather, and many other processes of industrial activity.

* Memorial on Occupational Diseases, p. 3.
† Ibid., p. 13.

The United States Census of Manufactures for 1910 includes under the heading of chemical and allied products some 25 or 26 separate industries, from the manufacture of axle grease, baking and yeast powders, explosives and fertilizers, to the manufacture of soap, salt, starch and wood distillates. The Census gives the growth of the chemical industry in the United States as follows:

In 1900 there were 8820 establishments with 185,515 wage-earners; in 1910 there were 11,863 establishments with 242,961 wage-earners. The capital invested had increased for the ten years from $1,180,000 to $2,053,000, and the value of products had also doubled.*

The large increase in the chemical industry has also been followed by a very large increase in the extent of occupational diseases produced by this industry and in the increased number of persons suffering from industrial poisons, gases and fumes. This is true of the chemical industry abroad as well as in the United States.

Leymann found in one chemical establishment of 1000 workers, 285 cases of poisoning in a period of less than twenty-three years. Grandhomme found 122 cases of industrial poisoning in three years.† Schneider ‡ cites statistics from Austria in which the cases of occupational disease in the chemical industries exceeds all others by 137 per cent at certain age periods and at others by 50 to 91 per cent. He also quotes Weyl, who has shown an increase in cases of diseases in the chemical industry over all other industries of more than 120 per cent.

In certain white-lead factories, out of 580 persons insured there were 76.63 cases of sickness and 1430 days of sickness per hundred persons. In aniline dye factories the cases of sickness were 70.63 per cent with 1212 days of sickness for every hundred persons.§

There were reported in Great Britain in 1911, 755 cases of industrial poisoning besides 263 cases of lead poisoning which were separately reported among house painters and plumbers. Of these, 669 were cases of lead poisoning, 12 were due to mercury, none to phosphorus, 10 to arsenic and 64 to anthrax, an infectious disease. In 1912 there was a total of 656 cases reported besides 256 cases of lead poisoning reported under painters and

* Report of Director, Second Report of the N. Y. S. Factory Comm., p. 460.
† Rambousek, Gewerbliche Vergiftungen, p. 2.
‡ Gefahren der Arbeit in der chemischen Industrie, p. 13.
§ Ibid, p. 19.

plumbers. Of these 587 were due to lead poisoning, 17 to mercury, and 5 to arsenic.

In the United States only seven states have established laws for reporting of industrial poisons, and only very few poisons are reported. During the twelvemonth ending in 1913, 121 cases of industrial poisoning, including 21 fatal cases, were reported to the Labor Department of New York State. In the same period for the year previous 162 cases were reported with 11 fatal cases. Of the fatal cases 25 were from chronic lead poisoning, 5 from other lead poisoning.*

Classification. Many attempts have been made to enumerate and classify the various harmful substances used in modern industry. Such attempts, however, have invariably failed because of the multiplicity of the morbific agents and of the rapid changes in industrial life, especially in the development of chemical industries. Enormous strides have been made within the last ten or twenty years in all chemical processes, great secrets have been wrested from nature, innumerable inventions and discoveries have been made which have changed entire industrial processes; and new materials, products and processes are daily cropping out whose dangers and hazards it is difficult to estimate.

Nor is the classification of the various harmful substances an easy matter. Some of them are at times found in the form of dust and at other times in the form of gases or fumes. There is no distinct line of demarkation between poisons and gases. Some substances belong to several different chemical groups and a scientific classification either by the nature of the material, or by its form, or by the industry, or chemical group to which it belongs is extremely difficult.

The committee of experts of the International Association for Labor Legislation which was to make a classification of industrial poisons, confessed its inability to present a classification according to the harmfulness of the substances or to the branches of industry in which they are used. In their list of poisons which was prepared and later issued by the Department of Commerce and Labor, the enumeration and classification of the industrial poisons is according to alphabetical arrangement.

The following is a selection from the enumeration of the substances which is included in the list of industrial poisons.†

* Report of the Commissioner of Labor, New York State, 1913, p. 59.
† List of Industrial Poisons, Bulletin of Bureau of Labor, No. 100.

Substances	*Industries in which They Occur*
AMMONIA	Ovens, mirror-silvering industry, coating iron plate with tin zinc, manufacture of solidified ammonia, sulphide and chloride of ammonia. sal-ammoniac, manufacture of carbonate of soda, dyeing industry, manufacture of bone-black, varnish and lacquer manufacture, tanning, manufacture of ice and refrigeration plants.
ANILINE AND ANILINE COLORS	Manufacture of aniline and its derivatives as well as of aniline dyes, manufacture of photographic materials, aniline dye factories, dye houses, manufacture of explosives, etc.
ANTIMONY AND COMPOUNDS	Preparation of type and white metal, fireworks, paints, pottery glazes, red rubber, tartar emetic, burnishing of rifle barrels and steel ware, manufacture of antimony wares, stereotype metal, ammunition factories, remelting of old and scrap metal, paint making, etc.
ARSENIC AND COMPOUNDS	Mining, manufacture of glass, colored chalks, aniline and other dyes, wall paper, oil cloth, artificial flowers, tanning, fur curing, felt-hat making, pottery glazing, making artificial stones, paints, taxidermy, preparation of organic dye stuffs, etc.
BENZINE AND BENZOL	Benzine distillation, chemical cleaning plants, removal of fat from bones, for solvents, lacquer, varnish and India rubber industries, waterproof materials, dye works, illuminating- and water-gas factories, etc.
BRASS AND ITS COMPOUNDS	In bronze, bronzing and allied industries.
CARBON MONOXIDE	In illuminating gas, water-gas and producing-gas manufacture, coal mines, blast furnaces, coke ovens, smelting furnaces, gas machines, foundries and where-

Substances	*Industries in which They Occur*
	ever illuminating gas is used, or heating with coal is done without special precautions.
CARBON BISULPHIDE	Extraction of fats and oils, sulphur from gas-washing materials, vulcanization of rubber, preparation of chlorine compounds, dissolving of fats and treating rags, bones and raw materials, oil factories, etc.
CHLORINE	Manufacture of chlorine, chloride of lime, organic chlorine, bleacheries, paper mills, laundries, ironing, manufacture of chlorine disinfectants, chloroform, etc.
CHROMIUM	Manufacture of chrome steel, mineral tanning, bleaching, chrome colors, oxidizing agent in the card-color industry, manufacture of Swedish matches, bleaching, fats, oil and wax, staining of wood, etc.
HYDROCHLORIC ACID	Potteries, enameling, manufacture of acid, glass factories, manufacture of chloride, artificial fertilizers, bleaching, cotton-print works, India rubber, etc.
LEAD, ALLOYS, COMPOUNDS, ETC.	In lead mining, manufacture of various lead products, in preparation of lead pigments, in pottery glazing, painting, varnishing and in hundreds of different processes in which lead or its compounds are used in one form or another.
MERCURY	Mining, smelting, extraction of gold and silver, making of mirrors, thermometers, barometers and other scientific instruments, photography, taxidermy, artificial flowers, antiseptics, rubber industry, etc.
METHYL ALCOHOL	In distillation of wood and refining, in varnishes, lacquers, polishes, perfumes, in denatured alcohol, in the production of coal tar colors and pharmaceutical prep-

Substances	*Industries in which They Occur*
	arations, in electroplating, polishing and many other processes.
NITRO-BENZOL	In coal-tar color industry, perfumery, soap factories, pharmaceutical laboratories, etc.
NITRO-GLYCERINE	Manufacture of explosives, use of dynamite.
NITROUS GASES	In manufacture of nitric acid, in electroplating, in metal etching and refining, manufacture of celluloid, sulphuric acid, aniline colors, etc.
PHOSPHORUS	In manufacture of phosphorus, and matches.
SULPHUR, SULPHUR CHLORIDE, SULPHUR DIOXIDE, SULPHUR HYDROGEN, SULPHURIC ACID	In manufacture of sulphur, in roasting of sulphur-bearing ores, in manufacture of sulphuric acid, and in many industries where one or more of these materials are used.

For a fuller list see Bulletin 100, U. S. Dept. Labor, or Dr. W. G. Thompson's book on " Occupational Diseases."

The Effects and Results of Industrial Poisons. Of the many workers exposed to the action of industrial poisons, gases and fumes, not all are affected alike by these toxic agents. A great number of the workers in these trades seem to be entirely immune and do not suffer at all. Other workers succumb to the effects of these toxic agents after but a brief exposure. A prolonged exposure to the action of the poisons seems to be necessary before other workers are affected, if at all. Observation and experience have demonstrated that there are workers who are extremely susceptible to industrial poisons, and, on the other hand, that many of them seem to be very tolerant to their effects.

Numerous examples are cited of persons working daily for many years in places where they are at all times exposed to lead poison who have entirely escaped the effect of this poison. At a hearing of the New York State Factory Commission at Niagara Falls, one of the companies, in whose plant many cases of lead poisoning were found by the agents of the Commission, tried to disprove the evidence by presenting affidavits made by employes who claimed that they had worked for over thirty years in the establishment and never had an attack of lead poisoning. On inspection of various establishments in the dangerous trades one often meets workers who have been exposed to the dangers of poisons, gases and fumes for from ten to twenty and more years, and who deny to have ever been affected by their work.   In a factory where workers were packing Paris green without any precautions whatever and where the air was full of arsenical dust, I found a worker who has worked at this process for ten years without any seeming effect upon his health.   Another man who came into the factory and worked for only two hours had an attack of acute arsenic poisoning from which he died within a week.

Legge and Goadby cite the case of two brothers working in one shift of men, who developed lead poisoning, although no other persons in the shift showed any signs of it.   In another factory three sons, two daughters and a father, suffered from lead poisoning within a period of four years.   Italians show considerably less susceptibility to lead poisoning than English workers as long as they adhere to their own national diet; but as soon as they become addicted to alcohol, the resistance to lead poisoning rapidly diminishes.*

These and many other cases which could be cited demonstrate the fact of tolerance existing among workers to poisons and also of the extreme susceptibility of other workers.

Certain factors such as age, sex, etc., have an important bearing upon the relative tolerance and susceptibility of persons to the effect of poisons.   Undoubtedly children and minors are more liable to industrial poisoning than adults.   Hence, the unanimity in the legislation of various countries in prohibiting the work of young persons in all factories where certain industrial poisons are employed.   Women are also said to be more susceptible to the effects of industrial poisons than males.   According to Legge and Goadby,† females are, at least twice, and probably three times, as susceptible to lead poisoning as males.   The liability of women working in lead factories to abortions and miscarriages is conceded by all writers on the subject.

Other persons who are extremely susceptible to the effect of industrial poisons are those suffering from anaemia, from diseases of the excretory organs, from constipation, from nephritis, enteroptosis, general weakness of the constitution, digestive diseases, tuberculosis, cardiac trouble, neurasthenia, epilepsy and

* Lead Poisoning and Lead Absorption, p. 30.
† Ibid, p. 42.

Courtesy Wm. C. Hanson, U. S. Dept. Labor, Bulletin 127.

Removing Lead from Oven into Metal Pan.
The Workman is Unprotected against Lead Dust and Heat.

nervous diseases. Alcoholics are especially susceptible to lead poisoning.*

The mode of entrance into the system of an industrial poison differs with the character of the poison as well as the form in which it appears, i.e., whether as a dust or gas or fume. Some poisons are absorbed through the unbroken skin; most of them are absorbed through the digestive organs either by swallowing the poisonous dust or by getting the poisonous dust and particles through food contaminated with poisonous materials and dusts. Others affect the organism by inhalation of the gases and fumes. According to Teleky, Kurschmann and other German scientists, lead is never absorbed through the unbroken skin. On the other hand, it has been shown that certain drugs applied to the skin produced the effect of these poisons. This is especially the case with mercury and other drugs. The mode of entrance may differ not only according to each poisonous element, but also according to the individual susceptibility of the worker.

The season of the year is also said to have an influence upon the effect of lead; and lead poisoning is said to be more serious in winter than in summer. Professor Thompson quotes Laureck, who claims that 71 per cent of cases arise in winter and 29 per cent in summer in Austria. On the other hand, he cites several French authors, who claim that in France lead poisoning is twice as common in summer as in the other seasons. The claim is also made that chewing tobacco leads to lead poisoning because of its liability to be contaminated with lead.†

Rambousek classifies industrial poisons according to their effects as follows:

(1) Poisons which act superficially. They are the poisons which cause in the organs which they reach gross anatomical lesions, irritations, corrosions, etc. To this class belong irritant and corrosive poisons.

(2) Blood poisons. Those poisons which are absorbed by the blood and which produce important changes in it.

(3) Poisons with definite internal action—so-called remote or specific effect. To this class belong the poisons which after being absorbed into the system act upon the definite organs and tissues in a specific manner. (Nerve poisons, heart poisons, etc.)‡

* L. Teleky: Die Aerztliche Ueberwachung und Begutachtung der in Bleibtreiben beschäftigten Arbeiter, p. 22.
† W. Gilman Thompson: The Occupational Diseases, p. 217.
‡ J. Rambousek: Industrial Poisoning, p. 158.

Effects and Symptoms of Lead Poisoning. Lead toxaemias are either acute or chronic. The initial symptoms are pallor of the skin, general lassitude, loss of appetite, nausea, constipation, or constipation alternating with diarrhoea. Anaemia, less than 90 per cent hemoglobin on the Talquist instrument, a wasting of the subcutaneous fat, first noticed in the infra-orbital region, are some of the early manifestations of lead poisoning. Another manifestation which may not appear early in the history is the so-called blue line on the gums which appears as a dark, blackish incrusta-

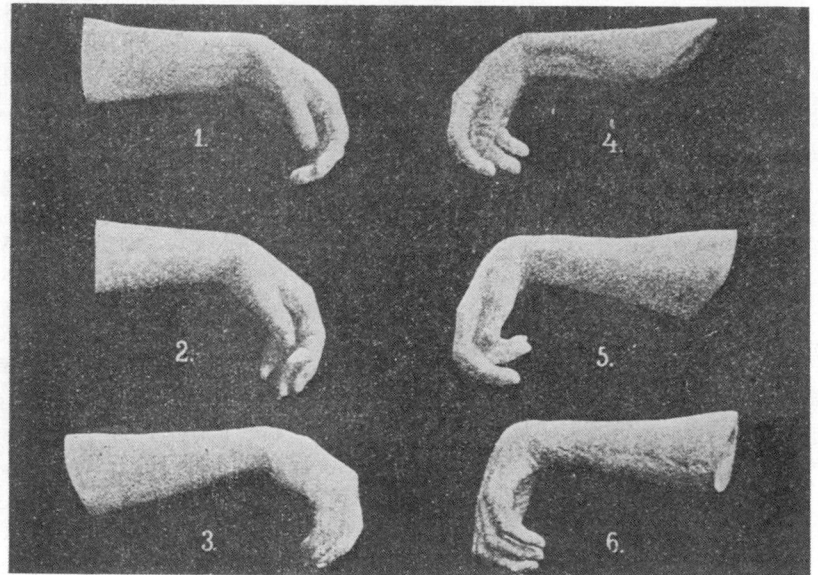

J. Rambousek " Gewerbliche Vergiftungen."

Various Types of Wrist-drop among Hungarian Potters.

tion on the edges of the gums, especially in persons who suffer from neglected and bad teeth. Abdominal colic, radiating from the navel to the sides, pains in the joints, muscles and in the back, general nervousness, persistent headaches, dull mentality, appear either early or later in the history of the case. Arthritis, paralysis of certain muscles, wrist drop and other paralyses appear later, as well as evidence of effects upon the secretory, nervous, vascular systems of the body. Loss of weight is usually present in many cases of lead poisoning, at times also fever.

Chronic lead poisoning manifests itself in severe recurrent

headaches, in defective vision, in peripheral neuritis, in the various lead palsies and, sometimes, in temporary or permanent blindness.

Effects and Symptoms of Arsenic Poisoning. Arsenical poisoning by ingestion or through inhalation of arsenical fumes has been known to cause acute poisoning and death. The effects of chronic arsenical poisoning are shown at first upon the gastro-intestinal organs and later upon the nervous system. The first symptoms are nausea, vomiting, loss of appetite and diarrhea. General gastro-intestinal disturbances may also be accompanied by local affections of the eyes, also by ulcers of the nose, mouth, hands and feet. The later effects on the nervous system show themselves in multiple neuritis and paralysis in the extremities.

Effects and Symptoms of Mercurial Poisoning. Mercurial poisoning is shown at first by extreme paleness, loss of weight, general weakness, headache, loss of muscular power, muscular pains, sleeplessness, a sallow complexion, metallic taste in the mouth, fetid breath, at times vomiting and diarrhea, inflammation of the gums, "stomatitis" and salivation, and later in muscular tremor of the limbs and facial muscles, rolling of the eyes from side to side, in tremors, a staggering and drunken gait, and a general loss of mental and muscular energy.

Effects and Symptoms of Phosphorus Poisoning. The symptoms of chronic phosphorus poisoning are loss of appetite, pallor of the skin, diarrhea, bronchitis and gastric disorders. The most important effect of phosphorus poisoning is a painful subacute and chronic inflammation of the bones of the jaw, which usually starts with the roots of decayed teeth and results in final necrosis of parts or the whole of the jaw and may sometimes result in total loss of the lower or upper jaw.

Effects and Symptoms of Chrome Poisoning. The principal effects of chronic chrome poisoning are observed upon the skin in the formation of chrome ulcers in the nose and upon various parts of the skin. The ulcers are rarely superficial, but are usually perforating and may be seen in the nose of chrome-workers not at great distance from the nostrils. Some inflammation may also be seen upon the mucous membrane of the mouth and throat. All chrome-workers suffer from nasal catarrh, a great many from ulceration and a large number from perforation. Out of 176 chrome-workers, 126 were found to be suffering from perforation of the nasal septum, 20 with ulceration, and only 30 had a normal septum.*

* Thompson: Occupational Diseases, p. 184.

Effects of Various Gases, Fumes, Acids and Alkalies. The effects of working in industrial establishments where chemical acids are being manufactured or worked with, or where alkali compounds are manufactured, and in all places where poisonous gases or fumes such as ammonia, carbon monoxide, chlorine gas, bromine, hydrocyanic gas or benzine are produced, vary according to the nature of the agent, the quantity absorbed and to various other factors. Some of these deleterious agents act simply as corrosives or irritants upon the skin, cause burns, sores and erosions, or injure the delicate mucous membrane of the eyes, nose and throat with which they come in contact. Others affect the worker upon being inhaled; A number of the gases and fumes may also be absorbed by the blood and cause acute or chronic intoxications, some of which may result in death.

II

SOME OF THE DANGEROUS TRADES

Of the large number of so-called dangerous trades, I shall discuss here only one or two of the more dangerous lead trades, several trades in which arsenic and mercury occur, and establishments in which alkalies and chemical acids are manufactured.

The Dangerous Lead Trades. Lead poisoning occurs in so many trades that it is difficult to even enumerate all of them. Layet gives a list of 111 processes in which lead or its salts are being employed in France. Sir Thomas Oliver states that lead is used in not less than 138 industries. Professor W. Gilman Thompson gives in his list of important lead trades 86 industries in which lead is used.

From the list of the reported cases of industrial poisoning in various countries, it appears that by far the largest number are due to lead. Indeed, they represent from 85 to 90 per cent of all the cases of industrial poisoning. With the present lack of diagnostic skill among general medical practitioners, with the laxity of the reporting laws, and the absence of such laws in many states the number of lead-poisoning cases must be much greater and cannot be definitely determined. In Great Britain there were about 7000 cases of lead poisoning reported in eighteen industries in the course of ten years from 1900 to 1910. When Dr. E. E. Pratt began to make an examination for the New York State Factory

Commission in 1911, he found no less than 376 cases of lead poisoning recorded in New York City alone in the years between 1909 and 1911. The Illinois Commission on Industrial Diseases found 640 cases of plumbism in that state in 1910. In an investigation of lead poisoning in Perth Amboy in 1910, records of 94 cases were supplied by a single physician. Dr. Hamilton reports that she found lead poisoning in 33 out of 56 factories in the State of Illinois.*

Manufacture of White Lead. A large number of cases of lead

New York State Factory Commission.

Stripping the Corroding Beds in a White-lead Factory. A Very Dusty and Dangerous Operation. Workmen not Protected by Respirators.

poisoning is found in the manufacture of white lead used for paints. There are several processes of manufacture of white lead. The Dutch process, which is the oldest process in use, is mostly employed in the United States and in England. The chamber process is used extensively in Germany. There are also several quick or " precipitate " methods of manufacturing carbonate of lead, which are employed in a limited number of factories in the United States and abroad.

* The Occupational Diseases, Dr. W. Gilman Thompson, p. 204.

The first process of manufacturing white lead is that of casting buckles or transforming the pig lead arriving into the plants into small thin disks of various shapes. In this country this is done by machinery and the buckles are semicircular and perforated. In England, I have seen the same process done by hand instead of machinery, and instead of small buckles there are cast flat plates about 4 by 12 inches with one-half dozen holes punched through them.

New York State Factory Commission.

An Unprotected Worker Stripping the Corroding Beds.

In the Dutch process the transformation of the lead buckles into white lead is done in a so-called corroding bed. These beds are housed in a large structure tightly enclosed on all sides, with only a few small windows near the roof. The floor of a bed is about 20 by 20 and is covered with a layer of tan bark to a thickness of about 14 inches. On this are placed, as closely as possible, earthenware jars containing about $2\frac{1}{2}$ per cent of acetic acid solution. The jars are made so that the upper part is much wider than the lower part, and the lead buckles are placed in these jars above the acetic acid, so that they cannot enter the acid. Boards are placed upon the jars which are covered with a layer of tan bark and the same process is repeated until the bed is filled to a height of about twenty feet. Here the lead buckles remain for about from ninety to one hundred days. The temperature within the sheds reaches from 150 to 180° F. When it is thought that the lead has been corroded and transformed into lead carbonate the beds are "stripped"; that is, the workers take off the layers of board from the top, remove the tan bark and expose the parts full of the lead buckles, which by this time have become corroded and present a brittle white appearance. The men take out the brittle buckles, load them into barrels or baskets and send them to be further acted upon in the other parts of the establishment, where the fully corroded buckles are separated from those in which metallic lead still remains, and where the carbonate of lead is subjected to further action.

In the chamber process, which is practically the only process used in Germany, and which is said also to be used in one factory in England, the lead is cast into long, thin strips which then are hung upon bars in a large chamber, under which are placed tubs, producing carbonic acid gas and acetic acid vapor, which corrodes the lead strips, transforming them into lead carbonate. This process takes from eight to ten weeks. Most of the metal strips, after full corrosion, fall down to the floors. In order to remove the corroded and partly corroded strips the workers enter the chambers, which are close and dark and full of lead dust in spite of their wetting with streams of water.

There are a number of patented quick, or "precipitate" processes for the manufacture of white lead. In a factory which I inspected near Frankfort a.M., belonging to Dr. Kalkoff, the metallic lead was cast and passed through a very fine meshed sieve, the lead coming out in long, thin threads, which were then put into drums and cylinders, where they were exposed to the action of acetic acid and carbonic acid gas. By this process the metallic lead was transformed into lead carbonate within a very short time —less than forty-eight hours. The carbonate of lead is taken out from the cylinder in a moist state and is packed into barrels without danger to the workers.

In the further work of separating, grinding and mixing the white lead which is received from the stripping beds, there are several processes which are extremely dusty. In all of these the workers come in close contact with the lead, which is deposited upon their clothes, hands and other body surfaces.

Other Lead Trades.   Other important trades in which there is
much danger from lead poisoning are potteries, tile works, manufacture of porcelain enameled sanitary ware, and the painting
and printing trades.

Dr. Alice Hamilton has shown that compared with British
potteries, American potteries with less than one-half the work-
people show almost twice as many cases of lead poisoning.   Among
796 men in the white-ware potteries, 60 cases of lead poisoning

New York State Factory Commission.

Unsuccessful Attempts by the Workers to Protect Themselves against Poisonous
Dust while Stripping the Corroding Beds in a White-lead Factory.

were found to have occurred during the two years 1910–1911, 39
of which occurred during the latter year.   Among the 150 women
workers there were 43 cases, 29 occurring during 1911.   A single
local of the Dipper's Union which gave accurate records of 85 men
for one year showed that 13 had acute lead poisoning during that
year.   Taking all the men and women employed in these three
industries, viz., white-ware, potteries, and tile works, it was found
that among 1100 men there were 87 cases of lead poisoning in a
single year, or one for every 12 or 13 employed, and among the
393 women 57 cases, or one for every 7 women employed.   In the

fourth industry, the porcelain enameling of iron hollow ware, 309 cases of lead poisoning were found to have occurred in ten factories studied within two years' time.*

The causes of lead poisoning in the pottery trades are the lead ingredients, of which the glazes are partly composed. The most dangerous process is that of mixing the glaze, applying it to the ware and then removing the excess of the glaze from the ware, handling the ware while the glaze is still wet, decorating and paint-

New York State Factory Commission.

Filling Barrels with Lead Litharge.

ing the ware and also sweeping the rooms in which the glaze has been handled. Much of the glaze is without lead and is harmless. In a large percentage, however, of the various pottery wares lead glazes are used. According to Dr. Hamilton, in most of the glazes the amount of lead used is under 20 per cent, and only in very few of the factories she investigated did the percentage of lead exceed 20. In certain tile works, the percentage of lead in the glaze ranges from 40 to 60.†

* Alice Hamilton: Lead Poisoning in Potteries, Tile Works, Porcelain Enameled Sanitary Ware Factories, Bull. U. S. Bur. of Labor, No. 104, pp. 8-9.
    † Ibid, p. 13.

In these industries the workmen, besides being exposed to lead poisoning, also inhale much mineral dust and suffer from the effect of great heat in the firing of the enamels.

Painting Trade. A large amount of lead poisoning is found among workers painting the inside and outside of buildings, coaches, automobiles, tanks, furniture, etc. Prof. Teleky found in one firm employing 114 painters no less than 56 cases of lead poisoning, or 49.12 per cent, and his figures show that the percentage of lead poisoning among painters in Vienna is about the same through-

New York State Factory Commission.

Lead Refining. Pot of Lead Drawn from the "Sweater" from which the Caster is Ladling Molten Lead.

out the city. He has also shown that since the prohibition in Vienna of using lead paint for interior work, the number of cases of lead poisoning among the painters has greatly decreased.*

According to statistics published by the Prudential Insurance Co., the mortality from lead poisoning among painters is very low—42 out of 2743 cases. According to the figures of the Illinois Commission on Occupational Diseases, of the 587 cases of industrial lead poisoning occurring between 1908 and 1910 exclusive, 27 per cent were among painters. Out of 119 cases of industrial

* Bericht über die Bleivergiftung unter den Anstreichern, Lackierern und Malern in Wien, Dr. Ludwig Teleky.

poisoning found by Dr. E. Pratt in 1912, in N. Y. City, 42 were among painters. Dr. Hayhurst made an examination of 100 painters for evidence of lead poisoning and the result of this examination is published in Dr. Hamilton's report on the hygiene of the painters' trade.* According to this report there were no cases of acute plumbism, but there were indications of chronic plumbism in at least 59 cases.

It is probable that only very few cases of the lead poisoning among painters came to note in hospital records and in the reports of the Labor Department. Some of the symptoms of lead poisoning among painters, especially such as colic, are not attended to by the employes, or are not properly diagnosed by practitioners to whom the painters apply for treatment.

Lead poisoning in the painting trade is caused by handling paints in which there is a certain amount of white lead or other pigments which contain lead. In the mixing of the dry lead, the grinding of lead with linseed oil, considerable dust is inhaled by the worker. Much more dangerous, however, is the process of sandpapering of painted surfaces, during which process a great deal of dried lead paint is being inhaled by the worker. This is probably the most dangerous part of the painter's work.

Of the various lead salts which are used in paints, red lead is said to be more dangerous than white lead in a dry state. In other forms, white lead is said to be more dangerous than red lead. Lead sulphate when used as a substitute for carbonate is also said to be quite dangerous.

Printing Trade. The dangers of lead poisoning in the printing trade among compositors and stereotypers have been described in many monographs and reports in this and other countries. Hand compositors handle the lead types. There is a great deal of dust in the cleaning of the lead type cases, and linotype-machine operators also handle much of the lead. Monotype operators in the casting room are also subject to lead fumes.

The diseases to which printers are specially subject are plumbism and pulmonary tuberculosis. According to Sommerfeld, "We but rarely meet acute lead poisoning among printers. As a rule, the intoxication is very gradual and insidious. The disease never begins with distinct diagnostic signs, but rather with general reduction in health, especially disturbances of the digestion." The substitution of machine for hand composition does not seem

* Bull. Bureau of Labor Stat, No. 120, p. 51.

to have improved the health conditions of the workers, and as Ducrot says, "The suppression of hand composition and its replacement by machine composition has not reduced the danger; while in Holland they have come to the conclusion that the type-setting machine has increased the dangers of lead poisoning.*

There is very much dust in all printing shops and the lead contents of this dust are quite considerable. Professor Steingrabe analyzed the dust in a printing shop and found it contained in some places 43.16 per cent of lead.†

New York State Factory Commission.

Lead Oxidizing Furnace.   Mechanical Type; Discharging the Furnace.

Trades in which Workers are Exposed to Arsenical Poisoning. Arsenic is used in a great many trades and arts and a large number of workers are exposed to the effects of this virulent poison. Dr. Rogers in his report to the New York State Factory Commission states that there is danger to the worker from arsenical poisoning in the following occupations: furriers, manufacture of candles and wax, ornaments, manufacture of japanned goods, manufacture of carpets, fancy bookbinding, preservation of wood, manufacture

* Beyer: Die Volkswirthschaftliche und Sozialpolitsche Bedeutung der Einführung der Setz-machine im Buchdruckgewerbe. p. 134.
† Oliver: Bulletin Bureau of Labor, p. 69.

MASS. STATE BOARD OF HEALTH

Courtesy Wm. C. Hanson, U. S. Dept. of Labor, Bulletin No. 12.

Lead Working in the Manufacture of Storage Batteries.

In Mixing Red Oxide of Lead and Litharge, Employes are Exposed to Lead Poisoning. The Employe Shown was Wearing a Respirator, but was not Willing to wear Long Gloves.

of gloves, manufacture of sheep dip, electroplating, lithographing and bronzing, manufacture of artificial leather, manufacture of oil cloth and linoleum, manufacture of cut glass, manufacture of hat linings, manufacture of beer, soaking of silk cocoon, and enameling.

The results of their investigations were summarized by Rogers and Vogt as follows:

" Arsenic and its compounds are powerful poisons, and their use in the industries is attended with danger to health of workers exposed to them.

" Poisoning may occur accidentally through the use of material which, unknown to the worker, contains arsenic as an impurity.

" Poisoning may occur through the handling of, or exposure to the dust of arsenic or its compounds.

" The form of poisoning most seen is that limited to local lesions of the exposed portions of the body (hands and face), and to the mucous membranes of the nose.

" The greatest danger exists in industries devoted to the manufacture of Paris green and Vienna green.

" Danger exists in the following industries: Paint works; plant vermin exterminator; glass works, other than bottle and window glass; artificial leather and oilcloth; electroplating; taxidermy; rubber goods, other than for insulating purposes.

" In a number of industries there is danger of a mixed poisoning, which is liable to render a proper diagnosis difficult.

" The majority of the workers are unaware of the poisonous nature of the material handled, and where precautions are taken it is only because lead compounds are also used." *

In my investigations of chemical factories in the United States I have come across several places where arsenic was used in the manufacture of Paris green in which no protection whatever was given the workers in the process of grinding, mixing, weighing and packing of the product in small paper packages. Foreign labor was exclusively used in one of the factories and there were records of several cases of sudden death and of numerous cases of chronic arsenical poisoning which caused temporary or permanent disability. The same kind of factories investigated abroad in several places in Germany were found to use very great precautions. The workers were protected by special clothing and were obliged to wear respirators; the processes of mixing, drying and weighing

---

* Second Report of the Factory Investigating Commission, 1913, Vol. II, p. 1161.

were practically automatic and there was very little dust or chance for the worker to be contaminated by it.

Mercury. In addition to miners of quicksilver the danger of mercury poisoning is great in the following industries: the silvering of mirrors, making of barometers, thermometers and other instruments where mercury is employed, making of electric light bulbs in which a vacuum is produced by mercurial pumps, making electric meters, antiseptics, corrosive sublimate, rubber manufac-

New York State Factory Commission.

Paris Green Factory: Automatic Packing Machines for Filling Small
Packages with Paris Green.

ture, hair dyes and cosmetics, bronzing, sole stitching of shoes by the Blake machine, the manufacture of felt hats, and the manufacture of felt from skins.

The illustrations on pages 415 and 418 are from a factory which I inspected, in which the hair is scraped from the skins of hares and rabbits imported from abroad, manufactured into felt and sold to hat manufacturers. In this factory, the bundles of skins from rabbits, nutria, hares, etc., are opened, sorted and the hair is then clipped by machine. The fur is then brushed over with a solution of silver nitrate from 10 to 20 per cent, this process being called

carotting. The skins are then dried on trays in ovens at a high
temperature and then are cut by machines to rip off the skins.
The 30 to 40 workers at " carotting " were all Greeks. They stand
all day at their benches and dip their brushes in the solution of
nitrate of mercury. The temperature in the room must be not
less than 70° F. and there is considerable volatilization of the
mercury, especially near the drying room and when the workers
carry the pelts from the drying-room to the other rooms in the
factory.

The industries where workers are exposed to mercury were
studied by Mrs. Lindon W. Bates and published in her report
issued in 1912. In several factories manufacturing mirrors in
New York State no mercury was used in the process of silvering
mirrors, silver nitrate being used instead, which is said to give just
as good results.

Professor Thompson quotes Dr. Tylecote of England, who
reported 20 cases of industrial mercurial poisoning, chiefly among
hatters, who presented tremor of the hands and arms and blackening
of the teeth with gingivitis.* The investigations of Mrs. Bates
and of Dr. Rogers in 1911–1912 cover a study of 122 cases of
mercurial poisoning in the felt hat manufacture.

Phosphorus Poisoning. Since the practical prohibition by
the United States of the use of white or yellow phosphorus in the
manufacture of matches, the subject of poisoning among phos-
phorus-workers has lost the great importance which it had until then.
As a matter of fact, only a comparatively small number of workers
were exposed to danger from this industrial poison, and it is
expected that the international prohibition of the use of poisonous
phosphorus in matches will eliminate this poison from industry.
In a factory manufacturing phosphorus which I inspected in Niagara Falls I was struck with the very careless way the workers were
handling this dangerous product, showing how familiarity with
the materials produced contempt for their dangers. The workers
in this factory were handling with seeming indifference solid phosphorus sticks which were fuming and burning their fingers. The
inspection was made just prior to the going into effect of the law
taxing white phosphorus out of manufacture.

The Manufacture of Acids and Alkalies. There is considerable
danger to workers in the branches of the chemical industry in which
commercial acids such as sulphuric, hydrochloric, nitric, acetic

---

* Occupational Diseases, Thompson, p. 289.

and hydrofluoric, and also alkalies, such as sodium, potassium and their products and by-products, caustic soda, caustic potash, bleach powders, etc., are manufactured.

The dangers which arise in the manufacture of these products come from the gases and fumes evolved in the various procésses, such gases and fumes being given off at times in such quantities that workers are sometimes killed by their inhalation or absorption. Besides the possible fatal effect of concentrated doses of these gases and fumes, the workers may be affected with chronic blood

New York State Factory Commission.

Putting Paris Green into the Bolter.

or other diseases, are exposed to the irritant action of many of these elements upon the skin, eyes, and respiratory tract, and are also frequently subjected to acid burns which are apt to result in permanent disfigurement and disability.

During the summer of 1912, while directing the general investigations of the New York State Factory Commission, I made an inspectorial tour through New York and other states accompanied by Dr. Charles F. McKenna, and inspected a large number of chemical factories, especially those where commercial acids and alkalies were manufactured. The results of the investigations have been embodied in my report on the chemical trades and in the report of Dr. McKenna on the manufacture and use of commercial acids. The impression which remained with us after a study of the conditions was that very little was being done by the owners and manufacturers to remove the dangers to workers which are so prevalent in these industries.

The general conditions of manufacture of commercial acids and alkalies were found defective in many respects. The build-

New York State Factory Commission.

Filling a Barrel with Paris Green.

Workers Wear Special Overalls, Gloves, Goggles and Linen Cloths Covering Nose, Mouth and Throat.

ings were mostly wooden structures, of flimsy construction, and often entirely unfit for the purposes for which they were used. Serious defects were found in the matter of lighting, illumination, ventilation and sanitation of these factories, as have been described in detail in the reports mentioned.

What interested us most, however, was the absence of any safeguards against specific dangers to workers in these industries, such as dust-removing apparata, or arrangements for removing the deadly gases and fumes evolved in many of the processes;

the neglect to provide the workers with means of protection; the large number of foreigners and unskilled workers in these industries, and the total ignorance of the workers as to the risks and dangers which they met daily, and their extreme carelessness to their dangerous surroundings.

In very few shops did we find any precautions taken during the firing and tending of the furnaces in which ores were being burned and from which gases and fumes were allowed to escape, in the mixing of dangerous materials and ingredients, in the large amounts of dust which were allowed to fill the air of the rooms, in the careless handling of acids and other dangerous liquids, in the carelessness with which workers tended the unprotected caustic pots and caldrons, in the absolute lack of protection to workers in dipping metals into strong solutions of nitric and sulphuric acid, and other unprotected processes, which fully explained the large number of accidents reported in the chemical industry. In the manufacture of sulphuric acid, either by the chamber or by the contact processes, there was considerable danger from the sulphurous acid; from roasters and brimstone burners; from nitrous gases from the pots or from the nitric acid supply; from sulphuric acid; from the interior of towers; from the concentrators, or the fumes from this acid encountered in the repair of the chambers.

In the manufacture of nitric acid, leakages have often been found in the apparata and much nitrous gas was liberated in these factories. In the inspection of the electroplating processes in a large number of metal trades where metal articles were dipped into a solution of nitric and sulphuric acid, dense and voluminous clouds of red fumes were often seen, and as there was very little effort made to convey or to remove these gases, there was no protection for the workers from breathing these dangerous fumes.

In the manufacture of hydrochloric acid, whether by the Le Blanc or by the electrolytic process, much hydrochloric acid is liberated and many of the workers had their teeth rotted and corroded and also showed evidences of frequent burns.

One of the characteristics of the chemical industry is that in one industrial plant or factory there may be a number of various processes housed in the same plant. Thus, factories which manufacture commercial acids manufacture also various alkalies. This is notably the case with the Solvay and electrolytic processes of manufacture of acids, soda and potash where, in these plants, sulphuric acid and hydrochloric acid are also manufactured, and

Courtesy Wm. C. Hanson, U. S. Dept. of Labor, Bulletin 127.

The Jewelry Industry.

The Workmen are Exposed to Fumes of Cyanide of Potassium.

where caustic soda or potash and bleach powders are often manufactured at the same place.

Reference has already been made to the unprotected condition in several factories in New York State, of the big caldrons 15 feet in diameter filled with burning cuastic soda and potash and to the accidents which often occur in these places.

Bleach Works. In the manufacture of bleach powders, several plants of which I inspected at Niagara Falls, New York, I was greatly impressed with the dangers in these factories, and also with the lack of protective devices and appliances. A description of these factories and their dangers may be of interest.

The electrolytic process of manufacturing chlorine gas is used in these plants; the bleach chambers, however, are such as were used in the old Weldon process. These bleach chambers consist of large rooms approximately 25 by 100 feet in size and 7 feet high. The lime is spread on the floors several inches thick and harrowed into narrow furrows; then the chlorine gas is let into these chambers until the lime absorbs a sufficient quantity of the gas, when the chambers are opened and fresh air is let in. The workers then go into the chambers and rake up the lime saturated with the chlorine gas and pass it down the chutes through traps in the chamber floor. In spite of the opening of the door and of a window opposite the door, considerable gas is left in the chambers and much is set free during the raking up of the bleach powder. This process raises clouds of dust, and the chlorine gas in the air of the chamber is so overpowering that it is impossible for one to stay in the chamber for even a short time without some protection. The work must be done with great speed in order not to waste the chlorine gas; the heat in the chambers is excessive, and the conditions are such as to make this work more trying and exhausting than almost any other process whatsoever.

The workers wear special clothes, caps and gloves, for the bleach powder is very irritating and destructive, sores resulting when it comes in contact with the bare skin. The eyes are protected by goggles, the head is covered, the mouth is covered by six or seven folds of heavy flannel through which the man must inspire, while expiration takes place through the nostrils, which are in close contact with the flannel. The apparatus is called by the men a " muzzle." It requires much experience for a man to be able to use it properly. Only those who are able to wear such muzzles are allowed to work in the bleach chambers. Even to those accustomed to wearing them they cause considerable difficulty in breathing, and they cannot be worn for a long period. When the muzzle is worn in a gassy bleach chamber, with the dust, heat and gas, and with the speed required for the work, the time that the workers may remain in the chamber with comparative comfort is very short, ranging from ten to thirty minutes. The men coming out from the chambers present a pitiful appearance. They are all covered with bleach dust; their eyebrows and exposed parts are permanently whitened by the action of the bleach; perspiration is profuse and runs down the face; the breath is labored and hurried; the pulse is high, ranging, in my examination of several workers, from 96 to 110 beats per minute. The workers in this exhausted condition quickly throw off their "muzzles" and rush for the open windows, gasping for breath.

My inspection was made in the summer when the windows were open, and the ghastly faces of the exhausted chamber workers as they thrust their heads through the windows into the outer air made a gravely impressive picture. Whether the windows are open in the bleach chambers during the winter time could not be definitely ascertained, as the testimony of the different workers varied in regard to this. It frequently happened that the workers are "gassed," i.e., overcome by the chlorine gas. This produces nausea, fainting, vomiting, and occasionally, unconsciousness. Sneezing and coughing are always attendant upon work in the bleach chambers.

Most of the men are robust and strong, for only such are able to do the work; there is, however, no physical examination of applicants for this work. Those who were found working were generally between the ages of twenty and thirty, although much older in appearance; in fact, they seem quite aged at thirty.

The work in the bleach chamber is done by gangs of four or five, and consists not only in removing the bleach from the chambers, but also in preparing the lime in the chambers and in the general care of these rooms. Their work inside the chambers is fortunately not continuous; while one gang goes in for fifteen to thirty minutes, the other gang is preparing the lime in another part of the plant, thus alternating the work. The system of compensation for the work is based on a ton of product and is considered quite high; at least, it is known that these workers are the most highly paid in the plant outside of the skilled workers. Their earnings range from $12 for beginners to $25 per week, the largest number of

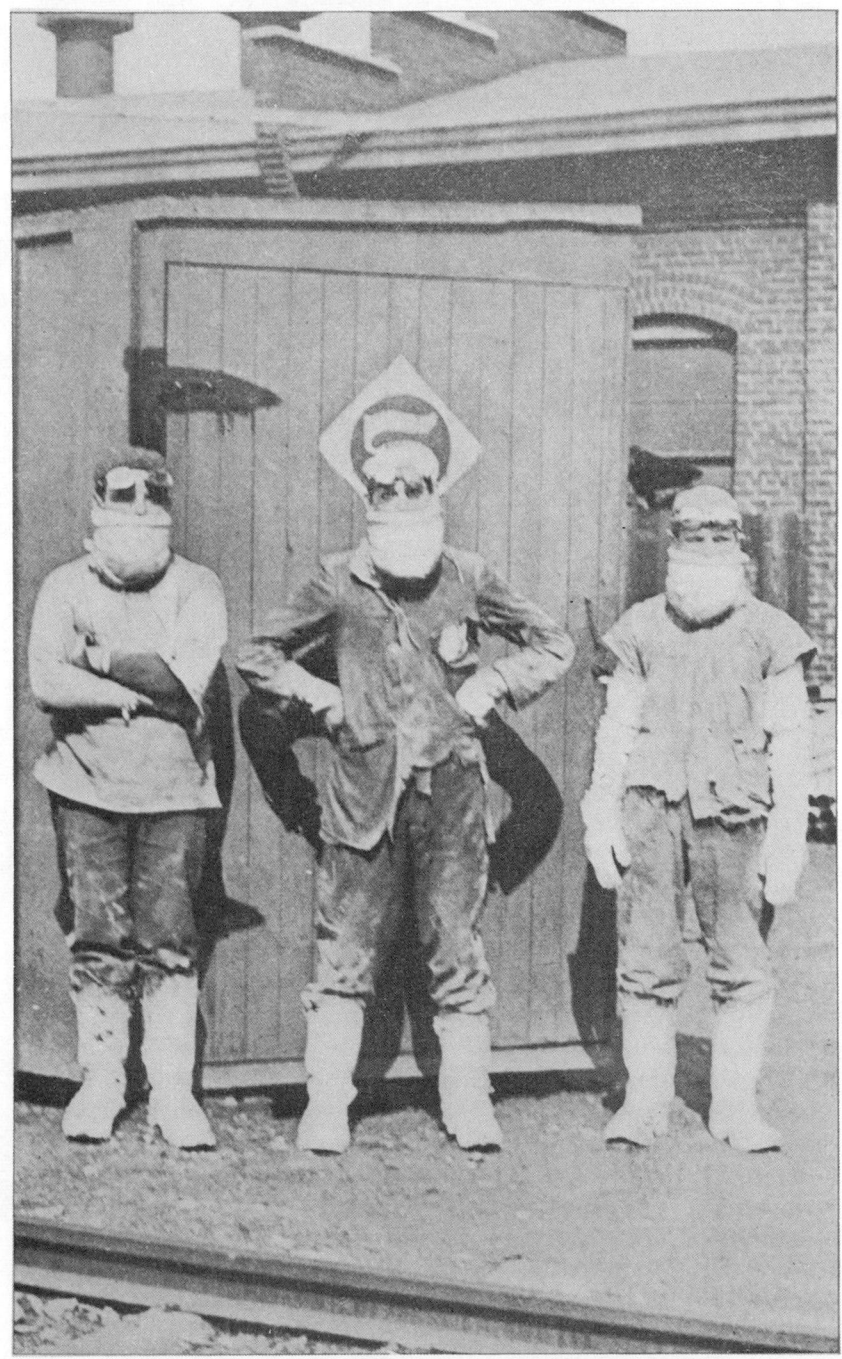

New York State Factory Commission.

The " Muzzles " and Costumes Worn by Bleach Workers.

bleachers making between $18 and $25 per week. Comparatively few of these bleach-chamber operatives had been long at this work, only ten or twelve among them having worked over five years.

Out of the 59 bleach-chamber workers whose individual histories were taken, there were only 16 who did not complain of some affection of the nose, throat, eyes, or who did not suffer from a cough, nausea, headache or other ailment.

The gangs work in shifts, in some plants there being two, in others three shifts. Of the 59 workers, 2 were found to work forty hours per week, 17 worked forty-eight to fifty-two hours per week, 12 worked sixty per week and 3 worked sixty-six to seventy-two hours per week. Out of the 59 bleach-workers whose histories were taken, 46 claimed to have knowledge of the dangerous character of their work and 37 said that instructions were given to them how to take care of themselves.*

In an illustration on page 422 the Hasenclever method of manufacture of chloride of lime is shown as used in Germany and in a chemical establishment in Brussels, Belgium, which I inspected in 1913. By using this method the necessity for " bleach-workers " is obviated, and the process becomes harmless.

III

PREVENTION AND PROTECTION

The problem of eliminating occupational diseases and preventing human waste caused by industrial poisons, gases and fumes is one of the most important tasks of the age, and is closely interwoven with the general subject of the conservation of human resources. The crux of the problem is not whether we shall have industry *with* disease and poisons, or *no* industry at all. It is rather whether we shall allow industry to take its annual toll of human life by permitting the captains of industry to decimate the industrial ranks by poison and disease, or whether we shall insist that industry must be free from all dangers, hazards and risks and subordinate production and output to the weal of the human factor in industry.

Just as theoretical considerations and experience have demonstrated that our industrial accidents are wasteful and unnecessary

* General Report of the Director of Investigation, New York State Factory Commission, pp. 470–472.

to industrial efficiency, and, that many, if not most of them, may be prevented, just so has it been proved that many of the effects of industrial poisons, gases and fumes are not a necessary concomitant of industrial life, that many occupational diseases may be prevented and the fearful waste of human life due to these causes avoided.

The general principles of prevention and protection of workers in dangerous trades do not differ much from the methods of protection and prevention that have been discussed in the other chapters, notably those on accident prevention and industrial dusts. In order to present the various methods of prevention and protection in logical sequence, I shall here give a scheme of the principal and subordinate methods which are being introduced in different countries to protect the workers in dangerous trades from occupational diseases.

I. *Legislative Protection*

(1) Investigation.   (2) Notification.
(3) Inspection.   (4) Special rules.
(5) Licensing.   (6) Special prohibitions.

II. *Social Protection*

(1) Hours of labor.   (2) Industrial control.
(3) Workmen's compensation.   (4) Sickness and social insurance.

III. *Industrial Protection*

(1) Substitution of harmless   (2) Wet and automatic processes.
    materials for dangerous
    ones.
(3) Removal of dust, gases and (4) Sanitary protection.
    fumes.

IV. *Medical Protection*

(1) Personal hygiene.   (2) First aid.
(3) Medical supervision.

Legislative Protection. Since the breaking down of the *laissez faire* policy, the principle of state regulation of industry has been accepted by all legislatures of the civilized world. The extension of legislative protection is progressing in all countries in about the same direction. At first, protection is given by the state only to children and women in industry. The protection is then extended to all adults and embraces regulation of industrial conditions, provisions for sanitation of factories and the safeguarding of workers against the dangers of accidents. After these steps have been taken attempts are then made to control and regulate the special hazards specific to dangerous trades.

Investigation. The first natural step toward any regulation of dangerous trades is to study these trades, investigate occupational diseases and the hazards specific to certain industries. Hence, we find almost in all countries that preliminary to enacting laws on dangerous trades, general or special investigations more or less thorough are ordered by the state and given over to competent scientific authorities, upon whose investigations and report the restrictive legislation is then based. Thus we find, for instance, in England, all the provisions of the factory acts relative to specially dangerous trades have followed the report of the Departmental Committee on Dangerous Trades, which was sitting for several years in the nineties. All the extensions of the factory acts to other dangerous trades since then have been made after special investigations ordered by Parliament.

Restrictive legislation on dangerous trades in Illinois followed the report of the Occupational Diseases Committee and the same has been the case in New York and other states. Such procedure is especially necessary in dealing with occupational diseases, which are only known to specially trained scientists. Hence, investigation is the first step in legislative protection in dangerous trades.

Notification. The second step in legislative protection is the compulsory reporting of certain occupational diseases and cases of industrial poisoning. Unless such data are gathered and unless all the cases of disease due to occupation and industrial poisons are known, the extent of protection needed in the dangerous trades cannot be known; and therefore many countries and states have already enacted laws compelling physicians and employers to report cases of certain occupational diseases and industrial poisoning. The results of this reporting and notification are not yet of much value, because of a lack of proper medical supervision; but this is undoubtedly a very important and beneficent step in industrial protection.

Inspection. Another corollary of the attempt at legislative protection is the extension of state inspectorial service to dangerous trades. This means not only more frequent visits by inspectors to industrial establishments in which poisons, gases and fumes are found, but also the inclusion by the state factory inspection departments of competent scientists and specially trained physsicians, engineers and chemists in their inspectorial service so that state inspection of dangerous trades may be a real force and service instead of a farce.   In European countries, factory inspectors are a highly technically trained corps of men, and in several of the countries special divisions in the inspectorial department have been created to take care of the dangerous trades and establish-

Danneberg & Quand, Berlin.

Showing how the Lead Fumes in a Lead Smelting Shop are Properly Carried Away by a Local Exhaust Ventilating System Devised by a Famous Firm in Germany, making a Specialty of Ventilating Apparata for Dangerous Trades.

ments. The same tendency is also manifest in this country, as several of the large states have appointed a number of special technically trained inspectors to take care of this work.

Special Rules. Legislative protection in dangerous trades begins first with investigation, then notification and reporting, and is followed by a more thorough and special inspectorial service. The next step is the issue of special rules and regulations adapted to specially dangerous industries and processes. The more the question of industrial hygiene is studied, the more it becomes apparent that legislative protection does not lie in the enactment of general laws covering all industrial conditions, but in the possibility of issuing from time to time according to necessity rules and regulations applicable only to certain industries or processes, or even to individual establishments where specific dangers are likely to be found. Hence, in almost all countries and states, provision is made for some authority after proper investigation and study, to issue such rules and regulations. In most of the European countries the ministers of commerce and labor (or however they are designated), are the usual authorities who, together with the specially trained higher inspectors, have the right to make such rules and regulations. In the United States, this matter has only recently been brought to our attention and several states have made attempts to solve the problem, each in its own way. In Wisconsin, the right of making special rules and regulations has been given to the Industrial Commission; while the same right, perhaps more restricted, has been given to the Industrial Boards in the States of New York, Massachusetts and Pennsylvania.

Those who make a study of the large number of special rules and regulations which have been issued abroad covering so many industrial processes and conditions, cannot help but admire the thoroughness with which this work has been done, the utility of such special rules and regulations, and the benefit that has accrued to the workers in dangerous trades.

Licensing. A further extension of legislative protection of the worker in dangerous trades is found in the system of licensing such trades. It is not sufficient to make special rules and regulations guarding the workers in establishments already erected and existing. It is always easier to prevent than to cure. The protection in dangerous trades should extend to establishments before they are erected. It is then possible to prevent certain conditions which it may be too late to amend later on; hence the practice of legislatures of different countries of compelling the owners of establishments in certain trades to apply for an authorization and to receive a license from the state inspection and industrial service after a thorough investigation of the plans and specifications. Such licensing is a very efficient method of legislative protection and is destined to be extended to all dangerous trades and to be accepted by all states in this country.

Special Prohibitions. The right of the state to protect the workers in dangerous trades goes even further. Not only does a state make special rules and regulations which must be followed in these establishments, not only are such trades often required to be licensed, but the legislatures also enact laws prohibiting certain classes of persons from participating in any dangerous trade. Many laws have been enacted by the legislatures of different countries and states, by which children under a certain age and sometimes all children and minors, and all women or only women of a certain age, etc., are prohibited from participating in any work which is specially dangerous or from working in establishments where certain poisons, gases and fumes are being used.

Social Protection. By social protection of workers in dangerous trades is meant the protection given not only by legislative action, but by a general combined social effort to raise the economic, social or health standard of the workers either by legislative enactments or by general combined efforts of states, industries and social institutions.

Hours of Labor. An important protection to workers in dangerous trades is the limitation of the hours of labor of workers in these trades. The principle of decreasing the hours of labor according to the extent of the danger in the industry has been accepted as a legislative standard in only a few instances. This is notably the case with the law restricting the hours of workers in caissons. The New York State Law has limited such work from two to four or six hours according to the air pressure in the caissons. It is probable that a limitation of hours of labor in other dangerous trades would be a great step in the protection of the workers, as it has been proved beyond doubt that in trades where there is no possibility of eliminating certain dangerous elements, the less hours a person works therein, the less he is liable to be affected.

Industrial Control. Another significant tendency in the protection of workers in dangerous trades is the extension of industrial control by industries to the organized heads of all the establishments in such industries. The owners of establishments in one industry have at last come to the conclusion that while individually they may compete with each other as to output and commercial undertakings, their interests as far as the human factor in industry is concerned are almost identical. It is to the benefit of their industry and to industrial efficiency in general to take proper care of their workers and common cooperative attempts have been made by whole industries or groups of industries to this end. This has been done especially in Germany, where Trade Associations have been formed in sixty-six various industries. Each Trade Association has been given the right by the government to issue special rules and regulations which are binding for their respective industries, and also to appoint a special inspectorial corps who have the right to make frequent inspections in the various establishments, and even to fine the members of each Association in case they do not comply with the rules and regulations of the Association. A further tendency in the same direction is seen in the attempts made by either large corporations or by organized manufacturers in certain industries to better the conditions of the workers in the whole industry. Reference has already been made to the great work done in this direction by the United States Steel Trust, by the International Harvester Company and by a great many other corporations in the United States. Attention must also be drawn to the latest example of industrial control of an industry by the industry itself in the two large industries in New York City, viz., the Cloak, Suit, and Skirt and the Dress and Waist Industries, in which there are in New York City alone 2500 factories and workshops, and which have created a Joint Board of Sanitary Control to take special care of the sanitary conditions of the workshops in these industries and also of the health conditions of the workers.

Compensation. An extension of the principle of industrial control is the enactment of workmen's compensation. If there are certain dangers and hazards inherent in a certain industry, the industry as a whole should be responsible for them and should also be made to pay the cost of the injuries, diseases and death due to the industrial hazards. The manufacturer and the capitalist recognize that a certain breakage of materials, machinery and appliances is inevitable. They all compute a certain amount annually for depreciation in the structure and in the physical properties of their plant. They include in their calculations possible loss by fire, accident and bankruptcy. If there are certain inherent dangers to the life and health of the human factor in industrial establishments, one cannot see why this element should not also fall as a toll upon the industry and be taken into consideration by the manufacturer and capitalist. There is no reason why the ills and injuries to which the worker is liable in the industrial plant should all fall upon himself and his nearest kin. There is every reason why these burdens should be shifted upon the industry itself.

Workmen's compensation, which is an established fact in a number of countries abroad, has only been lately accepted as a cardinal principle of industrial justice in the United States and has been enacted by legislatures of many states, and will doubtless be extended to all states of the Union and to the Federal Government. The enactment of workmen's compensation laws will

Danneberg & Quand, Berlin.

A Linotype Room of a Daily Newspaper in Berlin, Germany.   Each Machine is Connected with an Efficient Exhaust System.

not only lead to a curative effect by compensating the workers for their injuries in industrial establishments and for certain occupational diseases, but will also act as a powerful force in the prevention of occupational diseases and the effects of industrial poisonings. For, as soon as the industry becomes cognizant of the fact that every injury, impairment of health, or death of the worker in industry must be compensated, it will then become apparent that it is perhaps cheaper for the industry to eliminate the dangerous elements.

Sickness and General Social Insurance.   The social protection extended by state and society to all industrial workers is bound to go still further. For thirty years Germany has had a social insurance law which is a model of its kind, and has been copied by other states in Europe. In that law provision has been made for a general insurance of workers in case of sickness, invalidity, disablement from disease and old age, and in case of death. Austria, Switzerland and, lately, England have followed the example of Germany and have enacted extensive social insurance laws protecting the whole industrial population against disease, invalidity and old age. Social insurance is now a live, burning question in the United States. It is an inevitable step following the enactment of workmen's compensation laws. No one can prophesy how soon social insurance may become a living fact in the United States; but no one can doubt that it will come.

Industrial Protection. The general methods of prevention of industrial diseases by legislative and social protection are but a part of the scheme to put industry on a healthy basis, to avoid all preventable diseases, and give proper protection to the working class in industry. The important prophylactic measures are those which may be designated as industrial protection. They are imposed upon industry and upon employers in the endeavor to free work from its concomitant dangers and hazards.

Prohibition and Substitution. Many of the poisonous materials used in industry and art are not absolutely indispensable. They are valuable; they seem to be necessary; they are convenient and commonly used. It is possible, however, to replace some of them by harmless materials. Even when the poisonous materials cannot be replaced, it has been determined judicially that a state has a right to prohibit their use in the interest of public health. Such prohibition, however, is not always necessary, as experience has shown that a great many of the most harmful substances may be and are being replaced by non-poisonous or less poisonous materials.

Perhaps the best example of a poisonous substance being legislated out of industry is the history of the international agreement to eliminate white or yellow phosphorus in the match industry. For years phosphorus poisoning and horrible necrosis of the jaw were rampant among the workers in phosphorus match factories. Due to agitation and to the vigorous protests against the baneful results of the poisonous phosphorus, a non-poisonous substance, the sesquisulphid of phosphorus, was discovered and successfully applied in the match industry, thus, with one stroke, freeing the whole industry from a terrible burden.

Strenuous attempts are being made in a number of countries to lessen the dangers of lead poisoning, the most prolific cause of industrial poisoning, by finding some substitute for the dangerous lead. White lead has been successfully replaced by zinc white in both exterior and interior painting, though the painting trade still clamors for white lead, claiming certain superiorities for its use, especially for exterior decoration. It has been found, however, that zinc white serves the purpose nearly as well, that the cost of the two products is about the same, and that for interior painting white zinc is superior to lead because it does not turn yellow. For exterior surfaces, white zinc has proved excellent when used in the proper manner. Experiments have been made by the Society of Public Medicine and Sanitation in concert with the Society of Painters and Contractors of the City of Paris in regard to the comparative merits of white lead and white zinc paint, both on the exterior and interior of the annex of the Pasteur Institute. The result of these experiments showed that white zinc was entirely or very nearly equivalent to lead under many different conditions.* In France, the use of all white lead in painting has been prohibited by law, the prohibition to take effect on January 1, 1915. In Switzerland, white lead cannot be used on any government work.

There are also other zinc preparations which may be substituted for white lead in painting. Red lead paint, which is used on metals, can be replaced by gray zincs, which are composed of pulverized zinc. Zinc white or barium white and manganese dryers may be used in place of white lead and lead dryers in lacquer and ebony work. Zinc oxide, sulphate of barium or talc are generally used nowadays in place of lead by designers of embroideries or laces.

Zinc white and sulphate of barium have been substituted for lead in making the foundation, the mordants, the colors and the porcelain glazes used in the paper industry. It can also be used for various papers colored in yellows or greens by chrome yellow, which is lead chromate. Zinc chromates have been substituted for lead chromates.

In all pottery work and enamels a large proportion of white or colored lead is used. In some of the pottery work the proportion of lead is less than 20 per cent, but some potteries use a larger percentage. This matter has been given much attention especially in England and France. It has been demonstrated by many experi-

* Courtois-Suffit et Levi-Sirugue: Hygiene Industrielle, p. 414.

ments that it is practicable to make pottery glazes without lead ingredients, that it is possible to diminish the use of lead glaze for certain colors, and that a leadless glaze has been and is being widely used. There are a number of formulas for leadless glazes as well as leadless enamels.

In the polishing of glass a lead powder was formerly and is still widely used. This, however, has been successfully replaced by an iron oxide rouge which is extensively used in this country for all glass polishing.

In the manufacture of certain colors, a mixture of Prussian blue and zinc yellow is often substituted for arsenic green; and in dyeing materials it is possible to avoid the use of poisonous green dyes by suitable substitutes.

Nitrate of silver is at present widely used instead of mercury in coating mirrors. It is replaced by glycerine in the manufacture of air pumps, and substitutes have been found for mercury in a number of other industries. In the manufacture of incandescent lamps the danger of mercurial poisoning has been done away with by using vacuum pumps without mercury.

Tetrachloride of carbon, which is non-toxic and the vapors of which are not inflammable, has been successfully substituted for benzine and other poisonous solvents used for fatty materials, rubber, resins, etc.

It is manifest, therefore, that with industrial and hygienic progress, it is possible to eliminate a great many of the toxic materials by substituting for harmful substances less harmful or non-harmful ones. It is, however, necessary for the state or society to accelerate industrial and hygienic progress by legislative enactments, without the incentive of which the captains of industry do not seem to be anxious to prevent many of the industrial diseases.

Wet and Automatic Processes. Where poisonous materials are dangerous because of the dust created, the adoption of wet processes or of automatic machinery eliminates the danger. This matter has been fully discussed in the chapter on dusts. I have seen a number of white-lead factories where no dry grinding of lead was done, which were entirely free from lead dust. The wet process should be extended to all poisonous materials wherever possible.

In processes where the wet method cannot be adopted it is often possible to use automatic machinery which would eliminate poisonous dust. I have already referred to the example of the manufacture of bleach powders. This work, which is extremely dangerous, has become innocuous with the adoption of the Hasenclever method, an illustration of which is given on page 422.   There is no doubt that automatic methods and machinery may be invented in many other dusty and poisonous processes, which would decrease the dangers of industrial poisons.

Removal of Dust, Gases and Fumes.   Wherever poisonous dust, gases or fumes are evolved in industry the principle of their immediate removal at their place of origin should be applied.   Such

Danneberg & Quand, Berlin.

An Electro-plating Shop of a Metal Pipe Factory in Germany, Showing an Efficient Removal of Fumes and Proper Protection of Workers.

removal is feasible and is successfully accomplished in a large number of factories.

The removal of poisons by exhausts, fans, etc., does not differ from the methods described in the removal of dust.   When dealing with gases and fumes, modifications in the hoods, tubes and methods of removal must, of course, be made with regard to the substance which is to be removed.   The illustrations on this and next page show some of the methods used in Germany for the removal of gases and fumes in electroplating establishments.   Much attention is paid to this matter in the Charlottenburg Museum of Safety, where

special investigations and studies are being pursued all the time
for the discovery of the best methods of removal of gases and
fumes. Some of these methods, if adopted, would certainly eliminate much of the danger of inhalation of various gases and fumes
in industry.

Sanitary Protection and Prevention. It is unnecessary to enter
in detail into the general sanitary prophylactic measures to be

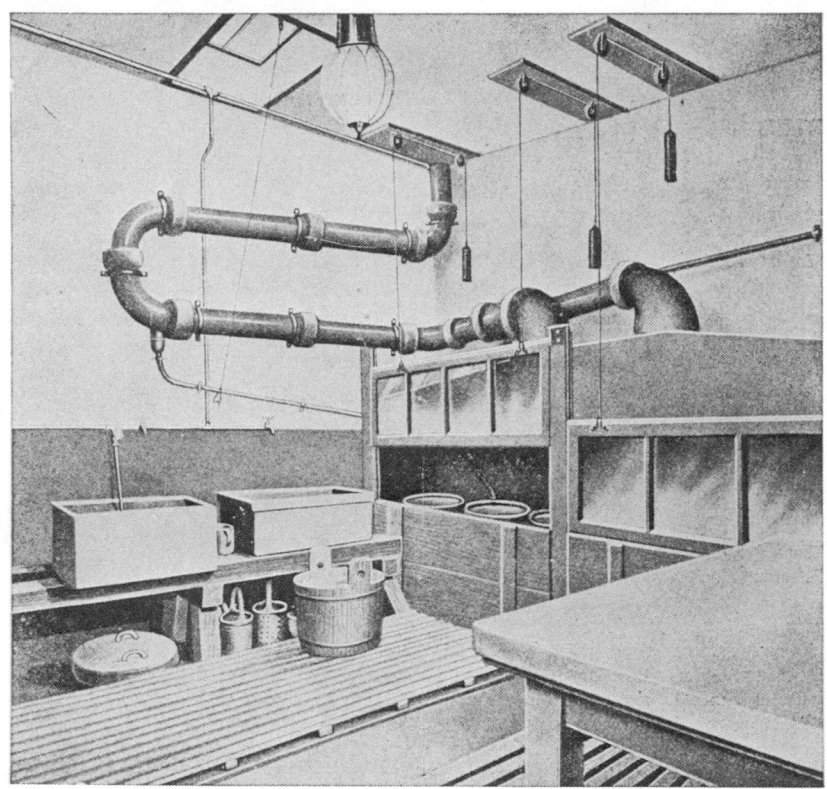

Ferdinand Bäume Nuremberg.

Another Method of Local Ventilation to Remove the Fumes in an Electro-
plating Shop in Nuremberg, Germany.

used in industrial establishments where poisonous dusts, gases
and fumes are found. The sanitary precautions are those which
have been described in previous chapters and relate to proper
construction of walls, ceilings and floors, to the safeguarding of
machinery, to the provision for adequate lighting and ventilation,

and to the installation of sufficient drinking, washing and other sanitary facilities.   The sanitation of factories in dangerous trades is an even more important matter than the general sanitation of industrial establishments.

Medical Protection. *Personal Hygiene.* Work in dangerous trades demands extra precautions for individual health. The worker must be instructed in the principles of hygiene and inculcated with habits of personal cleanliness and care. A worker who knows the risks and dangers of his calling and who practices all the precepts of personal hygiene will not fall a prey to industrial poisons, gases and fumes as easily as the careless, slovenly and uncleanly worker.   The matter of proper washing of the hands, face, etc., the cleaning of the teeth and washing of the mouth, frequent bathing, wearing of proper clothes outside and inside of the factory, the use of nourishing and simple foods, the taking of frequent exercise and wise use of the time for recreation—all play an important part in the health of the worker.

In some of the factories in Germany, factory owners and medical supervisors have not only instructed the worker in general hygiene and in special prevention of the dangers of his calling, but have attempted to give a daily schedule of the life of the worker in the factory.   One such schedule is cited by Blum in a hygienic plan for lead-workers.*   The schedule is as follows:

(1) Breakfast at home, vegetable soup, etc.

(2) On arriving at factory, removal of street clothes and donning overalls, etc.

(3) Work for $1\frac{1}{2}$ to 2 hours.

(4) Pause of $\frac{1}{2}$ hour, $\frac{1}{4}$ hour of which is for removing overalls, scrubbing of hands for one minute with a 0.1 per cent solution of sodium sulphide, afterwards scrubbing hands with sand soap, water and brush; washing face and using mouth wash containing 0.1 per cent of solution of sodium sulphide, then $\frac{1}{4}$ hour pause.

(5) Change clothes and work for $1\frac{1}{2}$ hours.

(6) Noon-day pause. Before pause $\frac{1}{4}$ hour to be used for the purposes of dressing and washing according to same routine.

(7) Work from $1\frac{1}{2}$ to 2 hours.

(8) $\frac{1}{4}$-hour pause and $\frac{1}{4}$ hour for cleaning and washing as before.

(9) Work for $1\frac{1}{2}$ or more hours.

(10) $\frac{1}{4}$ hour before stopping work for dressing and washing before leaving the factory.

* Dammer: Handbuch der Arbeiterwohlfahrt.

Under such a régime, the worker would have to use about one hour a day for washing and dressing purposes alone, and about 1½ hours during the day for pauses. This is probably more than American employers would permit unless such a daily routine is made compulsory by law.

First Aid. The need of an organization for first aid in every factory is self-evident. In all factories the workers are subject to various accidental injuries and diseases, and in every industrial plant there should be some means for treating such cases.

The medical and surgical cases which may need treatment in a factory are burns, wounds, amputations, fractures, dislocations, hemorrhages, acute poisoning, acute gassing, or loss of consciousness due to various causes, such as shock, heat, epilepsy, gassing, etc.

In all such cases time is very precious and life may often be saved by prompt attendance and treatment. This is possible only when there is some organization for first aid in each factory.

The organization for first aid implies (*a*) proper place, (*b*) proper personnel, (*c*) adequate instruction and education of the personnel, (*d*) sufficient and proper appliances, (*e*) materials, drugs, etc., which may be necessary and are to be used.

Many factories have special dispensaries or clinics where first aid is given to injured employes. In some factories the foremen or superintendents are the persons who administer the first aid. In larger factories and in some large corporations special crews or corps have been specially trained for this purpose, and nurses and physicians are drawn into the service of the first-aid organization. In a great many establishments notices are posted as to various methods of first aid, as to proper treatment of burns, loss of consciousness, etc. These notices, however, are of very little value unless there are persons instructed in the work whose duty it is to administer the first aid.

Among the appliances especially needed in large establishments are stretchers, pulmotors, oxygen tanks, and various other appliances and devices for resuscitation and treatment. Among the materials and drugs which are found in a great many factories besides cotton, gauze and splints, are also various disinfectants and neutralizing agents according to the character of the material which is used in the industrial establishment.

Medical Supervision. An important phase of protection in dangerous trades is a complete system of medical supervision.

Such a system embraces the following: (1) preliminary examination, (2) periodical reexamination, (3) dispensary and clinic treatment, (4) sanitary supervision of the plant, (5) supervision of the personal hygiene of the workers, (6) medical and hygienic instruction and education of the workers, and (7) general medical care of the workers and their families.

It is unnecessary to enter into the detail of the items belonging to a general scheme of medical supervision in factories in dangerous trades. Reference has been made to this subject in various parts of the book.

The need of medical supervision in industrial plants has been emphasized over and over again. The importance of preliminary examination of workers is self-evident in all work in dangerous trades where the health of the candidate for work must be perfect in order to prevent industrial poisoning. A periodical reexamination of workers in dangerous trades is also necessary in order to detect incipient symptoms of poisoning and to take the proper precautions to prevent further inroads of disease. Daily treatment in dispensaries and clinics is necessary to prevent the spread of industrial disease and to cure incipient cases.

The medical supervisor in a factory in a dangerous trade should exercise general sanitary supervision over the plant, so as to be sure that the general sanitary cleanliness, light and ventilation receive proper attention. The medical supervisor of such a plant should also take special care of the personal hygiene of the workers, especially in regard to sanitary and hygienic instructions to foremen and workers in teaching them the dangers of their trade and the risks of their calling, and instructing th m in the methods of prevention and personal care. He must also supervise the wearing by the workers of special clothing, gloves, goggles, and respirators which are necessary in the dangerous trades.

The proper organization of this work implies also an intimate influence of the medical supervisor not only upon the workers within the factory, but also upon their home relations and surroundings.

Only by such a comprehensive scheme of medical supervision of work and workers in dangerous trades can we hope to eliminate the dangers of industrial poisoning, and to prevent many of the occupational diseases to which such a large number of workers succumb.

CHAPTER XI

FACTORY LEGISLATION

I

GROWTH AND TENDENCIES OF FACTORY LEGISLATION

ALL labor legislation began with the protection of children. This protection was gradually extended to women and finally to all adults. Only after a considerable period of such general legislation were any attempts made to improve working conditions in factories and workshops.

From the beginning of the modern factory system there was strenuous opposition on the part of manufacturers and employers to any restrictive legislation. While this opposition was chiefly directed against any limitations imposed on the labor of women or children, all state interference with working conditions in the factory was bitterly fought by the manufacturers, who claimed that the state had no right to interfere in contracts between employers and employes or to supervise the conditions under which work was carried on. It was only when the principle of state regulation of industry had been firmly established that factory legislation, meaning by this legislation for the improvement of working conditions within the factory, became an integral part of general labor legislation.

Early Factory Legislation in Europe. The first labor legislation in *England,* and in the whole world, was the Factory Act of 1802, which applied only to cotton factories with more than three apprentices or with twenty other persons at work and which, as its name indicated, "The Health and Morals of Apprentices Act," was promulgated chiefly for the protection of apprentice children in factories, whose exploitation and abuse was so vividly described in the reports of Parliamentary Commissions. This first act already contained embryonic sanitary provisions in a clause calling for the whitewashing of mills and factories twice a year. The subsequent Acts of 1819, 1825, and 1831 contained numerous provisions restrict-

486

ing the work of children and young persons, but added little to the sanitary provisions of the first law. Indeed, the sole sanitary provision existing was greatly attenuated by decreasing the required number of whitewashings from twice a year to once in twelve months.

The chief importance of the next Act of 1844 lies in the fact that this Act was the first to include women among protected persons. They were placed in the same class as young persons from twelve to fourteen years, whose hours of labor were limited to twelve daily and to sixty-nine weekly. This Act also contained the first provision for accident prevention. It prohibited the cleaning of machinery while in motion, and required the fencing of flywheels and the safeguarding of dangerous parts of machinery. Provision was also made to protect working people from excessive dampness in the process of wet spinning. The one sanitary requirement of the former laws was still further weakened by making whitewashing in factories obligatory only once in fourteen months, and painting only once in seven years.

The Acts after 1844 and up to 1878, when all the factory laws were consolidated, are significant in that they mark the steady extension of the scope of factory legislation and the further limitation and restriction of the work and hours of labor of women, young persons, and children, and the extension of all provisions of the law to all industries. During this time occurred the battle of manufacturers organized in the National Factory Owners' Association against accident-prevention provisions of the law, especially against the fencing-in of horizontal shafts more than 7 feet from the floor. By the consolidated Factory Act of 1878, labor and factory legislation was established on a firm basis and state regulation was gradually extended until it embraced all working conditions within the factory.

No serious attempt at factory legislation was made in *France* until late in the second half of the nineteenth century, although a number of attempts were previously made to protect children in industries; and the first Act of 1813 prohibited the work of children under ten years in mines, and made other protective provisions in this industry. The Law of 1841, and the subsequent Laws of 1848, while giving some protection to children and women, contained no provisions for the supervision of industrial conditions within the factory. Very little progress was made until 1874, when a special inspection service was organized and some standards set for the improvement of sanitary conditions in the workshops. Since that time, by the labor Laws of 1882, 1883, 1892, etc., the extent of protection given to certain persons was increased and in 1893 the Hygiene and Security Law was passed, in which detailed provision was made for sanitary conditions in industrial establishments.

In *Germany* the first act to regulate the employment of young persons in factories was passed in 1839; but not until 1869 was the Industrial Code for the North German Union promulgated and an attempt made to regulate working conditions in factories by Article 107, which contained a general provison that every manufacturer should, at his own cost, establish and maintain all necessary appliances for safeguarding employes against dangers to health and life. This provision was extended by Article 120 of the Industrial Code of 1891, which is at present the basis of all factory legislation in Germany. The provisons of the Act are general in character; but the inspectors and the local authorities have power to define exactly the provisions of this Article. The essence of Article 120, upon which all factory legislation is based, reads as follows:

" Employers are to establish and maintain their establishments, their workrooms, machines and utensils so as to protect workers, as far as the nature of the industry permits, against dangers to life and health. Especially are they to provide for sufficient light, adequate air space and air change, removal of gases, dust and fumes arising in the process of the industry. They are also to provide such devices as are necessary for the protection of the workers against dangerous machinery or parts of machines, or against any other dangers which are to be found in the nature of industrial processes; also those dangers which arise from factory fires. In establishments where, because of the nature of the process it is necessary for the workers to undress and to cleanse themselves after work, special washing- and dressing-rooms must be established."

In other countries, factory legislation began much later than in the countries named. Labor legislation in *Austria* began with the Law of 1852, and was followed by the Industrial Code of 1859, and the revised Industrial Code of 1885, although there was some legislation for the protection of children prior to the first act. Only after the Law of 1883, when a factory inspection department was established, was recognition given to the importance of sanitary conditions within the factory, and inspectors given the right to investigate and make recommendations for their improvement. The present Industrial Code of Austria contains in Article 74 a general provision for the improving of factory conditions which closely follows the wording of the German Article 120 of the Code. It reads as follows:

" Every employer is obliged to establish and maintain at his own cost all such sanitary appliances and devices, and to furnish all safeguards as, according to the nature of the industries and processes, may be needed for the protection of the health and life of the employes. He must take care that all machines, their parts and all their appliances should be so arranged that injuries to workers may not easily be possible. He must also make provisions for proper light, cleanliness, and freedom from dust in the workrooms, for the needed artificial illumination, for change of air in the rooms corresponding to the number of workers, for prevention of injurious gases and fumes, and for the conduct of industry and its processes in such a manner as to protect the health of the employes."

Upon these provisions are based the detailed rules and regulations issued by the ministers and other industrial authorities.

Early Factory Legislation in the United States. Early factory legislation in the United States, as in Great Britain, began first with laws protecting child-workers in cotton factories and mills. The first cotton mill in America was established in Rhode Island, in 1790, and began to work with four spinners and carders; but five children were soon added, whose ages ranged from seven to twelve years. The number of children in the industry rapidly increased. In a letter written by Samuel Slater, the founder of the American Cotton Industry, in 1827, he says: "Wool business requires more man-labor, and this we study to avoid." So successfully did Slater and his fellow-employers avoid man-labor that in 1831 the number of children working in the cotton mills in Rhode Island was almost half of the total number of employes.

It took some time before public opinion in America was aroused on the subject of child-labor. Our forefathers were accustomed to see children busily occupied about the house and on the farm, and they had no experience to enable them to see the difference between such occupations and factory work, with its long, confining hours and bad effects upon the physique and character of the children. Indeed, the cotton manufacturers were considered great benefactors of the community in so far as they employed women and children in mills.

Massachusetts took the first steps in factory legislation. Characteristically, it was concern lest the education of the children should be neglected, which led to the passage of the first law pro-

tecting child-workers in factories.   This Act of 1836 provided that
" no child under fifteen years shall be employed to labor in manufacturing establishments unless such child shall have attended
school at least three months out of the twelve next preceding any
and every year in which such child shall be so employed."   In 1842
this Act was amended to provide a ten-hour working day for children under twelve years of age.

In 1842, *Connecticut,* following the example of Massachusetts,
passed a law requiring three months' schooling per year for every
child under fifteen working in factories in the state, and a ten-hour
day for children under fourteen years.

In 1847, the legislature of *Maine* passed a law requiring three
months of schooling in each year for every child under fifteen years,
and four months' schooling for every child under fifteen working
in the factories in the state.   As in Massachusetts, the school
committees were to enforce this law and could impose a fine of fifty
dollars upon every manufacturer not complying with its requirements.

As early as 1827, *Pennsylvania* legislators were interested in the
problems connected with child-labor in the cotton mills in the
state.   A bill was introduced in that year which provided that no
minor between twelve and eighteen should be employed in cotton
or wool manufacture unless producing a certificate signed by the
school master or two citizens that the minor could read and write
English, German, or some modern language, or unless the manufacturer should provide for instruction of said minor.   The enforcement of the law was left to the tax assessors.   The penalty was
fixed at five dollars.   The bill was passed by the House but thrown
out by the Senate, and no more attempts were made to protect
children in the mills until 1837, when the Senate appointed a committee to investigate child-labor.   This committee found that one-
fifth of the whole number of workers employed in cotton mills in the
state were under twelve years of age; the working time ranged from
eleven to fourteen hours and their average working week was
seventy-two hours.   This committee also reported that only one-
third of the cotton-mill workers under eighteen could read or write.

No action, however, was taken by the legislature to remedy these
evils until ten years later when, in 1848, a bill was passed which for-
bade the employment of minors in any cotton, woolen, silk or flax
factory.   The bill provided a legal working day of ten hours in
all such factories, with a proviso that minors above the age of fourteen might be employed more than ten hours by special contract

with parents or guardians. In 1849 the minimum age was raised to thirteen years and the protection of the law was extended to paper and bagging industries.

Labor legislation in the United States, therefore, as in other countries, began with the protection of children; and only very much later was any attention paid to the improvement of working conditions in the factory. In *Massachusetts* the first provisions as to protection of steam-machines were passed in 1852, and the supervision of boilers was provided for in 1870. In 1877 the first requirements for dust removal were made. In *New York* the first school law was established in 1852, and only in 1874 was the first compulsory schooling of fourteen weeks' duration made a law. In 1886 the first factory law to regulate employment of women and children in manufacturing establishments was passed, and only in 1887 was cleaning of machinery while in motion prohibited and washing and toilet rooms required. In 1892 provisions were made for ventilation and overcrowding, and the law was extended to apply to all establishments where persons were at work.

In *Illinois*, an Act to prevent and punish wrongs to children was the first attempt made to restrict child-labor; and only in 1893 was a law enacted creating the Department of Factories and Workshops and regulating factory conditions. Since that time, by the Acts of 1897, 1901, 1903, and subsequent acts, Illinois has rapidly gained foremost rank in the galaxy of states which are providing progressive factory legislation.

Factory Legislation Standards. In legislation regulating hours of labor, wages, night work, etc., it has been customary for legislatures to state the provisions of the law and to promulgate definite rules, regulations, and standards for its enforcement. Provisions for a normal day's work, for prohibition of night work, for a minimum age for child-workers, for the limitation of the working week, for payment of wages in cash, etc., easily lend themselves to standardization. Not so with provisions regarding working conditions within the factory. Factory legislation, meaning by this term legislative enactments for the prevention of industrial accidents and occupational diseases, for the promotion and preservation of the health of the workers, cannot be so readily standardized. Hence, in all countries and states provisions as to construction, fire-protection, light, ventilation, safeguarding of machinery, and general sanitation of factories, have always been, and still are, indefinite and unstandardized.

The German Industrial Code, in Article 120, quoted above, states that employers are obliged to provide such appliances as are necessary to prevent dangers and risks to health and life of the employes. Similar provisions exist in the factory acts of other countries. The same conditions prevail in the United States. Our factory legislation abounds with general provisions, with vague and indefinite rules and regulations, with terms such as " proper," " adequate," " suitable," " sufficient," " sufficiently guarded," " if practicable," " whenever necessary," " in the discretion of the commissioner," etc. There is hardly a paragraph in the state factory laws which does not contain these general terms, which leave so much to the imagination and interpretation of the employer and manufacturer and so little power of determination of what is to be done to the inspector or commissioner.

The results of this lack of definition are that manufacturers and employers have no specific standards which they can follow and are in doubt as to the exact meaning of the law; that inspectors are unable to enforce the vague provisions without arbitrarily setting up their own standards; that discretion must necessarily be given to the commissioner to interpret the law; that different interpretations are made by individual inspectors and officials, and that real enforcement of the law becomes impossible.

The chief reasons for the lack of standardization of factory legislation is, that there is an absence of such standards among the scientists themselves. Hence, legislators cannot be blamed for their failure to embody in factory legislation standards which do not as yet exist. But even if such standards could be scientifically determined, it would be unjust and impracticable to have these standards embrace all groups of industries, all kinds of industrial processes, and all sorts of industrial establishments. Industrial conditions differ so much from place to place and from time to time that no single standard made by any scientific body can possibly apply to all cases. If standards are to be set, if provisions are to be made and rules promulgated, they must be issued so as to cover definite conditions, separate industries, and, at times, separate industrial establishments.

This difficulty is overcome somewhat differently in European countries and in the United States. In Europe the problem is solved in two ways. One is to give the Secretary of State or the Ministers having charge of enforcement of labor and factory laws power to issue from time to time special rules and regulations, to set standards, and to make such provisions for groups of industries or for special trades and industrial establishments as to insure the proper enforcement of the law. This method allows the inspectors no discretionary powers to set up their own standards and to differ in their modes of application of the law. This is the practice in England, in France, in Austria, and in other countries.

On the other hand, Germany tries to solve the same problem not by allowing the industrial authorities to make special rules and regulations, but by selecting for inspectors such highly trained experts in industrial hygiene and safety that there is no need for the setting of special standards or for the promulgation of special rules, leaving the application of the general provisions of the law to the sound judgment and ripe experience of the industrial inspectors. This, of course, may be done only in a country like Germany, where the general standard of industrial hygiene is very high, where there are so many museums of safety and chairs of industrial hygiene in the universities, and where industrial inspectors are recruited from a most highly technically trained body in any country.

In the United States, legislators continue to experiment and annually tinker with factory laws, and neither employers nor factory inspectors are able to enforce the law properly. The remedy which is applied in some states is the creation of industrial commissions and boards. The Wisconsin Industrial Commission was created by the adoption of a general provision " that the Commission take charge of the safety of the workers," leaving the definition of *safety* and the making of rules to the Commission, permitting it to " make such rules and regulations and set up such provisions and standards as, after proper investigation, it may deem fitting."

With the high character of the personnel of the Industrial Commission of Wisconsin, the remedy seems to have been the right one and has worked well so far. In New York, Pennsylvania, and Massachusetts, Industrial Boards have been created with no executive power but the right to investigate industrial conditions and, after proper investigation and conferences with those interested in the matter, to promulgate an industrial code and set special provisions and standards for groups of industries or industrial establishments. One cannot as yet judge what the results of this departure in factory legislation will be. It is to be hoped, however, that some order will be established by these boards in the anarchy and chaos hitherto reigning in existing factory legislation.

II

REGISTRATION AND AUTHORIZATION OF INDUSTRIAL ESTABLISHMENTS

No proper enforcement of the provisions of factory legislation is possible without a knowledge of the location of industrial establishments in which the law is to be administered. All reports on factory legislation and factory inspection have urged the necessity for a system of general registration of all industrial establishments which come under the law.

The Massachusetts Commission on Inspection of Factories, etc., came to the conclusion that the registration of all industrial establishments subject to inspection should be enforced by law. " The lack of authoritative information regarding the number and location of factories, workshops and mercantile establishments leaves many loopholes for the evasion of labor laws." * " It would seem that the first task of a board entrusted with the administration of these laws would be to inform itself concerning the exact extent of the field in which its work lies, and this task involves registration of all industrial establishments under its jurisdiction."

The New York State Factory Commission also came to the conclusion that a general registration of industrial establishments was necessary; and a law recommended by this Commission became part of the new state law of 1913. The law reads as follows:

" The owner of every factory shall register such factory with the state department of labor, giving the name of the owner, his home address, the address of his business, the name under which it is carried on, the number of employes and such other data as the commissioner of labor may require. Such registration of existing factories shall be made within six months after this section takes effect. Factories hereafter established shall be so registered within thirty days after the commencement of business. Within thirty days after a change in the location of a factory the owner thereof shall file with the commissioner of labor the new address of the business, together with such other information as the commissioner of labor may require."

Outside of New York State there is, however, no state that has as yet introduced compulsory registration of factories; although

---

* Massachusetts: Report of the Commission to Investigate the Inspection of Factories, etc., p. 76.

the principle that the state has a right to insist upon a license or authorization for certain industrial undertakings is well established. Certain trades, such as plumbing, which have important bearing upon public health, must be licensed; and in certain states bakeries, dairies, slaughter-houses, etc., must apply for a license for each establishment.

In European countries not only registration but authorization and licensing of trades is a firmly established principle, and has been accepted by many legislatures. The *English* provision for registration reads that " every person within one month from the beginning of occupation in a factory or workshop is required to serve a written notice on the district inspector stating the name of the factory or workshop, its location, business address, nature and amount of motive power of factory, nature of work, and name of the firm. The district inspector is required to forward this notice to the district council in the district in which this workshop is situated."

In continental countries the law goes much further. According to Article 16 of the Industrial Code of *Germany*, authorization is demanded from the proper authorities for the establishment of such plants which, because of their location or because of the nature of the operations within them, may cause considerable dangers, injuries or nuisance to the inhabitants of the neighboring places or to the general public. The Code gives a list of 26 various plants and groups of plants which need authorization and which may be added to or changed by special resolutions of the Federal Council with the sanction of the Reichstag.

The application for authorization must contain a description of the proposed plant, a plan of location, and a construction plan. Plans and description must cover the following points:

(a) The size of the plot.

(b) A map of the surrounding property and the names of its owners.

(c) The distance between the proposed establishment and the adjacent buildings, establishments, and public highways.

(d) The height and form of construction of the adjacent buildings.

(e) The location, extension and form of construction of the proposed establishment.

(f) The designation of each room and its general arrangement.

(g) The object of the establishment.
(h) Principles of the various processes and of the apparata utilized.
(i) The expected extensions of the establishment.
(j) The gases formed and the devices used to prevent the formation of the gases.
(k) The character of the fluid and solid waste products, also the methods of their disposal.

A commission of experts then reports upon the authorization, and public hearings are held in case objections are made to any of the details of the proposed establishment. The members of the commission are usually the district physician, chemist, architect, industrial inspectors, and others. Appeals may be taken from the decision of the district commission to the higher industrial authorities.

In *Austria* all trades must be registered, and the Code requires that one desiring to enter any trade or establish any plant must give due notice to the proper authorities. A tax varying according to the location, is levied, and objections may be entered against the conduct of such establishment. Aside from this general registration of free trades, there is a list of thirty-one trades, industries and groups of trades for which a special license is required. A license is also required in every establishment where, because of furnaces, steam-machines, motors or water works, or because of influences injurious to health or safety, or because of foul odors, or excessive noise, it may injure or become a nuisance to the neighborhood. Provisions are made for the forms of application, for the hearings before the various authorities, and for appeals, etc., upon these applications.

Belgium requires authorization for certain classes of establishments having special dangers or those which are unsafe, unhealthy or unsuitable. The scope of the classification of such establishments requiring authorization is so wide that it includes nearly every type of factory.

The application for authorization must set forth the nature of the establishment, the objects of manufacture, the apparata and processes to be used, as well as the approximate quantities that are to be manufactured or stored. The employer must in addition state the measures which he has in mind for diminishing the inconveniences connected with the establishment, as well for the workers employed as for the neighbors and the public. Every demand for authorization must be accompanied by two plans, one showing the interior arrangement of the factory, such as the location of the workrooms, storerooms and machinery; the other the situation of the factory in relation to other buildings, roads, railroads, water-courses, etc., within a radius of 200 meters. Establishments of the first class must also state the approximate number of workers to be employed, age, sex, length of work-day, and length of daily and weekly rest periods. In addition, the application must state the methods of heating, lighting and ventilation to be employed; the arrangements for cleanliness in the factory and on the part of the workers; the cubic air space allowed for each worker; the provisions made for medical and surgical care in case of accident; provisions for securing workers against dangers of explosions or fire, escape of vapors, gas or dust, breaking of machinery and pulleys. Lastly, the application must state the various measures to be taken to assure sanitary conditions in the workshop, such as alternation of work, provisions for meals, bathing facilities, toilet facilities, use of disinfectants, etc.

In *Switzerland* the law requires anyone proposing to construct a new factory or any industrial establishment, or to reconstruct or to add to already existing industrial establishments, to obtain an authorization from the cantonal government.

III

CONSTRUCTION, FIRE-PROTECTION AND ACCIDENT-PREVENTION

The construction of factories, as far as the materials of buildings, plans, forms of construction, thickness of walls, etc., are concerned, is usually under the jurisdiction of municipal authorities, subject to local building laws, rules and regulations. These building laws are not uniform throughout the state, with the result that there is a difference in the standards of factory construction in different cities and localities.

In a few European countries there is some special legislation on the subject. Thus, in *Switzerland*, the construction of all new factories is regulated in detail. No cellar is permitted to be used as a workplace except by special permission and on condition that it is well lighted and protected against dampness. The height and cubic air space of workrooms, the size of the windows, the methods of lighting, ventilation and heating, are all prescribed.

The law gives details as to construction of stairways, number and size of exits, doors and elevators, and contains provisions for insuring the safety of the persons using them.

In *England* the construction of factories is under the jurisdiction of local and municipal authorities.

In countries where certain trades are required to obtain an authorization or license, there is usually a very strict supervision of the plans of new buildings, and the form of construction as well as the arrangements in the factories in trades for which authorization or license is required.

It would be a great advance in factory legislation if states and countries would require all new industrial establishments to file their plans before construction and to have the state authorities supervise and control the methods of construction and proper hygienic arrangement of the future factories. It would obviate a great deal of the later need for correction of evils due to faulty construction.

Fire Protection. All states set some standard for fire-protection and prevention in factories. These standards usually cover the character and construction and materials of windows, doors, walls and floors, methods and form of construction of stairways, elevators, exits and fire-escapes. In general, Europe is far ahead of the United States in fire-protection and fire-prevention.

German regulations are probably the most thoroughgoing and drastic. In all buildings of more than one story in height the following specifications are ordered as a means of minimizing the dangers of fire.

(1) The outside walls and partitions must be made of fire-resisting materials.

(2) The ceilings and floors must be fire-resisting.

If openings cannot be avoided, precautions must be taken to prevent the spread of fire.

(3) Large, many-storied buildings should be divided by fire-walls.

(4) The stairways must be in specially constructed stair-towers. The latter, as well as the stairways, should be constructed of fireproof materials.

(5) In all buildings of three and more stories there should be at least two stairways remote from each other when the number of persons on upper floors shall be more than forty, or the length of the building more than fifty meters.

(6) The windows of the upper stories must be arranged so that a full-grown person can get through the window into the air.

The following regulations must be complied with in every workroom:

Factories and workshops in which more than twenty workers are employed, or in which light inflammable materials are manufactured, must be provided with two fire-proof stairways. At least two such stairways must lead to every workroom in the upper stories, except in such factories where stairways are on opposite sides of the building and enclosed in fire-proof walls on all sides.

In buildings already existing iron steps are permitted which are fire-proof above and below and are easily reached.

Direct communication of the workrooms with the stair-towers is to be avoided. An indirect connection between the workrooms and the fire-towers by means of iron galleries is preferable. These iron galleries must be closed on all sides in order that the smoke from the workrooms may not enter the stair-towers.

In the same way the doors leading to the stairways must be fire-proof, must open into the stair-tower and be self-closing. The doors of the workrooms, especially those in boiler-houses, must be so arranged that they open outwards. The same holds good for windows which in case of fire must be used as a means of exit.

Shed workshops must have a sufficient number of exits on all sides.

Storerooms for light inflammable materials must be only placed at the side of workrooms, and not in any case beneath them, and must be shut off from them by fire-proof walls.

In *France* the Labor Code requires the doors of all workshops where more than ten workers are employed, and all places, regardless of the number of workers, where inflammable materials are manipulated, to open from within out. The stairways, in addition to being constructed of incombustible material, where they must serve for the simultaneous exit of twenty or more persons, must have a minimum width of 1 meter, which must be increased by 15 centimeters for each new group of employees from 1 to 50. Municipal regulations in France forbid the construction of buildings more than seven stories in height. Other provisions of the Code insure the safety of establishments in which combustible materials are used or inflammable liquids or gases are employed for lighting or heating. The French Law requires periodical fire-drills.

The *English* Factory Law makes a distinction between old and new buildings:

Every factory erected since Jan. 1, 1892, and every workshop erected since Jan. 1, 1896, in which more than forty persons are employed, must be furnished with a certificate from the District Council (in London from the County Council) that reasonable provision has been made for the escape, in case of fire, of all persons employed. The certificate must specify in detail the means of escape provided. It is the duty of the district council (or county council) to examine every such factory and workshop, and to supply the certificate if they are satisfied that reasonable provision has been made.

In every factory or workshop erected after Jan. 1, 1896, the doors of each room in which more than ten persons are employed must, except in the case of sliding doors, be constructed so as to open outwards.

With regard to every factory erected before 1892, in which more than forty persons are employed, and every workshop erected before 1896, in which more than forty persons are employed, it is the duty of the District Council (in London of the County Council) to ascertain whether the factory or workshop is provided with reasonable means of escape, in case of fire, for all persons employed.

While any person is within a factory or workshop for the purpose of employment or meals, neither the external doors, nor the door of any room in which any such person is, may be locked, bolted, or fastened in such a manner as not to be easily opened from the inside.

The means of escape must be maintained in good condition and free from obstruction.

In the case of a tenement factory or workshop the owner is responsible instead of the occupier, and the whole tenement factory or workshop is to be taken as one factory or workshop.

District councils are given powers, in addition to those they possess, to make bye-laws providing for means of escape from fire. And the existing powers of the London County Council to make bye-laws on this subject with respect to buildings over 60 feet in height are extended to all factories and workshops of whatever height.

In *London*, under the London Building Acts (Amendment) Act, 1905, the following additional requirements apply:

(1) Means of escape in case of fire must be provided in " high

buildings" and in factories and workshops in which more than twenty persons are employed, with two exceptions:

   (a) If the whole of the building is a factory or workshop within the meaning of Section 14, of the Factory Act of 1901.

   (b) If the building while used in part as a factory or workshop has been so provided in compliance with the Factory Act of 1901 between the 11th August, 1902, and the 11th August, 1905.

(2) In the case of " new buildings " to which the above requirements apply plans must be submitted to the London County Council showing the means of escape it is proposed to provide.

(3) Precautions are also required in the case of workshops or workrooms connected with premises used for the storage of inflammable liquid.

In America, *New York State* has the most rigid and detailed fire standards. The following is a summary of the New York State Law, which will probably serve as a model for similar fire laws in other states, although many of the New York requirements are necessitated by special conditions prevailing in New York City, which would not exist in many of the other states.

The New York Law makes a distinction between buildings to be erected in the future and already existing buildings.

All buildings to be erected in the future, which are over four stories high, must be of fire-proof construction and have roofs covered with incombustible material. All exterior walls within 25 feet of any non-fire-proof building must be not less than 8 inches thick and extend 3 feet above the roof.

Two means of exit remote from each other are required from every space between fire-walls. One of these exits must be an interior enclosed fire-proof stairway; the other may be a similar or horizontal exit. No point in any floor area is to be more than 100 feet distant from one of these exits. An additional means of exit is required for every 5000 square feet in addition to the first 5000 square feet of floor area.

Stairways must be of incombustible material, 44 inches wide, and they must not be more than 12 feet, 6 inches, in height between landings. Winder stairways are not permitted. The width of the treads and the height of their rise is prescribed.

All doors and doorways must open out, and their width must not be less than the aggregate width of all the stairways leading to them. The width of the doors leading to stairways must not be less than 44 inches.

All partitions must be of incombustible material.

All elevators, shafts, hoistways, etc., must be enclosed with fire-proof material and must extend 3 feet above the roof.

REQUIREMENTS FOR EXISTING BUILDINGS

(1) *Required Exits.* Every building over two stories must have on every floor at least two exits remote from each other; one exit to open on interior stairway. Such stairways must be enclosed with fire-proof partitions extending from basement to three feet above the roof; all openings in these partitions to be provided with self-closing fire-proof doors.

The other means of exit may lead to a similar stairway to a horizontal exit or to an exterior screened stairway or to fire-escapes on the outside of the building (at the discretion of the Industrial Board). No point in any floor is to be more than 100 feet distant from an exit. Stairways must lead to the street or to unobstructed passageway, affording safe passage to street (Industrial Board has discretion over character of stairway enclosures).

(2) *Doors.* All doors to open outwardly or be double-swinging doors in all factories where five or more persons are employed.

(3) *Fire-escapes.* Fire-escapes must be constructed of wrought-iron or steel and safely sustain a live load of not less than 90 pounds per square foot, with a factor of safety of four; continuous stairway to be used wherever practicable.

Exits leading to fire-escapes to be 2 feet wide and at least 6 feet high and must extend to floor level and within 6 inches of floor level. Exits leading to fire-escapes must be fire-proof; windows opening on fire-escapes must be fire-proof.

Fire-escape balconies must be 4 feet wide. They must have a landing 24 inches square at the head of each stairway; passageway, between stairway opening and side of building must be at least 18 inches wide; stairway opening to be guarded by iron railing 3 feet high; balconies to be surrounded by iron railings 3 feet high.

Stairways must be 22 inches wide and have an incline of not more than 45 degrees, with 8-inch treads, and not over an 8-inch rise, and must be provided with hand-rail 3 feet high. Stairway from lowest balcony to landing must remain down permanently or be arranged to swing up and down automatically by counterbalancing weights. Exceptions to operation of this provision are made for certain factories.

ADDITIONAL REQUIREMENTS

(4) *Stairways.* Stairways must be provided with substantial hand-rails and must all extend to roof.

(5) *Doors and Windows.* Doors and windows must be unobstructed by metal bars, grating or wire mesh, unless readily remov-

able. Doorways opening on stairways must not obstruct passageway. Exits must be plainly marked.

(6) *Access to Exits.* There must be passageways on each floor at least 3 feet wide throughout leading to every exit, including outside fire-escapes. Such passageways must be unobstructed. No doors may be locked, bolted or fastened during working hours. Industrial Board has power to adopt rules, establish standards, etc.

(7) *Limitation of Number of Occupants.* In buildings hereafter erected 14 persons only permitted to work on any floor for every 22 inches in width of stairway.

In existing buildings no more than 14 persons can work on any floor for every 18 inches in width of stairway. Industrial Board has discretion in enforcing this regulation.

For every additional 16 inches over 10 feet in height between two floors, one additional person may be employed. On the upper of such floors one for every 18 inches in width of stairway in existing buildings, and one for every 22 inches in width of stairway in future buildings. If winder stairways are used a deduction of 10 per cent is to be made in counting capacity of the stairway.

In a fire-proof building, approved by the superintendent of buildings, as many additional persons may be employed on any floor as can occupy the enclosed stairhall on that floor, allowing five square feet of unobstructed floor space per person.

Where horizontal exit is provided on any floor, as many additional persons may work therein as can occupy the smaller of the two spaces on either side of the fireproof partitions; or as can occupy floor of a nearby building connected with this floor, allowing 5 square feet of unobstructed floor space per person, provided that such horizontal exits shall have doorways wide enough to allow 18 inches for each 50 persons or fraction thereof employed on each floor in the case of horizontal exits in the existing buildings and 22 inches in the case of horizontal exits in future buildings.

When a floor is sub-divided by partitions of brick, terra-cotta or concrete, not less than 4 inches thick, with all openings protected by fire-proof doors not less than 44 inches or more than 66 inches wide, as many persons may be employed on each floor as can occupy the smaller of the two spaces on either side of the partition, allowing 5 square feet of floor space per person, provided there be on each side at least one fire-proof stairway.

The number of persons employed on any one floor may be increased 50 per cent where an automatic sprinkler system is installed. The number of persons employed on any floor shall never exceed the number that can occupy the floor, allowing 36 square feet floor space per person, if the building is not of fire-proof construction, and 32 square feet per person if the building is fire-proof.

The Industrial Board has the power to make further rules and regulations in respect to fire-protection as well as in respect to other parts of the Labor Law.

The legislation in relation to accident-prevention and safeguarding of machinery has been partly discussed in the chapter on safety and accident-prevention. Legislation for this purpose is usually too general, as it is not feasible to encumber statute books with detailed provisions about the methods of safeguarding machinery, transmission apparata, or other devices and appliances which are of such great variety in every industrial establishment. Standards for safety and accident-prevention are made by accident insurance companies and by trade associations. Factory laws usually set down general principles of safety which are then applied according to the needs in each case.

IV

LIGHT AND ILLUMINATION, AND VENTILATION AND HEATING

There are very few definite standards in factory legislation as to the quantity and quality of light and illumination. This is natural when we consider that the science of illumination has not as yet progressed sufficiently to give definite solutions to the problems which confront the engineer in the illumination of different parts of industrial establishments. The legislation found in different countries and states may be summarized in the following excerpts from the provisions on the various statute books.

The *English* law contains no provision or standards for light and illumination of factories and workshops. Recommendations made on this subject have been in relation to special industries only.

France, Belgium and *Switzerland* require only "sufficient" natural or artificial light in workrooms, on staircases, in wash-rooms, toilets, etc. Switzerland requires in addition the installation of a sufficient number of safety lamps.

The *German* Industrial Code gives no standards for daylight or artificial light, but standards have been set by industrial inspectors according to the demands of the Federal Health Council, as follows:

Provisions for Natural Light.

(a) Minimum window area for each work-place from 0.25 to 0.05 square meters.

(b) Minimum window area of 1 square meter for each 30 meters of room space.

(c) Minimum window area of 1 square meter for every 5 square meters of floor-space.

Provisions for Artificial Light.

1 to 2 incandescent lamps from 16 to 32 N.K. power must be
provided.

In *Holland* the royal decree of Jan. 31, 1897, relating to the
conditions of working of female and young employes under unhealthy
or dangerous conditions does not allow the persons protected to
be employed on premises where, between nine in the morning and
three in the afternoon, artificial means have to be resorted to in
order to secure sufficient illumination (save only in exceptional
cases when the condition of the atmosphere renders artificial light
essential). Moreover, the intensity of illumination must conform
to certain definite requirements. In the case of the following trades—
embroidery, working in precious stones, gold, and silver, engraving
metals or wood, the manufacture of instruments, printing, mechanical knitting and quilting, sewing, draughtsmanship, the repairing
of clocks and watches—an intensity of at least fifteen bougie-meters
is prescribed. In the case of other works requiring good lighting
an intensity of ten bougie-meters is necessary.

Requirements for light and illumination of the different *American*
states are for the most part general in character, requiring only that
factories, workrooms and dependencies shall be properly and sufficiently lighted. The *Connecticut* law requires colored and corrugated windows to be removed if they are injurious to the eyes.
Illinois requires a light to be kept burning in passageways, on
staircases, in front of elevator shafts, etc., except in cases where
natural light is sufficient. *Wisconsin* alone attempts to set a standard
of illumination, requiring every place of employment in which hand
or machine operations are performed to be supplied during working
hours, when daylight is not available, with artificial light equivalent
in amount, for each 4 square feet of floor space, to not less than
the light produced by a one-candle-power lamp hung ten feet from
the floor.

Ventilation and Heating. The same reasons which have compelled legislators to make vague and indefinite provisions for light
and illumination in factories have also been potent in the matter of
setting standards for ventilation and heating. Ventilation engineers
are not as yet agreed on the proper methods of ventilation and the
qualitative and quantitative needs of different industrial establishments. Owing to this indefiniteness, the enforcement of the laws
is also very difficult. The present legal standards for ventilation
and heating may be summarized as follows:

The *English* Factory Acts stipulate for 250 cubic feet of air-space per person during regular working hours, and 500 cubic feet per person during overtime work. The *French* Code requires 7 cubic meters of air-space per person, which must be increased to 10 cubic meters in laboratories and kitchens, and in shops, stores and offices which are open to the public. The windows must be sufficient to prevent excessive rise in temperature. The air of workrooms must be renewed when necessary for the health of the workers. *Belgium* requires 10 cubic meters of air-space per worker. The height of work-place must be at least 2.51 meters and arrangements must be made to introduce new air and let out vitiated air at the rate of 30 cubic meters per hour per worker. The air must be renewed during work-pauses by draughts when circumstances permit. Work-places must be sufficiently heated in winter, and workers must be protected from excessive radiation from heating apparatus, furnaces, etc. *Germany* requires the same number of cubic meters of air-space per worker as Belgium, but German work-rooms must be at least 3.5 meters high and under special circumstances 4 meters high. The temperature of workrooms must be uniform, between 12 and 18° C.

In America the legal standards for ventilation in most states are general and indefinite. " Factories must be ventilated," or " Work places must be ventilated so as not to be injurious to health," are usually the only allusions to this subject in the labor laws. Six states only require a definite amount of air-space per employe, varying from 250 cubic feet in *Pennsylvania* to 500 cubic feet in *Illinois*. *Indiana* and *New Jersey* require 250 cubic feet of air-space per employe from 6 A.M. to 6 P.M., and 400 cubic feet of air space from 6 P.M. to 6 A.M.

Illinois requires fresh air to be supplied in such a manner as not to cause injurious drops of temperature. The air-supply must not be taken from the cellar or basement. Where the lights do not consume oxygen, 250 cubic feet are considered sufficient. Rooms with 200 cubic feet per employe and outside window and door area one-eighth of floor space, do not require artificial ventilation, but must be properly aired before beginning work and at noon hour. Rooms with 500 to 2000 cubic feet of air-space per employe with outside windows and doors one-eighth of floor space, must have artificial ventilation when weather requires windows closed, supplying 1500 cubic feet of fresh air to each employe. Rooms with less than 500 cubic feet per employe rooms without outside windows or doors, rooms with less than 2000 cubic feet per employe and outside windows and door area less than one-eighth of floor space, must have artificial ventilation supplying 1800 cubic feet of fresh air per employe each working hour.

The general orders on sanitation of the Industrial Commission of *Wisconsin* contain the following general standards for ventilation of workrooms:

Rooms with Less than 900 *Cubic Feet of Air-space Ventilation.* All rooms in places of employment where there is less than 900 and more than 300 cubic feet of air-space per person, and in which there is no smoke, gas, fumes, dust, vapors, or fires consuming oxygen, must be provided with a ventilating system which will furnish 1800 cubic feet of fresh air per hour to each person. In all rooms specified above where there are lights or fires which consume oxygen, an additional amount of air must be supplied to make up the loss of oxygen.

Rooms with 900 *Cubic Feet of Air-space Ventilation.* All rooms in places of employment where there is 900 cubic feet of air-space per employe, and in which there is no smoke, gas, fumes, dust, vapors, or fires which consume oxygen, must be provided with a ventilating system which will change the air in the room not less than twice each hour. Such system must be so designed as not to produce injurious drafts or reduce the temperature materially below the average temperature maintained.

(a) *Standard Secured by Window Ventilation.* The above standard of ventilation can be secured in rooms in which there is sufficient window-space if the windows are opened at top and bottom, and a board is placed at the bottom to prevent drafts. This holds true in winter as well as in summer.

(b) *Temperature for Health.* It has been found that in rooms where the employes are engaged in active work, a temperature of 60 to 65 degrees is the best standard to maintain. In this temperature the men are invigorated and are less liable to catch cold when they go out of doors. In rooms where the employes are engaged in sedentary occupations, it has been found that a maximum temperature of 68 degrees is advisable.

Minimum Cubic Feet of Air-space. In all places of employment not less than 300 cubic feet of air-space must be provided for each person.

V

SANITARY CARE AND COMFORTS

It is more feasible to make definite provisions as to standards
for installations for the sanitary care and comforts of the workers
in industrial establishments. Hence, factory legislation on this
subject has been more extensive, although not always satisfactory.
Factory laws make either general or definite provisions as to the
provision for drinking-water, washing-facilities, cleanliness in shops,
lunch-rooms, bathing, rest-rooms, etc. A résumé of the standards
of the various countries and states is given below.

Cleanliness. The *English* law, in addition to a general provision
requiring cleanliness and freedom from effluvia from drains in
factories, calls for whitewashing of walls and ceilings of workrooms,
halls and stairways once every 14 months, or a painting with oil
and varnish once every seven years. In the latter case, they must
be washed with hot water and soap every fourteen months.

France requires factory floors to be cleaned at least once a day
outside of working hours and scoured at least once a year. Walls
and ceilings must be kept clean and painted or plastered whenever
necessary. Organic matter must be removed immediately from
the workrooms unless kept in hermetically sealed receptacles.

Belgium has only general provisions for cleanliness in factories,
but requires all organic waste to be removed daily.

Most American states have only the most indefinite legal provisions for general cleanliness, such as "must be kept clean," "clean
as nature of business permits," etc. *Indiana* and *New York* require
factories to be limewashed when conducive to health or cleanliness.
Illinois requires removal of rubbish and waste at least once a day,
and all cleaning, as far as possible, to be done outside of working
hours.

The general orders issued by the Industrial Commission of
Wisconsin in regard to cleanliness are as follows:

" In all places of employment the floors and walls of the rooms,
and the machines, benches, vessels, and other things in the room,
must be kept as clean and sanitary as the nature of the industry
will permit. Where wet processes are used, the floors must be so
drained that there is no measurable depth of water in which the
operators must stand while working. Where practicable, dry

standing-room must be provided for employes. All waste, sweepings and decomposed matter must be removed from the workrooms each day, and their removal must be made in such a way as to avoid the raising of unnecessary dust or noxious odors. When possible, the sweeping and the removal of waste should be done outside of working hours.

Cuspidors. The doctors who have had the widest experience in the treatment of consumption (tuberculosis) state that *spitting on the floor spreads this dread disease more than any other one cause.* The commission wishes strongly to urge every employer to provide cuspidors for his employes. These cuspidors should be made of paper, which can be burnt, or of some impervious material which can be easily cleaned and kept in a sanitary condition. The cuspidors should be filled with a solution of borax, boracic acid or some other odorless disinfectant solution which will prevent the germs in the sputum from becoming dry and floating in the air."

Washing-facilities and Dressing-rooms. *French* and *Belgian* codes require employers to provide dressing-rooms with wash-basins for their employes. *Germany* requires one wash-place with running water for every five persons, and separate dressing-rooms for each sex must be provided in industries where workers need to change their clothing. Arrangements must also be made to dry wet clothes.

Only seven American states make any provisions for washing- or dressing-rooms. Five states require separate wash- and dressing-rooms for the sexes. *Illinois* requires one wash-basin for every thirty employes and separate wash-rooms for workers in specially dusty or dirty trades, provided with hot and cold water. *New York* State requires separate wash-rooms provided with running water in every factory, and separate dressing-rooms in factories where more than ten women are employed. *Wisconsin* prohibits the use of the common towel.

Drinking-water. *Switzerland* and *France* require the employer to provide good drinking-water for his employes. Where good drinking-water is lacking, the *Belgian* law requires the employer to provide a hygienic infusion. *German* factories must have pure drinking-water on every floor. No drinking-water faucets are allowed in toilet-rooms, and where water is objectionable it must be filtered.

Massachusetts and *Rhode Island* require fresh and pure drinking-water to be provided during working hours. *New York* requires a sufficient supply of clean and pure drinking-water to be provided at all times for the use of employes. It must be supplied through proper pipe connections with water mains used for domestic purposes or from spring, well, or body of pure water. If the water is placed in receptacles in the factory, these must be properly covered to prevent contamination and be thoroughly cleaned at frequent intervals.

The *Wisconsin* Industrial Commission requires each place of employment to be supplied with sufficient pure drinking-water, and the faucets or outlets for same to be placed convenient to the employes. Common drinking-cups are prohibited. Individual cups must be used or sanitary drinking-fountains must be installed.

Toilets. All European countries require separate toilet-rooms for the sexes. *Switzerland, England* and *Belgium* require one toilet for every twenty-five persons. *England*, however, modifies this requirement for large establishments, requiring one toilet for every twenty-five males up to one hundred, and one for every forty over that number. Where the number of males exceeds 500, one sanitary convenience for every sixty males is deemed sufficient, in addition to proper urinal accommodation. *France* requires one toilet for each fifty persons. *Germany* requires one for every twenty males and for every fifteen females.

The *German* Code requires all toilets to be located within a reasonable distance from the workers, but never in direct connection with the workrooms. The toilet-rooms must be arranged so as to be easily cleaned. The wall surfaces must be smooth and covered with a washable material up to 1.5 meters in height. Floors must be of non-absorbent material. Each toilet must be properly lighted and ventilated and heated during winter. Each toilet seat must be separated from the others by sound-proof partitions at least 2 meters in height and provided with doors. Each toilet compartment must have not less than 75 cubic meters capacity.

Most states in America require separate toilets and wash-rooms in factories where men and women are employed. The usual stipulation is for a "sufficient number." In *Tennessee*, separate water-closets for the sexes are not required unless there are fifteen or more employes. Six states require a definite number of toilets in proportion to the number of employes. *Illinois* requires one for every thirty males and twenty-five females; *Michigan, Indiana* and *New York* require one for every twenty-five persons; *Wisconsin* requires a separate toilet for each twenty persons or fraction.

The orders of the Industrial Commission of *Wisconsin* in regard to toilet-rooms are the most detailed of any state, and as they are being used as a model for similar orders in other states, they are given in detail as follows:

"*Toilet-rooms Required.* Every place of employment must be equipped with adequate toilet-rooms which must be distinct and separate from the other parts of the building and must be so constructed as to insure privacy.

"Where the two sexes are employed, separate toilet-rooms must be maintained. Toilet-rooms for the two sexes, when adjoining, must be separated by a partition made of material which is soundproof and which cannot be easily cut or defaced.

"*Sex Designated.* Each toilet-room must be distinctly marked with regard to the sex which uses it, and no person shall be allowed to use the toilet-room assigned to the opposite sex.

"*Indecent Pictures.* Indecent or suggestive marks, pictures, or words are forbidden in toilet-rooms, and such defacement when found by the employer must be at once removed.

"*Cleanliness.* Every toilet-room, and every part thereof, including walls, floors, and ceiling, and all fixtures therein, must be kept in a clean condition. In each toilet-room sufficient toilet-paper must be provided, and it must be made of material which will not obstruct the fixtures in each toilet-room.

"*Construction of Toilet-rooms.* In each toilet-room *hereafter installed* the floor must be constructed of material other than wood which does not readily absorb moisture and which can be easily cleaned.

"In toilet-rooms *at present installed* the walls must not be covered with paper. If the walls and ceilings are constructed of wood, they must be covered with a non-absorbent paint.

"In each toilet-room *hereafter installed* the walls and ceiling must be made of smooth cement, plaster, porcelain, glazed brick, metal tiling, or other smooth, non-absorbent material.

"*Location, Light, Ventilation.* Each toilet-room *hereafter installed* in a place of employment must be so located as to open to outside light and air. The minimum amount of window-space for a toilet containing one fixture must be 4 square feet, and for each additional fixture an addition of 2 square feet of window-space must be made. These windows must be so constructed that they can be opened to give adequate ventilation to the room.

"Each toilet-room *hereafter installed* must have not less than 10 square feet of floor space, and not less than 100 cubic feet of airspace for each fixture installed.

"In each toilet-room *heretofore installed*, and which is so located that it is impossible to secure light and air directly from the outside, a flue or mechanical ventilating system must be installed which will provide adequate ventilation.

"Each toilet-room which is not open to adequate outside light must be artificially lighted during the hours of employment, so that all parts of the room are easily visible.

"Each toilet-room must be furnished with adequate artificial light during the working hours when natural light is not available.

"Within five years after the date upon which these orders become effective, all toilet-rooms *at present installed* which are not open to outside light and air must be moved and so located that they are open to outside light and air.

"*Water-closets Hereafter Installed.* In each toilet-room *hereafter constructed*, individual water-closets made of porcelain or vitreous chinaware must be installed. These closets must be equipped with properly vented traps located above the floor, and with an adequate flushing device which uses not less than three gallons of water for each flush.

"Each water-closet must be set upon a solid base, and its connection to the soil-pipe or fitting must be constructed in such a manner as to be gas- and water-tight.

"*Water-closets at Present Installed.* Each water-closet *at present installed* must be provided with a flushing appliance, which will be as effective in its operation as the type of closet requires.

"Each water-closet must be kept in good repair, and obstructions must be removed at once.

"*Sewer Systems.* Each water-closet, urinal, lavatory, or slop-sink located in a toilet-room must be connected with a sewer system, where a sewer system is available.

"There must be a proper connection between the pumping system and the sewer, and such connection must be kept in good repair.

"*Seats for Water-closets.* The seat of each water-closet *hereafter installed* must be made of wood or other non-heat-absorbing material, and finished with varnish or other substance which will make it impervious to water. Under no circumstances will seats made of enameled ironware, porcelain, or similar heat-absorbing substance be allowed.

"*Number of Water-closets and Urinals Required.* Water-closets must be provided in places of employment in the following proportion: When the number employed is more than 20 of either sex, there shall be provided an additional closet for each sex, up to the number of 40, and above that number in the same ratio.

"Where males are employed, urinals must be provided in the proportion of 1 to every 40 employed. Where trough urinals are used, each 2 feet of trough shall constitute one urinal.

"*Urinals, Construction.* Each urinal must be made of impervious material and must be properly flushed and kept in clean condition. If iron is used in the construction of urinals, it must be enameled on the inside of the trough or bowl.

"*Partitions for Water-closets and Urinals.* Each water-closet or seat of range closet must be separated by a partition not less than 5 feet in height. Each individual urinal or urinal trough must be provided with a partition at each end and at the back, to give privacy. Where individual urinals are arranged in batteries, a partition must be placed at each end and at the back of the battery.

"In *new installations* the partitions between water-closets and urinals must be made of material other than wood, which does not readily absorb moisture.

"*Traps for Toilet-room Fixtures.* Each water-closet, urinal, lavatory, or slop-sink *hereafter installed* in a place of employment must have a trap. This trap must be equipped with a vent so constructed that adequate circulation of air will be secured in the waste-pipe; and so constructed that no siphonage will be possible, and the vent will not serve as a waste-pipe in case of obstruction.

"In installations where individual lavatory bowls are arranged in a battery, one trap may be used for six bowls.

"Each lavatory and slop-sink *at present installed* must be equipped with a trap properly vented. A mechanical trap may be installed where it is impractical to install a vented trap.

"On *old installations* each water-closet and urinal must be equipped with a trap, and where there are two or more water-closets or urinals on one sewer connection, the trap must be properly vented."

Lunch-rooms. Workers in *French* factories are forbidden to eat lunch in the workrooms, although permission to do so may be granted in case of need by the division inspector, under the condition that no toxic materials are employed, that no disagreeable or poisonous gas or dust is given off, and that other hygienic conditions are satisfactory. The *Belgian* Code forbids workers to eat lunch in work-places where poisonous substances are used. In all factories in *Germany* well-lighted lunch-rooms, separate for each sex, and heated during winter, and containing the necessary number of tables and chairs must be provided for workers who do not leave the factory during the midday pause.

In America, three states—*Illinois*, *New York* and *Missouri*—forbid employes to eat food in any room where white-lead, arsenic, poisonous substances, injurious fumes, dust or gases are present. A notice to this effect must be posted in such rooms, and the employes are not allowed to remain in these rooms during meal hours. The employer must make suitable provision whenever practicable for meals elsewhere in the establishment.

Medical Appliances. Two states in the Union, namely *Massachusetts* and *California*, require every factory where machinery is used to install a medical or surgical chest, maintained free of cost, for the use of employes. In Massachusetts the requirements for articles in the chest are made by the local boards of health. California requires a specified list of medicines and appliances costing not less than six dollars.

CHAPTER XII

FACTORY INSPECTION

The Beginning of Factory Inspection in Europe and in the United States. The extent of legal protection given to workers is determined not by the number of factory laws upon the statute books, but by the number of such laws as are properly administered and by the extent to which their provisions are actually enforced.

The promulgation of laws protecting workers against risks and dangers within the factory has always preceded by considerable periods the creation of administrative institutions for their enforcement. In Europe, as well as in the United States, factory inspection was practically thrust upon the governments and states because of the accumulated evidence that legislative enactments were futile without provisions for their administration and enforcement.

The first factory inspection department was organized in *England* in 1833. In the parliamentary debates preceding the enactment of the Law of 1833, it was conceded by all that the provisions of the Acts of 1802, 1819, 1825, and 1831 were never properly enforced and that those acts failed to give needed protection to factory workers. From the time of the enactment of the first factory law in 1802, the manufacturing interests bitterly opposed all endeavors to create special machinery for the enforcement of labor laws which they knew would remain ineffectual, so long as there was no special department for their enforcement.

The importance of the Act of 1833, which created the first factory inspection department, lay therefore in the recognition of the necessity of a special administrative body for the enforcement of labor laws. The history of factory inspection in England since that date shows the steady progress of this great social institution which was later adopted, copied and followed by other countries and states.

In 1834, the Factory Inspection Department of England began with four inspectors having jurisdiction over 2094 factories. From this small beginning it has grown and developed until it has a per-

514

sonnel of 224 inspectors having jurisdiction over no less than 117,275 factories and 155,697 workshops (1913), a total of 272,972 industrial establishments.

In *France*, the Labor Inspection Department was not established until 1874, although there had been considerable factory legislation, beginning with the ordinance of 1806 and followed by numerous acts since that date. Between 1874 and 1892, the inspectorial service of France was not compulsory for all the departments. Only in 1892 was it established on a firm basis and reorganized in its present form.

In *Prussia* and in the German states, administrative departments for the enforcement of labor laws were not established until 1878, although factory legislation began with the Regulativ of 1839 and was followed by the Laws of 1845 and 1853 and by the promulgation of the " Industrial Code " of the North German Union in 1869. As in France, the first inspection department created in 1878 was experimental and not compulsory for all states; and only in 1891 was the whole service reorganized. Since that time the progress of the department has been steady.

In *Austria*, as in the other countries, there were attempts at factory legislation from the beginning of the nineteenth century, and in 1859 a complete industrial code was promulgated; but not until 1883 was industrial inspection organized and established.

The same conditions prevailed in other countries. Laws were enacted and put on the statute books, but were not enforced because administrative provisions were lacking. Only when their failure to protect the workers had been demonstrated was an endeavor made to establish a system of factory inspection. The following is a chronological table of the beginning of factory inspection in the various European countries: Great Britain, 1833; Denmark, 1873; France, 1874; Switzerland (Federal), 1877; Germany, 1878; Russia, 1882; Austria, 1883; Belgium, 1889; Netherlands, 1889; Sweden, 1889; Portugal, 1893; Hungary, 1893; Italy, 1906; Spain, 1907.*

Factory Inspection in the United States. As was the case in European countries, factory inspection in the United States lagged behind factory legislation and years elapsed before it dawned upon legislators that not only factory laws but provisions for their administration and enforcement were needed.

---

* The data on European factory inspection is taken from the report which I made to the U. S. Dept. of Labor, and which has been published by the Bureau of Labor Statistics in 1914 as Bulletin No. 142.

The first attempt at factory inspection was made in Massachusetts in 1886. Prior to that year, since 1842, the local school authorities and truant officers were the enforcing agents of the several laws which were passed, beginning with the Child Labor Law of 1836. In 1866 a single deputy was detailed by the police department to enforce the Child Labor and Compulsory Education Laws, and only in 1877 was the right of entry into factories granted to this inspector. By the Act of 1879, the governor was empowered to appoint two or more members of the district police to act as inspectors of factories and public buildings. Immediately upon the passage of this act the governor appointed Rufus R. Wade, John T. White and Joseph M. Dyson. The duties of these inspectors were (1) the enforcement of laws regulating the hours of labor in manufacturing establishments, (2) laws relating to employment of children, and (3) inspection of factories and public buildings.

In the first report of the chief of the district police, who was also one of the inspectors appointed by the governor, the question of fire hazards in factories was considered at some length. This section of the report might have been taken from a report of any one of the recent legislative commissions investigating industrial conditions, risks and hazards.

" In the matter of providing for speedy and safe egress in case of fire or panic, a large number of manufacturing establishments were found deficient. The horrors of Holyoke and Granite Mill at Fall River and other disasters that have occurred by reason of neglect to provide safe means of egress in case of fire or panic should not, through negligence or thoughtlessness of manufacturers or owners of public buildings, be repeated." *

This first report also states that the laws providing for education of working children were not enforced and that many children were employed below the legal age. In one mill the inspectors found thirty boys and girls working, the youngest being only nine years old. The two inspectors found their task a heavy one, as can readily be imagined, since they were supposed to inspect not only all the manufacturing establishments, but also all public buildings, such as schools, churches, hotels, boarding and lodging houses, etc.

The quote from the report again: " The task of inspection of factories is of sufficient magnitude and importance to justify making it a distinct branch of the service."

* Report of Rufus R. Wade, Chief of District Police for 1879, p. 8.

The report also asked that two assistants be appointed. The following year, 1880, the governor's message recommended that factory inspection be made a separate department; but not until 1888 was this established.

In discussing the work of these early inspectors, Miss Whittlesey, in her book on Massachusetts Labor Legislation, says: "It is curious to note the attitude of employers towards these labor laws. Invariably offering persistent opposition to the enactment of each new measure, they nevertheless fall one after another into line and obedience. The inspectors constantly attest their cheerful spirit of compliance and their general courteous treatment." *

In 1891 two women inspectors were added. In 1893 a separate boiler inspection division with ten inspectors was created. In 1907, a reorganization of factory inspection was made, by which a number of state health inspectors were appointed, who were given discretion to look after the health conditions in their districts, and who took over a considerable part of the functions of factory inspectors. The chief work of the health inspectors consisted in collecting data relating to industrial hygiene or occupational diseases. The division of functions of factory inspection between the district police and the State Board of Health created much dissatisfaction, and in 1910 a commission was appointed to investigate the matter and report upon conditions. The commission found that "neither the inspection department of the district police, nor that of the State Board of Health had a force of men in the field exclusively engaged in the inspection of factories, workshops and mercantile establishments specially qualified and selected for their work. In short, the Commonwealth had no specialized industrial inspectors at the time, and the commission therefore recommended the establishment of a separate department of industrial inspection." †

In 1913, the inspection department of Massachusetts was reorganized, an Industrial Board established and a larger force of inspectors engaged.

In *New York*, there existed a number of legislative enactments for the protection of women and children in manufacturing establishments; but only in 1886 was an act passed to provide for the appointment of inspectors to enforce the same. The act called for the appointment by the governor of a factory inspector at a salary of $2000 per year and an assistant at a salary of $1500 per year,

---

* S. S. Whittlesey: Massachusetts Labor Legislation, p. 28.
† Report of the Commission of Massachusetts to Investigate Inspection of Factories, Workshops and Mercantile Establishments and Other Buildings, June, 1911, p. 16.

the inspectors to hold office for three years. James Connelly was appointed as inspector and John T. Franey as assistant.

In their first report issued in 1887, the inspectors gave a record of three months' work. They complained of the ignorance of the children working in the mills and factories and stated that compulsory education was a dead letter. The inspectors seem to have worked hard and to have been anxious to fulfill their duties as best they could. They visited 857 factories in twenty-one counties in four months, and as a result of this first inspection they made a number of recommendations to the legislature, which read very much as though they were written just lately. Among the recommendations were a compulsory education law, prohibition of children under fourteen years from working in manufacturing establishments, screening of staircases, prohibition of cleaning machinery while in motion by women and minors under eighteen years, a ten-hour workday for women and minors under eighteen years, a three-quarter hour midday pause, proper construction of elevators and hoistways, provision for proper fire-escapes and stairways, physician's certificate for children under sixteen years, increase of air space for employes, screening and separation of water-closets, construction of all doors to open outward, and other provisions which even at present have not yet been all put on the statute books.

The growth of the factory inspection department in New York State was at first very slow. In 1887, eight male inspectors were added to the two previously appointed. In 1901, the Bureaus of Statistics, Inspection, Mediation and Arbitration were combined under one head and a labor department was formed. Since the creation of this Department its progress has been rapid and very great, until at present it has the largest number of inspectors of any state and has an annual budget of nearly $700,000.

Between 1870 and 1890 *Illinois* reached the rank of third state in the Union in the value of its annual manufactured product. But because this growth had been sudden, the state up to that time had done nothing to ameliorate the conditions of the workers by legislation, such as had been passed in the other manufacturing states. The Illinois Child Labor Act of June 17, 1891 carried with it no provisions for enforcement. By the Act of June 17, 1893, the Department of Factories and Workshops was established with one chief and an assistant chief, five male and five female inspectors. An appropriation of $20,000 for two years was made for salaries and $8000 for traveling and other expenses. The report of the factory inspectors at the close of the first year showed that 2363 places were inspected in which 76,224 persons were employed. Of these, 6456 or 8.5 per cent were children between the ages of fourteen and sixteen.*

In *Pennsylvania*, the enforcement of the labor laws, some of which were enacted as early as 1827, was left to tax assessors; and it was not until 1889 that any real provision was made for inspection of factories.

The first inspection department consisted of one chief and six district inspectors. In 1901, there were already forty-one inspectors. In 1913, Pennsylvania factory inspection was considerably reformed, reorganized and an Industrial Board appointed.

In 1883, a law was passed in *Wisconsin* requiring the appointment of a commissioner who was to constitute a bureau of labor statistics. This commissioner was to collect statistics in regard to wholesale and retail prices, the cost of agricultural products, wages of skilled and unskilled laborers of the state, hours of labor, number of workers in the different industries, etc. In addition to collecting these statistics, he was required to visit all the factories in the state and see that the laws were enforced. The commissioner was to receive $1500 a year, and no provision was made for an assistant or clerk. He was only allowed $500 for traveling expenses; and in his first report the commissioner stated that he had found it an impossibility to properly perform the work of inspection of factories with the small sum of money and with the limited time he had left from his other duties. In 1887, in response to repeated requests of the commissioner for assistants, two inspectors were appointed and penalties were attached to the laws which made it possible to enforce them. In addition to factories, these inspectors were required to visit hotels, lodging houses, churches and schools for the purposes of seeing that these buildings were safe from fire hazards.†

The first factory inspector in *Maine* was appointed in 1887, and in 1907 one female assistant was added. In Ohio, the first inspectors were appointed in 1884 and in 1904 there were thirteen inspectors.

In *New Jersey*, factory inspection began in 1883, and in 1889 six inspectors were appointed. In 1904 a separate department of factory inspection with eleven inspectors was established.

* Bulletin, State of Illinois, Department of Factory Inspection, Vol. I, No. 2, Chicago, April, 1914.
† Reports of the Bureau of Labor Statistics of Wisconsin, 1883 and 1887

In *Rhode Island*, factory inspection began in 1894 with two inspectors, one of whom was a woman.

In *Indiana*, factory inspection began in 1887 with one chief and five inspectors.

In *Tennessee*, factory inspection started in 1895, in *Delaware*, in 1897 (with one female inspector) and in *Missouri* in 1901.

In 1887, the first convention of factory inspectors was held in Boston. At this date, five states had factory inspection departments, Massachusetts being the first. The others were New Jersey, Ohio, New York and Wisconsin.

Scope and Work of Factory Inspection. There is great diversity in the number, scope and extent of the laws to be enforced by factory inspection departments as well as in the kind and character of the industrial establishments which are under their jurisdiction.

In some states the scope of the laws to be enforced by the inspection departments is very wide and includes child and woman's work, hours of labor, factory construction, fire protection, prevention of accidents, workmen's compensation, wage payment, arbitration and mediation, etc. In other states the labor laws to be enforced by the factory inspection departments chiefly consist in the protection of child and women workers and the maintaining of certain working conditions within the factory.

In some states the number of industrial establishments under the jurisdiction of the inspection departments is limited by legal definitions of factory or workshop which confine the application of the law either to establishments employing a certain number of persons or to establishments of a certain character. In other states every place where work is being done is considered a workshop and is under the jurisdiction of the factory inspection department.

There is also much diversity in the number and character of the administrative bodies or institutions which are empowered to administer the labor laws and to enforce factory acts. In some countries, notably in France and Belgium, the whole work is centered in the labor inspection departments, and the only assistance from outside bodies that these departments receive is from the regular prosecuting and judicial functionaries.

In other countries, for instance in England, the local authorities are a coexisting administrative institution, having jurisdiction over the enforcement of all sanitary provisions in workshops. This division of authority between the factory inspection department and the local government is the result of certain historical developments of administrative institutions in England.

In Germany, there are three great bodies in charge of the administration of factory laws: first, the industrial inspectors who inspect factories and workshops in relation to sanitation, safety and general industrial conditions; second, the inspectors of the trade associations who are charged with prevention of accidents; and third, the police authorities who do a great deal of inspection and reinspection work, gathering statistical data and having sole jurisdiction over actual enforcement by judicial and administrative procedures.

In Austria, there is considerable division of labor between the industrial inspectors and the local industrial authorities who have charge of the prosecution and the general administration of the laws.

In Switzerland, there is division of jurisdiction between the Federal factory inspectors and the cantonal inspectors, and the enforcement of the law is entirely in the hands of the local police and cantonal authorities.

Diversity of jurisdiction in the enforcement of labor laws is sometimes advantageous, because it gives much less work to the labor or factory inspection department and makes it possible for more industrial establishments to be inspected. On the other hand, it carries disadvantages in the division of authority between the enforcing institutions, in the lack of uniformity in standards of inspection, and in the inevitable friction resulting therefrom.

In the United States, labor laws are also enforced by different departments, boards and groups of officials. In New York, labor laws are enforced by the Department of Labor, by the Public Service Commission, by the State Fire Marshal, by the Workmen's Compensation Commission, by the local building construction officials, by local Boards of Health, etc. In the State of New Jersey the Department of Labor, the Bureau of Statistics of Labor and Industries, the Board of Health, the Boards of Public Utilities, the local school authorities, etc., each have various duties in respect to the enforcement of labor legislation. In Massachusetts, the provisions of the labor laws are enforced by the Board of Labor and Industries, the Bureau of Statistics, the Board of District Police, the Board of Railroad Commissioners, the Industrial Accident Board, the Board of Conciliation and Arbitration, the Minimum Wage

Commission, the local building inspector, the local Boards of Health, the local school authorities, etc., etc. Similar conditions prevail in other states where the enforcement of labor laws is shared by various departments.*

There is also great diversity in the designation of the institutions which are in charge of factory inspection. This is less so in Europe than in the United States. In eight American states factory inspection is under the jurisdiction of the the so-called "Bureaus of Labor Statistics." The next most frequent titles are "Department of Labor," which occurs four times; "Department of Labor and Industry," which occurs three times; "Bureau of Labor," which occurs three times; "Bureau of Labor and Industrial Statistics," which occurs in two states; and "Factory Inspection Department," "Department of Factory Inspection" and Bureau of Emigration, Labor and Statistics." "Industrial Commission" also occurs twice, and then follow twenty-two titles, no two of which are alike, making a total of thirty-one titles for officers doing practically the same kind of work.†

In most countries in Europe there are several methods by which special administrative provisions having the force of law may be issued for the guidance of factory inspectors.

In England, the Secretary of State is empowered to make rules and regulations for certain industries after special investigation. Appeal may be taken against the decisions, but the principle is well established and the Secretary of State thus has considerable legislative power.

In other European countries, the Ministers of Industry, Labor or Commerce who have jurisdiction over the factory inspection department, have considerable legislative and administrative power and have power to issue rules and orders interpreting and extending the industrial code.

In the United States, until lately, the factory inspection departments were simply the executive agencies of the state and had no power to make administrative rules and regulations or to add to the provisions of the industrial code. Only lately, in Wisconsin, and then in New York, Massachusetts and Pennsylvania were industrial commissions and boards created with power to issue rules and regulations and to adopt an industrial code without waiting for acts of legislatures.

* Administration of Labor Laws, Vol. III, No. 4, Publication 23 of the American Labor Legislative Review, Published by American Association for Labor Legislation.
† Ibid.

Almost all factory legislation provides penalties for violations of laws. These penalties are usually small, although at times they may reach hundreds of dollars. The department reports state the amount of fines which were recovered through the action of their inspectors; these fines sometimes reach very respectable sums.

In most of the states or countries the prosecution of offenders against the factory laws is carried on either by the state or local prosecuting officers or by special prosecutors, attorneys, corporation counsels, etc., who are assigned to the factory inspection department.

In England the factory inspectors themselves act as prosecuting officers. On the other hand, Germany is an example of an entirely opposite attitude toward the functions of factory inspectors. There, industrial inspectors have nothing whatever to do with enforcing the law or prosecuting offenders. They are simply technical experts, who give their advice and opinion as to conditions in factories and industrial establishments. Violations, wherever found, are referred to police authorities; and all work of prosecution and subsequent enforcement and penalization is in their hands. It is interesting to note the opinion of German legislators as to this special character of their industrial inspectors. The following quotation is from a speech made in 1887, during the discussion of the relations of factory inspectors to police authorities, by Minister Von Boetticher. He says,

" The factory inspector is not intended to become a police executive. The factory inspector is an official who, because of his technical knowledge is, on the one hand an adviser to the authorities in the establishment of various regulations for the safety of industrial establishments; and, on the other hand, is an adviser of the industry and of the workers in the sphere which is given to him. The real *police tasks* of factory inspection should not be within the sphere of the activities of the inspectors. For this the factory inspector is much too high. This function may be left to the *gendarmes*."

In the United States, factory inspectors are usually called as witnesses in court cases; but the prosecution is in the hands of attorneys who are specially designated for this purpose and attached to the factory inspection department, or are regular prosecuting attorneys of the county or the municipality in which the offense occurs.

The duties of factory inspectors differ according to the scope
of factory legislation in each state or country; but in most countries
they consist in enforcing the provisions of the labor and factory
acts, inspecting the various industrial establishments under their
jurisdiction, detecting violations of the law, advising employers
of such improvements in their establishments as would tend to prevent industrial accidents and occupational diseases, and in efforts
to improve conditions of work in the factories.

The inspectors are endowed with certain powers, the most
important of which is the right of entry. Next to this is the right
to take evidence, to require the production of documents and to
enforce compliance with the requirements of the law.

There is hardly any inspection department or administrative
body for the enforcement of factory laws in which there is no provision made for the right of entry of the inspectors at all times to
all industrial establishments under their jurisdiction. Indeed,
inspection would be a farce if such right of entry were not granted.
There is some divergence, however, in the provisions as to right
of entry during the night time or when no work is being performed.
In some countries, inspectors have no such right during the night or
at times when the industrial establishment is not in activity. The
right of entry is usually granted to all the officers of factory inspection departments.

Inspectors show their authority by special " cards of legitimacy "
which, in some European countries bear the photograph of the
inspector. In the United States, inspectors usually wear official
badges. In Germany, the right of entry gives the inspectors all
the powers of the local police authorities and in particular the right
to visit work places at any hour of the day or night. The right of
entry is extended in Austria to workmen's dwellings, which are under
the labor law; in Belgium to premises where wages are paid, and
in England to schools where children employed in workshops and
factories are educated. In Italy and Russia, the inspectors have
the right of entry to bedrooms, messrooms, crêches and all places
appertaining to the factory. In France and Luxemburg, all such
schools are subject to inspection even if the education given is of
an industrial nature or if they are charitable institutions. On the
other hand, in Holland, schools and institutions of this kind belonging to the state are not subject to inspection.

In the United States, the right of entry is given to all inspectors
in all states. The right of taking evidence and compelling the **giving**

of information by employers and workers is granted in most states where factory inspection departments have been established for some time, as it has been shown that this right is of great importance to the proper enforcement of factory laws.

Organization. All European countries have a system of factory or industrial inspection. In the United States, of the forty-eight states in the Union, only thirty-nine have provisions for factory inspection. The six states which have no such provisions are Arizona, Mississippi, Nevada, New Mexico, South Dakota and Wyoming. Idaho and North Dakota have no factory inspection, but only Bureaus of Statistics. In North Carolina, there is no enforcement of laws over factories but only over mines. In seven of the thirty-nine states, viz., Connecticut, Illinois, Indiana, Massachusetts, Missouri, New Jersey and Rhode Island, there are separate Bureaus of Factory Inspection and Collection and Publication of Labor Statistics.*

The centralized form of organization predominates among all factory inspection departments and is typified by the oldest factory inspection department, that of England. Factory inspection in England is a separate department of the Home Office, presided over by a chief inspector who is responsible for all the work of the department and who has full authority over the department; and the whole machinery of the organization is then divided and subdivided, classified and graded so as to form one compact, highly centralized and highly specialized body.

The Industrial Inspection Department of Austria has an organization somewhat similar to that of England, but is not so highly centralized and gives more authority and independence to the inspectors and to the industrial authorities under whom the inspectors serve.

The same form of organization is also found in Belgium, except that there the organization is still less cohesive and the district inspectors have much independent authority.

All inspection bureaus and departments of the United States have a strictly centralized organization. They are all presided over by a chief inspector or commissioner, who is responsible for the whole department or bureau, and who usually has full authority to organize his department according to the law and in most cases has great powers in the appointment of inspectors. The chief

* Administration of Labor Laws, American Labor Legislation Review, Vol. III, Publication 23.

inspector has also full authority to assign inspectors to various
functions.

The Prussian Industrial Inspection Service presents an antithesis
to the centralized government of England and the United States.
In Prussia, the department has no chief inspector, the organization
of enforcement being left entirely to the different states and district governments. Each district is presided over by a special industrial councilor, between whom and the district inspectors there
are no very close relations, each inspector of a district having supreme
authority over his district and his work. Between this extreme
decentralized form of organization and the highly centralized organization of England, there are a number of gradations, such as those
presented by the inspection departments in some of the lesser Germanic states.

A unique form of organization is that adopted in the State
of Wisconsin where the Industrial Commission was created in 1911.
This Commission consists of three members who have sole jurisdiction over factory inspection, labor law enforcement, gathering
of publications and statistics, workmen's compensation, employment offices, accident prevention and everything which "makes
the work place safe," *safety* being defined by the law as "such
freedom from danger to life, health or safety as the nature of the
employment will reasonably permit." This Commission has,
besides executive powers, considerable legislative and administrative functions and has been enabled by the legislature to issue special rules and regulations, set standards and issue an industrial code
which is binding on all concerned.

Owing to the high character and ability of the first appointed
commissioners, the *Wisconsin idea* has worked very well indeed,
and its extension and acceptance by other states has been urged
by a great many social workers and those interested in industrial
matters. Whether the Wisconsin form of organization would have
been as successful with a personnel of commissioners of the type
usually appointed in other states, is doubtful. At any rate, the
Wisconsin precedent has not been followed in New York, Massachusetts, Pennsylvania, California and Ohio, where industrial boards
have been appointed with considerable legislative but without any
executive power, this being left, as before, with the Labor Commissioner.

In the organization of all inspection departments, the personnel
consists mainly of the inspectors, upon whom devolves the chief

function and work of the department, that of inspection. There are different classifications and gradings of inspectors and there is considerable difference in the designation and grading of the supervising force,—such as chief inspectors, deputy chief inspectors, central inspectors, commissioner, deputy commissioners, etc.

The budgets for inspection work in each state or country differ according to the number of employes, to the number of industrial establishments and to the character and extent of the functions of the inspectors and of the inspection department. The budgets range from the lowest of about $3000 in the State of Delaware, to $691,220 in New York State in 1914.

There is also great difference in the extent of specialization in the inspection departments abroad and in the United States. In Prussia, there is hardly any specialization at all, as all the inspectors must be technically trained persons, able to make inspections in all different industries, processes, etc., although experts in various branches may be called in from time to time when necessary. There is no division of labor among the inspectors and no medical, chemical or other inspectors are appointed.

This is also the case in France, where there is hardly any specialization; and division as well as departmental inspectors perform all the functions, although some of the inspectors may be specially trained in certain branches of industry.

In England and in Austria there is considerable specialization among the inspectors; thus, there are in England inspectors for dangerous trades, for textile industries, for light, for electricity, besides the medical division. In Austria there are special inspectors for building construction, shipping and several other branches of industry.

In the United States there has developed lately a tendency towards specialization of functions among the higher grades of inspectors. Thus, in New York, there are special inspectors for safety, ventilation, fire, etc.; and in the Division of Hygiene there are technically trained engineers, physicians, chemists, etc. Specialization of functions also prevails in some of the work of the Wisconsin Commission and in the work of the Illinois, Massachusetts, and Pennsylvania departments.

The growing conviction that the supervision of sanitary conditions in industrial establishments, the prevention of occupational diseases and the improvement of the health of the workers are subjects of paramount importance, has led to agitation for the participation of physicians in factory inspection. So far, there are very few countries in Europe and very few states in the Union where medical factory inspection has been established.

The only European countries in which there is effective medical factory inspection are England and Belgium. In England, the first medical factory inspector was appointed in 1894 and at present the medical division consists of four physicians presided over by the chief medical inspector, Dr. Legge. In Belgium, Dr. Glibert, who was appointed in 1911, has organized and maintains a highly efficient division of medical factory inspection in the department, although the personnel of this division consists only of four physicians. Bavaria and Baden each have a physician in the inspectorial service; Austria has a medical consultant, and here and there in different countries are found physicians connected with the inspectorial service, although their function is not as separate and distinct as in England and Belgium.

New York was the first state to appoint a medical factory inspector. This was done in 1907, and when the department was reorganized in 1914, a section of medical factory inspection was instituted consisting of a chief medical factory inspector and three assistants. Illinois in 1912 appointed two medical factory inspectors, and lately Pennsylvania and Massachusetts have followed suit.

All labor and factory legislation in all countries and states had its origin in the necessity for the protection of children and women in industry; hence, all labor legislation began with the restriction of child and female labor. Such restrictions form at present a large part of every industrial code in all countries and states, and the enforcement of the child and women labor laws constitute a major part of the work in all factory inspection departments. The chief agitation for protective legislation for children and women has come from social workers and from women, and there has been from the inception of factory inspection, a strong agitation on the part of women for the appointment of women factory inspectors.

The first women inspectors were appointed in England in 1893, and since then there has been a separate division of women inspectors. This division at present consists of twenty women inspectors and is practically independent of the factory inspection department in its work and functions and is subject only to a general supervision by the chief factory inspector. The position of women factory inspectors in England is unique, and their standing is exceedingly high.

There are eighteen women inspectors in France, two female inspectors in Belgium, five female inspectors in Austria, fifteen in Prussia, none in the Federal Inspection Department of Switzerland and a few here and there in the Germanic states. Outside of England, the functions of female inspectors are limited to the inspection of smaller shops where chiefly women and children are employed. Their position is of a lower grade than that of the male inspectors; their salaries are much smaller; but their work is an integral part of the work of each district factory inspector, except perhaps in Belgium, where they work more or less independently and have charge also of the mercantile establishments.

In the United States there are a number of women in the factory inspection departments of the different states. Some of the women were appointed when the departments were created; others have been added to the inspection force from time to time. The following gives the number of women inspectors in the several states of the Union which have factory inspection departments: New York, 30; Ohio, 8; Pennsylvania, 5; Massachusetts and Minnesota, 4; Illinois, Michigan, New Jersey, Wisconsin and Maryland, 3; California, Connecticut, 2; Colorado, Delaware, Iowa, Kansas, Kentucky, Maine, Missouri, Rhode Island, Utah, and Washington, 1.

The main arguments for the appointment of women inspectors are (1) the very large percentage of women in industrial establishments, (2) the considerable number of provisions in every labor and factory code protecting women in industrial establishments, (3) the greater sympathy and understanding of women inspectors for the needs of their sex and the enforcement of the child labor law, (4) the greater confidence that women and child workers feel towards women inspectors, (5) the special adaptability and worth of women in inspectorial work, (6) the possible reluctance of women workers to complain about certain sanitary matters to male inspectors.

In this country the principle has been firmly established that women have a right to participation in factory inspection, and it has been proven that they are capable of doing good work; and that there is no reason for excluding women from a branch of state service in which they have shown themselves so efficient. The objection that women factory inspectors do not, as a rule, possess the highly specialized training in safety and mechanical appliances may hold good in Germany or in countries where only highly technically trained persons are accepted as factory inspectors; but

not in countries and states where inspectors are appointed without
any special technical training.

In Europe there is also great agitation for the appointment
of inspectors from the laboring class who have had practical training in manual and mechanical work. This subject has been discussed and agitated with considerable bitterness, especially by
representatives of labor organizations. The demand is made for
the creation of a lower grade of inspectors, composed of workmen
to be selected without examination or with a special examination.
There is, however, much opposition to this demand. The opposition comes often from the government and also from the inspectors
themselves. In England, we find the inspectorial service divided
into two classes, the lower grade consisting of workmen inspectors,
numbering fifty-five. Their functions are limited, their salaries
lower and their status different from that of the regular factory
inspectors. In Prussia, France and Switzerland there are as yet
no such inspectors, although the pressure on the government from
labor organizations and the social democratic and radical political
parties is very great. In some of the Germanic states a few inspectors from the laboring class have been appointed. In Austria there
are two workingmen inspectors for special functions, and there are
also a few in Belgium.

In the United States, there cannot be any division of classes
among regular inspectors and workmen inspectors, and most of
the inspectors are persons who have previously pursued some
mechanical occupation and who were either selected because they
had passed their civil service examination or because of their affilia-
tion with labor organizations.

Methods of Selection and Character of Factory Inspectors.
The efficiency of a factory inspection department depends partly
upon its form of organization, the functions it has to perform, the
scope of its work, the appropriations the state makes for the purposes of factory inspection, and in a large measure upon the character, qualifications and efficiency of the inspectors themselves.

The functions of a factory inspection department are three-
fold:—(1) detection of the violations of the factory acts; (2) prevention of industrial accidents and disease; and (3) education
of employers and employes in order to get their coöperation in the
enforcement of the factory laws and the prevention of industrial
accidents and disease. It is to be regretted that in most factory
inspection departments the detection of violations seems to be

their main and most important function; and this is especially true of the United States. The prevention of accidents and disease should be the paramount function of the department. Neither in Europe nor in the United States is there as much prominence given to the educational functions of the departments as they deserve.

For the efficient organization of factory inspection and proper enforcement of labor and factory laws, the inspectors should be possessed of the highest possible qualifications. Factory inspectors should be recruited from the most intelligent and best classes of the community. He who wishes to devote himself to the profession of factory inspector should be endowed with a good physique and robust health. He should have a gentlemanly bearing and be able to meet on an equal footing employers, superintendents and managers of the plants he inspects, and should also possess tact so as to be able to sail safely between the Scylla of capital and the Charybdis of labor and not seem to be partisan to either side.

The factory inspector should have a prolonged training and experience in industrial work and have the practical knowledge of industrial conditions so necessary for intelligent inspection of factories and workshops. A factory inspector should have a good general education so as to enable him to stand on a basis of equality with the average intelligent employer and manufacturer.

Aside from all these qualifications, the inspector should go through special technical training in matters of industrial hygiene, in architecture of factory buildings, in theory and practice of factory lighting, ventilation and sanitation. A good technical knowledge of machinery is also necessary in order to enable him to inspect all kinds of machinery, to criticize safeguards and suggest improvements.

The inspector should also have a general knowledge of the various kinds of dusts, their effects and methods of prevention, should know the different industrial poisons, their specific effects and means of prevention. He should also be able to make the necessary tests of air, light and ventilation which are within the province and functions of factory inspection; in short, be an expert in industrial hygiene. It is desirable that an inspector should be able to speak the languages which the working population in his district use and also be able to give lectures and talks to classes of workers and educational institutions.

It is with regret that one has to state that the general character of factory inspectors in the United States falls very far short of the above ideal requirements. Of the nearly twelve hundred inspectors in the bureaus and departments of factory inspection in the different states, there are few who fulfill all the above qualifications. This is admitted by all writers on the subject and all who are acquainted with the character of factory inspectors in the United States. There are a number of reasons for this condition, the principal being the method used in selecting factory inspectors and the general conception of state service in this country.

Selection for fitness is still a rare method of appointment of factory inspectors in the states. Labor laws and factory inspection departments have been won from reluctant legislatures by the efforts of partisan politicians and political labor unions; and when these laws are enacted and inspection departments established, the spoils usually go to victorious politicians without regard to the necessary qualifications of the personnel. As a writer on the subject aptly says, " As a rule, laws regulating the employment of labor have been won from indifferent legislatures as concession to the labor vote; and the offices created in this way have been usually conceded to the union as a sop to Cerberus."[*]

In a report issued in 1910 by the National Civic Federation's Committee on Improvement of Factory Inspection, the following statement is made:

" Obviously the effectiveness of the inspection of factories must depend first, upon the statutory requirements, and second, upon the efficiency of the individual inspectors. The collected returns from States show that the tenure of office of inspectors varies from two to four years or is at the will of the commissioner of labor, or of the governor, or during good behavior. The inference is that there is needed more protection of inspectors against political or personal influence in the performance of their duties. In nearly every state reported, no examination is required for appointment as inspector. Two exceptions are New York and Wisconsin, where the returns state a civil service examination is required. The inference is that there is a generally prevalent defect in statutes, which leaves the administration of whatever the statutory requirements as to inspection may be, open to personal or political interest or influence."

In a report on the efficiency of the factory inspection machinery in the United States, E. F. Brown has stated the conditions in a nutshell, as follows:

* B. Herron: Factory Inspection in the United States, American Journal of Sociology, 1907, p. 491.

" Finally, the most dangerously unguarded machinery I have known is the machinery of factory inspection in the United States, exposed to a most pernicious political influence, and to the parsimony of legislators, rendering possible the industrial diseases and accidents which a provident nation would promptly make impossible."*

Mr. Brown further states that

" in twenty states the head of the labor department is designated by the governor, and his term of office depends usually on the political fortunes of his chief. The absence of a permanent official in this important post makes it possible for politics to play no uncertain game, both in the choice and in the character of the man who is sworn to enforce the labor laws. The best type of man is not always attracted to the position. To my mind, no state, except possibly Massachusetts and Wisconsin, has entirely freed its labor department from a destructive political influence. This is, I think, the one cloud which hovers over the otherwise successful administration of labor laws by commissions. In only five states in the United States,—New York, Massachusetts, New Jersey, Wisconsin and Illinois—are inspectors required to qualify through the civil service test, and unfortunately, in even some of these five the test does not appear to be the last word in the selection of able and honest assistants."

Of the character of inspectors, Mr. Brown speaks as follows:

" In Pennsylvania, where I recently made an investigation of the administration of the department, I found that many of the factory inspectors were conducting private business enterprises while holding commissions in the department. One is alleged to have sold fire insurance to the establishments he was sworn to inspect impartially. Another kept a saloon. Still another was in the coal business. In another state, where the chief factory inspector divides his time between conducting a livery stable he owns and the business of caring for some 30,000 factory wage-earners, I found him contributing a remarkably concise annual report consisting of exactly fourteen words. It reads, under date of July 1, 1911, as follows: ' I have visited the same factories as last year and find conditions the same.' "†

In the most recent report on the administration of labor law by the American Association for Labor Legislation, the following data is given as to the methods of selection and appointment of inspectors:

* Report of the Sixth Annual Meeting of American Assoc. for Labor Legislation, p. 28.
† Ibid., p. 27.

California:—Commissioner is appointed by the governor. He in turn appoints deputies, assistant deputies and inspectors. Only special agents are under civil service.

Indiana:—Deputies and assistant deputies must have ten years' practical experience in their respective lines, but they are appointed by the chief inspector with the consent of the governor.

Kansas, Kentucky:—Some practical experience is required of inspectors.

Massachusetts, Minnesota, New Jersey, New York, Ohio, Wisconsin, Colorado, Illinois:—Inspectors are under civil service.

In other states inspectors are either political appointees or are required to have some practical experience, which is judged solely by the appointive powers; or else they must belong to labor organizations.

In most states the higher grades of inspectors, the chiefs, commissioners and deputies upon whose character the efficiency of the department greatly depends are political appointees, and their tenure of office usually lasts as long as the political party to which they belong is in power. They cannot, therefore, expect to remain in the factory inspection department for all their lives or during behavior and good work, and must necessarily regard their office as but a temporary sojourn in their meteoric political career. They are under obligations to the political parties or to persons from whom they receive their appointments and are necessarily guided in the selection of the lower grades of inspectors as well as in their official work by political exigencies.

The lower grades of inspectors are subject to civil service examinations only in the few states which have been noted; in all the rest no civil service examination is required and the appointment of inspectors is made for the same political reasons as that of their superiors.

Civil service examinations in the larger states such as New York, New Jersey, Massachusetts, Illinois, etc., have been greatly improved during the last decade, so that at present they are more or less an indication as to the character and knowledge of the candidates for inspectors. But even in these states the tenure of an inspector's office is not safeguarded because of the possibility of arbitrary discharge by his superiors either during probation period or after, and because of the character of the commissioners and chief inspectors.

No special technical training, diplomas or educational qualifications are required from candidates for factory inspectors even in those states where civil service examinations have already been established on a firm basis. The character of the questions given on the various examinations is such that a person with little experience and instruction may be able to cram the necessary knowledge within a few weeks and pass a satisfactory examination.

Not only is the inspector who has been appointed after a civil service examination insecure in his tenure of office and therefore unable to regard his work as a life service, but he is doubtful of his regular promotion, and in no state is there provision for a pension after a certain number of years of service or upon reaching old age.

The three fundamental principles upon which efficient state service must be based are (1) security of tenure of office, (2) regular promotion for merit and length of service, and (3) pension for years of service and old age. Without any one of these there can be no possible efficiency in state service, nor can employes regard their position as a life profession.

As is well known, it is the practice in the majority of states, even when civil service prevails, to appoint commissioners, chiefs, assistants and supervisors not from the rank and file of inspectors but from outside elements, usually from political henchmen of the powers that be. It is only in exceptional cases that promotion for years of service is attained by the competent inspector. The rule is that incompetent outsiders get the higher salaries and higher grade positions. With such a practice it is no wonder that the competent, the energetic and the bright inspector despairs of obtaining his due promotion, and leaves the department just at a time when his experience and services become valuable.

With the meagre compensation that most of the inspectors of the lower grades receive, they cannot posssibly save for old age,and there is no pension provided in any of the states for the factory inspectors. The salaries vary with the state and position from $900 per year to $1000 and $1200, which is the salary paid in New York and other large states to the ordinary factory inspector for a great number of years.

Factory Inspectors in Europe. In contrast with the conditions prevalent in the Unites States, it will perhaps be interesting to describe the methods of selection and examination in several European countries. In all the European countries which I visited, labor and factory inspection is considered as a profession just as law, medicine or engineering. Factory inspection is an integral part of the bureaucratic regime and a branch of state service. Those who enter this profession are hardly ever younger than twenty-five years of age and are usually not older than thirty years. They have to go through a rigid and arduous training and when they do become inspectors they remain such for life. In the practice of factory inspection as well as in the other intelligent professions there is no place either for the very young and inexperienced or for the very old or for those who have failed in other walks of life.

In all European countries, the personality of the candidate plays a most important role, apart from any scientific education, technical training and other requirements imposed. The appointive powers in all countries select only those who have passed certain tests and examinations, and also determine who shall take those tests. This system of nomination and appointment serves to exclude undesirable candidates, even those of superior education and technical training. Theoretically, it does not exclude appointment for political influence; practically, however, such appointments are hardly known in England and on the continent.

The principles as well as the methods of selecting candidates differ in each country. Prussia and most Germanic states demand very high special technical training, while England only requires a certain number in special departments to be technically trained men. In France, the inspectors are not all technically trained men, although the examinations are more technical than in England and the technical branches are the most important part in the competitive examination. In Austria, most of the inspectors are mechanics, chemists, electricians and engineers. In Belgium there is no examination whatever. The personnel of the inspectors is divided between the technically trained men and experienced mechanics coming from the working class. The countries which give rigid examinations and tests are England, France and Prussia.

The tenure of office of all the inspectors in European countries is absolutely secure. Once a candidate has been accepted as an inspector he remains in the service during his life and there are very few instances of an inspector losing his position.

Promotion in all European countries is regular, at stated periods and is given for length of service combined with competence and experience. So regular is the promotion that an inspector may calculate beforehand the date at which he will reach next higher grade. All inspectors of the highest grade, all supervisors, chiefs and heads of bureaus come from the ranks after due promotion.

There is no possibility of an outsider being appointed as chief inspector, a practice which would be resented by all; and only on rare occasions may an outsider enter the service in the highest ranks and then only by reason of special qualifications recognized and justified by all.

Every country in Europe gives a pension to the factory inspectors as well as to other officials in state service. The amount of pension differs according to the country.

In England, after the inspectors reach the age of sixty, they may retire upon their request and the consent of the Secretary of State. At the age of 65, their retirement is compulsory. The inspectors may also be retired for disability before the age prescribed. Pension is hardly ever given before the expiration of ten years of service. The amount of pension given upon retirement is one-eighth of the salary for every year of service. To this annuity is added a lump sum amounting to the salary of one year. For example, if an inspector has been in the service of his department for twenty years and has been paid at the rate of £800 per year during the last three years of service, he receives upon his retirement 20/80 or one-fourth of £800 or an annuity of £200 during his life, with an addition of £800 given to him upon the day of his retirement.

The German industrial inspectors are incorporated in the Prussian bureaucratic system and receive pensions during disability; and after twenty to twenty-five years of service. This pension is based upon the salary of the officials, upon their rank, upon the number of years in service, and upon their age at retirement. The amount of pension varies from one-third to two-thirds of the salary received at the period of retirement.

In France, labor inspectors have the right to pensions under the same conditions as all public functionaries. Inspectors may receive a retirement pension after twenty years of service upon reaching the age of fifty-five years. The pension is half of the average salary which an inspector has enjoyed during the last six years. Retiring inspectors, especially division inspectors, may at their retirement, receive the title of honorary division inspector.

In Austria, inspectors are entitled to pensions according to the pension system of the Austrian state officials. Such pensions may be given after ten years of service in case of disability when the sum does not exceed forty per cent of the salary. After thirty-five years of service pensions are given to the *full amount* of the salary.

In Belgium, inspectors are usually given a pension after twenty years of service. The pension usually ranges from 2000 francs up.

The compensation which factory inspectors receive in European countries is, with the exception of England, very meagre and hardly to be compared with the salaries given in the United States. Taking, however, into consideration the lower cost of living, the security of tenure of office, the regular promotion, the assured pension and the low compensation general in the state service in European countries, the compensation is not so very much lower than in America.

Americans are very often astonished at the ease with which continental governments are enabled to obtain for their inspectorial service persons of such high social and educational standing, especially for the small compensation that most of these inspectors receive. But the solution of the problem is, as already indicated, in the security of state service. State service is a high desideratum in all European countries; it is regarded with devotion and deep respect; it is the ideal of the youth of the country; and all persons after having gone through the middle and higher grades of educational establishments vie with each other in their efforts to enter the ranks of state officials and the series of bureaucratic departments.

What are the actual results to the country, to the service, and to the enforcement of labor and factory laws of obtaining so high a grade of inspectors?

In the first place, inspectors of this class having gone through such a long, arduous, and rigid preparation, regard their vocation as a life profession, look upon it seriously, hesitate before they hazard their life's work for a mess of pottage and are not likely to be led into temptation by dishonest employers. In the second place, a long preparation is of service in developing their tact, in teaching them the use of diplomacy in handling employers and employes, and in preparing them for the duties of responsible district inspectors.

Perhaps the most important result of the high character of the personnel of the inspectors is the regard and respect which they command from employers, manufacturers and technical managers of industrial plants. There is not, and cannot be, any of the contempt which is so often encountered in the relations of owners and technical managers towards the green and inexperienced factory inspectors in the States. The employers and their managers know that these inspectors are well trained and are specialists in their line; hence, they are willing to abide by the inspectors' advice and follow their requirements.

Within the department, the results are seen in the perfect comradeship among the inspectors themselves; the lack of bullying by superiors, the respect of one grade of inspector to another grade of inspector, no matter what the position may be. Where the chief supervisors and higher grade of inspectors are taken by regular promotion from the ranks and not from the outside, amicable relations and mutual respect exist between the different grades of inspectors.

Nowhere on the continent do factory inspectors receive as high salaries as they are paid in England. In respect to the salaries paid, England is the most liberal of all European countries. The salary of the chief inspector is, according to the original schedule, £1200 per annum, but this has been increased by special arrangement in the case of Sir Arthur Whitelegge, the present chief inspector, to £1500 per annum. The two deputy factory inspectors receive £750 to £900. The following table shows the minimum and maximum salaries of various grades of inspectors with the yearly increase.

	Minimum.	Maximum.	Yearly Increase.
	£	£	£
Medical Inspectors	500	800	25
Superintending Inspector	600	750	25
Principal Lady Inspector	400	500	..
Inspectors in Grade 1A	300	550	20
Inspectors in Grade 1B	300	400	15
Senior Lady Inspectors	300	400	15
Lady Inspectors	200	300	10
Inspectors—Grade 2	200	300	10
Assistant Inspectors (Seniors)	250	200	5
Assistant Inspectors (Juniors)	100	250	5

In Prussia the salaries of the inspectors are as follows:

(1) Industrial Referendars receive no salary.

(2) Industrial Assessors receive 2400 marks the first year, 3075 marks the second year, and 3450 marks the third year.

(3) Industrial Inspectors receive 3000, 3600, 4200, 4800, 5400, 6000, 6600 and 7200 marks.

(4) The State and Industrial Councilors receive 4200, 4800, 5400, 6000, 6600 and 7200 marks.

In France, there are three classes of division inspectors and five classes of departmental inspectors, who receive salaries as follows: division inspectors receive from 6000 to 8000 francs per annum, respectively; departmental inspectors receive 5000, 4500, 4000, 3500 and 3000 francs per annum, respectively. The inspector stagiares (probationary inspectors) receive 2400 francs per annum.

In Austria, the salaries of inspectors are rated according to their grade and length of service. Inspectors are given stated salaries with yearly increases. Besides salaries, a certain addition (zulage) is given to inspectors, which differs according to the grade of service. The salaries of inspectors range from 1600 to 12,000 Kronen (a Kron is about 19c.).

In Belgium the salaries of inspectors are as follows:

	Salary.
First Inspector General................	10,000 francs.
Chief Inspectors......................	9,000 to 10,000 francs.
Provincial Chief Inspectors............	7,500 to 8,500 "
Medical Inspectors....................	6,500 to 7,500 "
Inspectors...........................	4,500 to 6,500 "
Adjoint Inspectors....................	2,400 to 4,000 "
Editors..............................	2,400 to 4,000 "
Delegated Inspectors..................	2,000 to 2,600 "

In Switzerland, the salaries of inspectors and their adjuncts are as follows:

	Salary.
Inspectors............................	6,200 to 8,200 francs.
Adjunct—1st Class.....................	5,200 to 6,200 "
Adjunct—2d Class.....................	3,700 to 4,700 "
Office Clerks.........................	2,000 to 3,500 "

Methods of Supervision and Inspection. Factory inspection departments were established in order to enforce labor laws. The functions of the first factory inspectors and of factory inspection departments, therefore, were mainly the detection of violations and the discovery of those manufacturers who were disobeying the provisions of the law. The methods, therefore, which the inspectors had to pursue consisted in making unexpected raids upon industrial establishments in an endeavor to find children working contrary to the provisions of the law, or other transgressions of the factory acts. It is not to be wondered that such methods of inspection created great animosity on the part of employers, and that they regarded the inspectors as spies, informers, detectives, etc., and adopted concerted means by which the presence of an inspector in a town became at once known and his whereabouts signaled throughout the industrial community.

The detective function of factory inspectors still comprises a large part of the work of industrial inspection in this country as well as in others. Germany is practically the only country where a firm stand was made by the government from the beginning, where the factory inspector's function was strictly limited to preventive work and all detection or prosecution left to the police authorities. The same tendency, although not so pronounced, became the basic principle of English factory inspection.

The methods which are gradually superseding the detective functions consist in inspection by the factory officials for the purpose of determining what is best to be done in order to prevent accidents and disease, in conferences with owners, manufacturers and superintendents of industrial plants as to the best means of preventing the risks and dangers of trades and promoting the well-being of the workers.

There is still need, however, of both methods of inspection; and factory inspection departments have not as yet succeeded in inaugurating a campaign of education which would make the first method of inspection unnecessary. In most factory inspection bureaus, therefore, the inspectors give a large part of their time to making unexpected visits to factories in order to detect violations, especially those relating to child and women labor. Inspectors have also much to do with prosecution; they act as witnesses and assist with the proceedings against violators of the law. The higher class of inspectors usually strive to work in an advisory capacity, to persuade manufacturers to install safety devices and appliances and adopt methods which would lessen the dangers of certain industrial processes.

Every inspection department is divided into a number of principal districts which are supervised by a higher official, who has under his jurisdiction a number of inspectors of lower grade, each of these inspectors being given a smaller district or a special function in the larger district. With the limited force of inspectors in most of the departments, only one annual inspection can possibly be made in every industrial plant, and in some states even this is impossible and plants are not visited for two or more years.

There are as yet very few inspection departments where a complete record is kept of every industrial establishment in a district, of every condition in the establishment and a historical review of all the violations found in the establishment. Inspections are either made as a routine matter, visiting the establishments after certain intervals which may be a year or longer, or are made on complaints of citizens or workers, anonymous or signed.

The inspector is supplied with a number of cards or blanks on which are printed the items which he must inspect in each part of the factory and note whether there are any violations of the law. In most states the law compels owners to post an extract of the labor and factory acts in a conspicuous part of the factory; some states require the factory inspector to stamp this notice at every visit.

The routine method of inspection is as follows: The inspector usually presents himself at the office of an establishment, announces his authority, shows his credentials, if required, asks a number of questions as to the ownership of the plant, the number of employes, etc., looks for the notices posted on the walls and examines the books in which an account is kept of the employes under a certain age, and of such accidents as may have occurred since his last inspection. He then proceeds to go through the plant, either by himself or accompanied by a representative of the manufacturer, and notices the sanitary condition of the plant, the state of the walls, ceilings and floors, the adequacy of light and illumination, the methods of ventilation, the condition and adequacy of the sanitary fixtures in the plant. The inspector also notes the number of women and children employed in the establishment, the presence of any children who seem to be under age, and inquires about the number of hours of work during the day and the length of the midday pause as well as the beginning and closing hours of work. While on his tour of inspection, the inspector observes the mechanical appliances and machines in the plant and makes a note of such machines or parts of machines which are, according to his opinion, not properly safeguarded, and of such processes which may in his opinion be dangerous to the life or health of the employes.

The inspector is usually not permitted by his superiors to enter into lengthy conversations with employers or to tell employers the result of his inspection. He has to send to the office a detailed and complete report on each of his inspections, and if the inspector reports a violation of the law, the matter is taken up for further procedure by the office.

Inspectors are not usually required to make any special tests of light, illumination or ventilation, as these tests require special training and knowledge which is not possessed by the ordinary inspector. If photometric inspections are to be made of light and illumination, or air tests for carbon dioxide, carbon monoxide, dust, etc., these are usually made by specially trained experts, a few of whom may be found in some of the larger states.

There are as yet no scientific standards set for methods of factory inspection either in Europe or in the United States. The general routine method of factory inspection is about the same in all countries. I found very little difference in the methods used in the various European countries visited. The methods of taking notes and of keeping records differ very much; and it is my impression as far as methods of recording inspections are concerned, that those used in states like New York, Wisconsin and others are much superior to those employed by the factory inspection departments of some European countries.

CIVIL SERVICE EXAMINATIONS FOR FACTORY INSPECTORS IN ENGLAND, FRANCE, GERMANY AND NEW YORK STATE.

ENGLAND.

Candidates for nomination for factory inspectors in England make a formal application and present it with any testimonials which they wish to submit to the Private Secretary of the Home Office in London. In this application they give their names, addresses, date and year of birth, education, and particulars as to their past and present employment. The applicants are then personally interviewed by the chief inspectors or by the superintending inspectors, and sometimes by the district inspectors; and whenever a vacancy occurs selection is made from the list of applicants.

The nominations are never given except when an examination to fill a vacancy is about to be held. Only a very limited number of applicants, namely, " those who appear after careful consideration and inquiry, to be the best qualified in every way for the position, can be given the opportunity to compete." Nominated candidates receive not more than one month's notice of the examination. The prescribed age for candidates at the time of examination is between twenty-two and thirty years, but an extension up to thirty-eight is allowed in the case of a candidate who (a) for the last seven years has been occupied in one or more of the following capacities in a factory or workshop or in engineering work, viz., master, manager, foreman, workman, or apprentice, and has thereby acquired practical acquaintance with industrial relations and conditions; or (b) has served as a factory inspector's assistant, with a certificate of the Civil Service Commission from a time when he was under thirty. The candidate must pay a fee of three pounds for the examination.

The following is a syllabus of the obligatory as well as optional subjects for the civil service examination:

SUBJECTS FOR EXAMINATION

A. Obligatory Subjects

1. English Composition.
2. Arithmetic.

B. Optional Subjects

3. English Literature.
4. English History.
5. General Modern History.
6. French or German or Italian.
7. Mathematics.
8. Economics (including knowledge of the history of industry in modern times).
9. Chemistry.
10. Physics, including mechanics.
11. Practical Mechanics and Industrial Machinery.

NOTE. Four only of the optional subjects may be offered. Any candidate who does not satisfy the Civil Service Commissioners in three of them will be thereby disqualified.

SYLLABUS

A. Obligatory Subjects

1. *English Composition.* Candidates will be tested by precise writing as well as by an essay.

2. *Arithmetic.* First four rules, simple and compound, including English and metrical weights and measures, reduction, vulgar fractions and decimals (excluding recurring decimals), and the preparation of percentage and other tabular summaries.

B. Optional Subjects

3. *English Literature.* From Shakespeare to the death of Wordsworth.
4. *English History.* 1066 to 1880.
5. *General Modern History.* 1519 to 1871.

In the papers set upon each of these subjects a liberal choice of questions will be allowed.

6. *French, German or Italian.* Translation, Composition, Conversation.
7. *Mathematics.* Algebra, Geometry, Trigonometry.
8. *Economics (including knowledge of the History of Industry in modern times).* The economics of industry as treated in the ordinary text-books. The history of the chief forms of modern industry, and the outlines of legislation affecting the working classes in the last two centuries, with especial reference to the United Kingdom.
9. *Chemistry (chiefly inorganic).* In this subject there will be (1) a written paper, and (2) an oral and practical examination. The latter will include, among other things, such qualitative and quantitative analysis as has a bearing upon the administration of the Factory Act (e.g., the detection and estimation of lead, arsenic, mercury, and other poisonous metals used in manufactures, and the

detection and estimation of carbonic acid, carbonic oxide, nitrous fumes, and other gas, vapors, and impurities in air, etc.).

10. *Physics (including Mechanics).* The fundamental principles of mechanics; heat; light, electricity and magnetism, treated from the experimental standpoint. In this subject there will be (1) a written paper and (2) a practical examination.

11. *Practical Mechanics (including Mechanical Drawing).* In this subject there will be (1) a written examination including (*a*) an elementary, (*b*) an advanced paper. Candidates who take this subject must pass in the former, although more weight in the competition will be attached to the latter. There will also be (2) an oral and practical examination. The latter will include, among other things, questions upon the construction of machinery.

The knowledge of languages, especially French and German, is very advantageous for the candidates and is practically required for the examination. The examination usually takes place in London where the candidates are required to appear. The examination lasts about five days, an examination lately being held on Tuesday, Wednesday, Thursday, Friday, and Saturday of the week, each day from 10 A.M. to about 5 P.M., with an interval for lunch.

The examination is not only written, but also oral. Oral tests are given in French, advanced mechanics, chemistry, and physics. The rating is not only on the answers to questions, but also on the general appearance of the candidate. Such tests may last about an hour.

FRANCE.

All male and female inspectors are recruited by competitive examination. The division inspectors are chosen from the departmental inspectors of the first and second classes.

(1) AGE LIMIT. The applicants for positions of inspectors must be at least twenty-six years of age, and not older than thirty-five years. No exception is made to the age limit.

(2) PHYSICAL EXAMINATION. Candidates must undergo a physical examination by a physician designated by the Minister of Labor. A candidate may be accepted as a labor inspector who has been exempted from military service. The physical examination is made only after the candidate passes his written tests.

(3) Either diplomas or certificates showing the candidate's knowledge of French.

(4) A certificate of good character.

(5) A certificate that the candidate performed military service or has been exempted from same, with the statement of the causes for such exemption.

(6) A note signed by the candidate giving his autobiography, the place where he lives, with the changes of residence, the nature of his previous occupations, and an indication of the establishments in which he has been working.

(7) Such diplomas or certificates of universities, etc., as he may possess.

The following is the program of the competitive examination for admission as candidate for inspector.

The examination is written and oral. The written test consists of the following:

(1) *A Composition on " Labor Laws."* The candidate must show knowledge of the various laws applying to labor and inspection of labor as well as all decrees,

ministerial or otherwise relating to labor inspection and labor laws. The candidate must also write an essay on administrative law, on penal law. and on application of penalties, etc., on the forms of protocols to be made by inspectors of labor, on relations of inspectors to police officers, on penalties for various crimes, derelictions and contraventions, and on rules for applications for authorization. He must also have a knowledge of judicial procedures, appeals, etc.

(2) *Industrial Hygiene.* The examination on industrial hygiene consists of questions relating to the following: air and ventilation of workshops; heating of workshops; lighting and cleaning of workshops; plumbing; water supply; installation of various sanitary appliances; the dangers and removal of dust, certain gases, fumes and irritants; intoxicant and poisonous materials, infectious materials; labor in extreme temperatures; humidity; compressed air; electricity, fatigue, and accidents.

(3) The examination in electricity and mechanics consists in questions on the following topics: general mechanics; principles of inertia; gravitation, etc.; applied mechanics; transmission of movements; resistance of materials; motors; hydraulic; steam, etc.; labor machines; principles of machinery and textiles; other uses of machines; engines of leverage; pumps, ventilators, etc.

The examination in electricity covers the subject, theoretical as well as practical. In the subject of prevention of accidents the examination consists of practical tests on machines, motors, and mechanisms.

The written examination tests the candidate's knowledge of mathematics, algebra, geometry, and trigonometry.

All the tests must be finished within one day; three hours are given for the composition on law and one and one-half hours each for the other two compositions.

The oral tests are given only after three or four weeks after the written examinations, when the examiners have had time to pass upon the written tests. No candidate who has not passed the written tests is allowed to participate in the oral examination. The oral examination is also made in Paris.

The oral test consists of questions covering the three subjects already indicated in the written examination. The candidate must give proof that he possesses knowledge of the Penal Code and a general knowledge of the labor laws. Questions are also given as to wages, trades, industries, legal proceedings, trials, etc.

Candidates are generally questioned by two examiners on each subject. Besides the general oral tests, a special practical test is also given. These practical tests are two in number; one is obligatory, and one is optional. The first which bears on hygiene and applied mechanics is taken in the National Conservatory of Arts and Trades. There each candidate is placed before an apparatus; he must give a description of the different means of ventilation, the proper means of ventilation, the drawing off of smoke, gases, vapors, etc. He is also asked to explain the working of motors, machines, tools, and of any of the mechanisms indicated by the examiners. He must not only give a description of the apparata, but also their use and their provision against accidents.

The optional test is taken in a factory or industrial establishment in which the candidate claims special efficiency. The object of this test is to permit those who have a practical knowledge of their trade to get proper credit for their work. This test was made especially for those candidates who have had considerable factory experience, and who therefore are given a chance to prove their proficiency in industrial work. They are given credit which may counterbalance any deficiencies in other tests in the examination. The jury having charge of the examination may also give a mark for what is called " personal equation." This mark is, as the law states, justified by the nature of the powers which are given to labor inspectors. The functions of the inspectors demand considerable tact, besides knowledge, and also certain moral and personal qualifications, which the jury may take into account. The previous experience of the candidate, the inquiries made about his present connection, and the general impression which he produces upon the examiners are all taken into consideration.

All the tests which are required for male inspectors are also required for female inspectors except that in their examination mechanics and electricity are not included; nor does the examination include a practical test on industrial work. They are, however, called to take an examination in what is called " applied hygiene."

The practical work in the laboratory includes the handling of various instruments, such as psychrometers, hygrometers, anemometers, the analysis of potable waters, analysis of air, the tests for dust, etc.

Successful candidates are appointed on probation and are called " stagiares." They are assigned to districts and have the same powers as regular inspectors. They have also the right to traveling expenses and other indemnities. The male and female inspectors when appointed receive an annual salary of 2400 francs. At the expiration of the first year they are promoted to inspectors of the fifth class. The inspector stagiares as soon as appointed are installed in their functions by the chief prefect of the department, from whom they take the professional oath of office, as prescribed by the law, which specially relates to prohibition of revealing trade secrets. This oath is taken only once, upon entering the service, and is not repeated when an inspector is transferred from one department to another or from one class to another.

PRUSSIA.

The requirements from candidates for inspectorial service in Prussia are the following:

(1) A certificate of graduation of nine classes of gymnasium, or, what is called in German, " Reifenzeugnisz " (Certificate of Maturity).

(2) Proof of at least three years' technical study in a German High School.

(3) At least one and one-half years of study of law and political sciences.

The above are the absolute requirements for candidates before they are allowed to compete for the position of probationary inspector.

If the candidate satisfies the above requirements then he is subject (1) to two examinations, and (2) to a period of probationary work in the Industrial Inspection Department. The two examinations are respectively at the beginning and end of his probationary term of service.

The first examination may not be required if candidate possesses the following diplomas: (a) diploma of qualification from a state construction master in the construction of machinery; (b) diploma of a mining engineer or technical engineer certifying that candidate is a graduate of a mining academy or other

Prussian technical high school; (c) a doctor's degree at a Prussian University when chemistry was the principal subject taken in examination; (d) a diploma of chemist at a Prussian High School.

After the candidate is selected he is assigned to a district inspection office and begins his one and a half years' probationary period of service.

During the probationary service a candidate, or, as he is officially called, industrial "referendar," is under the immediate supervision of an industrial assessor or inspector, who acts as his preceptor, and under whose direction the candidate is pursuing his studies and work. The service consists first in an assignment to the keeping of the day-books and other registers in the office, as well as assisting in the correspondence with the various officials and with the employers, etc. The general plan of the preparation of the referendar is under the supervision of the State and Industrial Councilor, who reports to the State President of the Circuit.

During the second term of probationary service the referendar is taken by his preceptor to various industrial establishments and shown the methods of work and inspection; he is also shown different industrial conditions. The preceptor is instructed by the rules to frequently confer with the referendar upon various technical questions, to require him to make sketches of machines and apparata, and in general to convince himself of the progress in knowledge and experience on the part of the referendar.

During the last three months of his probationary period the referendar may be appointed as assistant to the inspection bureau, in order to learn the routine of work of inspection in its relation with the government. He must participate in the conferences of the district government and when necessary prepare reports before these conferences.

During all this period the referendar does not receive any salary whatever, except his traveling expenses. If the referendar is found to be lacking either in physical qualities or in the diligence or interest in the service, then the Minister of Commerce and Industry may on the report of the government president terminate his service.

At the end of his probationary period the industrial referendar must still undergo two tests. The first is a "great probationary work" (Grösserer Probearbeit). This consists of a report upon a theme which is given to him by the State and Industrial Councilor, and is based upon his experience in industrial inspection in the district where the referendar served his probationary term. The thesis must be written without the assistance of outsiders, and is passed on by the State and Industrial Councilor. It is then presented to the President of the Circuit government. Should the thesis prove unsatisfactory, the industrial referendar may get an extension of six months to prepare another thesis.

The second main examination which the referendar is subjected to at the end of his probationary period of service, study and his thesis, is (1) oral, and (2) written.

The examination is conducted by a board of industrial supervising officials in Berlin, appointed by the Minister of Commerce and Industry.

The written examination consists of questions (Aufgaben) on the administration of the Industrial Code and on political science and administration. The questions are given by the chairman of the examining board; the candidate is given *six weeks' time* in which to answer the questions. This period may be extended to two months. At the end of this term the candidate must present his answers, with the assurance that he has had no outside help in their preparation. The answers are presented to the examining board, each member of which must note his opinion when passing judgment upon the papers. Consideration must be given to the scientific conception, the conciseness, clearness, grammar, logic and good German in which the work is expressed.

The oral examination consists of questions which tend to show ability to determine and solve technical problems in practical service. Special attention is paid to the technical scientific training of the candidate and his practical experience in those branches which the candidate has been taught during his probationary service. The examination must also determine in how far the candidate is conversant with the Constitution of the German Empire and of the Prussian State, with the Prussian State administration, with the industrial supervision—its extent as well as practical administration and enforcement.

The examiners are required to determine whether the candidate has a thorough understanding of the methods of safeguarding machinery, of the principles of construction and establishment of factories and workshops, methods of heating, ventilation and removal of dust. He must also possess a knowledge of the ordinary methods of prevention of accidents, the prevention of dangers to health which are found in various industries, and of dangers of certain industries to their immediate neighborhood. Of course, a thorough knowledge of the Industrial Code, as well as of the Workmen's Insurance Code, is absolutely required.

The candidate must pay before the application for the second examination a fee of fifty marks ($12) for the examination.

After the candidate has passed the ordeal described above, the Minister of Commerce and Industry appoints him as industrial assessor, and as such he is assigned to work in an industrial district, in which he usually remains about two years. Every two years or more he is sent to other districts with different industrial conditions, and, is after a certain number of years of service—which is seldom less than five, or may reach ten—appointed as an industrial inspector and given charge of a district. Once a man is appointed industrial assessor, his tenure of office is secure.

NEW YORK STATE.

The following questions were given by the New York State Civil Service Commission as a test for Supervising Factory Inspector, on April 20, 1912:

INSPECTION

(1) Give a list of the machinery used in the textile industry. Name the elements of danger and the best methods of guarding each machine.

(2) Give a list of the machinery used in a general machine-shop, the elements of danger from each machine, and the best methods of guarding the same.

(3) Give a list of machinery used in a wood-working establishment. Name the elements of danger, and the best methods of guarding each machine.

(4–5) One of your duties will be to give instructions to newly appointed inspectors. Prepare a communication to such an inspector, giving definite instructions relative to the inspection of factories, covering the subject in the following order:

(*a*) A factory inspector's duties under the law.

(*b*) Employment and hours of labor of children.

(c) Employment and hours of labor of minors and women, and restrictions thereto.

(d) Dangers incident to the operation of machinery, fire hazards, and safety appliances.

(e) Sanitation, and conveniences prescribed by the labor law for employes.

(f) General instructions deemed best, if any.

(6) Prepare a communication to a newly appointed factory inspector regarding his duties while inspecting tenement houses.

(7) A factory inspector in your district has made an inspection; notice of changes as the result thereof have been sent the manufacturer; the manufacturer appeals; what would be your duty in the matter? State specifically and fully the course you should take. Assuming necessary facts, make a full report on same to the Commissioner of Labor, including your recommendations.

(8) How may accidents in factories, wood-working establishments, etc., be minimized, aside from safeguarding the machinery? Has a factory inspector any duty or obligation in avoiding accidents, aside from seeing that machines are properly safeguarded? Discuss both questions fully.

The following examination for Deputy Factory Inspector was given by the New York State Civil Service Commission on January 22, 1910:

LAW

(1) Describe the organization of the Department of Labor. How are appointments made therein? What is the general purpose of the State in maintaining such a department?

(2) Give the functions of (a) the Bureau of Factory Inspection, (b) the Bureau of Mercantile Inspection.

(3) Give the provisions of the labor law relating to (a) hours of labor, with the exceptions thereto, (b) wages. What is the purpose of these provisions? What kind of public employment is exempted from the application of these restrictions, and why?

(4) What are the provisions of the labor law in relation to the safety of persons employed in the construction, repair or renovating of buildings?

(5) Define the following terms as used in the labor law: (a) factory, (b) tenant-factory, (c) mercantile establishment.

(6) State concisely the provisions of the labor law relating to the employment of children in (a) factories, (b) mercantile establishments? Why these provisions?

(7) What are the provisions of the labor law relating to the employment of women in (a) factories, (b) mercantile establishments?

(8) State briefly the provisions of the labor law relating to the safety of life and limb of factory employes.

(9) What provisions are made in the labor law for the health and comfort of employes in (a) factories, (b) mercantile establishments?

(10) What are the powers of the Commissioner of Labor with reference to unsanitary conditions in (a) tenant-factories, (b) bakeries?

(11) What are the powers of the Commissioner of Labor relative to tenement houses?

(12) What class of employes are excluded from employment upon public works in this State? What further provision is there relative to preference in employment upon such works?

(1-2) A complaint, received by the Commissioner of Labor, alleging that a contractor for the erection of a state armory is violating the labor law by requiring his employes to work ten hours a day, has been referred to you for investigation. Prepare a report sustaining the complaint, and describing the facts in detail. Support your report with the sworn statements of two of the contractor's workmen who have been required to work more than eight hours a day.

(3) John Smith is charged with employing children in his factory after 5 P.M. How would you obtain evidence against him with a view to his prosecution? What evidence, and how much would you consider necessary?

(4) What is (*a*) a line-shaft, (*b*) a counter-shaft, (*c*) an idler or loose pulley, and a belt-shifter?

(5) Supplying all necessary facts, give an outline of the inspection of a machine-shop containing dangerous machinery upon which boys under sixteen years of age are employed. Give in connection therewith such orders as may be necessary to remedy conditions found in violation of law.

(6) Supplying necessary facts, give an outline of the inspection of a knitting-mill employing a large number of women and children. Assuming that the sanitary requirements for the health and comfort of employes have not been complied with, give orders to correct the defects in accordance with the law.

(7) Suppose on inspecting a paper-box factory in a tenant-factory you find that the floors and toilets are in a filthy condition, that the air in workrooms is superheated and charged with unpleasant odors and that all windows are closed. Indicate the course to be taken to remedy the conditions.

(8) Describe in detail the particular elements of danger of physical injury in connection with the operation of power-driven machinery while entirely devoid of safeguards. Indicate how the danger may be practically overcome without interference with the utility of such machine. Name several power-driven machines, describing the danger from each and the method of guarding against accident.

APPENDIX I

A SELECTED BIBLIOGRAPHY FOR THOSE WISHING TO MAKE
A FURTHER STUDY OF SOME OF THE TOPICS TREATED.

Rise and Development of the Factory System:

ASHLEY, W. J.: Introduction to English Economic History. New York, 1888. 2 Vols.

BAINES, EDW.: History of the Cotton Manufacture in Great Britain. London.

BRENTANO, LUJO: History and Development of Gilds and the Origin of Trade Unions. London, 1878.

BRIZON, PIERRE: Histoire du Travail et des Travailleurs. Paris, 1912.

BUECHER, KARL: Industrial Evolution. New York, 1906.

CLARK, ALBERT: The Effect of the Factory System.

COMAN, KATHERINE: Industrial History of the United States. New York, 1911.

COOKE-TAYLOR-WHATLEY: Introduction to a History of the Factory System. 1886.

CUNNINGHAM, W. D.: Industrial History of England. Cambridge, 1895. 2 Vols.

GIBBINS, H. DE B.: Industry in England.

GUIRARD, PAUL: La Main d'Œuvre Industrielle.

INNES, ARTHUR: England's Industrial Development.

LAMBERT, Rev. J. MALET: Two Thousand Years of Gild Life.

PORTER: Progress of the Nation.

ROGERS, J. THEOBOLD: Six Centuries of Work and Wages.

WING, CHARLES: Evils of the Factory System Demonstrated by Parliamentary Evidence. London, 1837.

In addition, see reports of English and American Governmental Commissions and other authorities mentioned in the text.

Fire Prevention and Fire Protection:

FREITAG, JOSEPH: Fire Prevention and Fire Protection. 1912.

CROSBY, FISKE: Handbook of Fire Protection. 1909.

McKEON, P. J.: Fire Prevention. 1912.

JOHNSON, JOSEPH: Report on Incendiarism in New York City. 1912.

New York State Factory Investigating Commission. First Report. 1912. Vol I. Second Report. 1913. Vols. I and II.

FISHER, WALTER L.: The Fire Waste.

553

Safety:

CALDER, JOHN: The Prevention of Factory Accidents. London, 1899.

EASTMAN, CRYSTAL: Work Accidents and the Law. New York, 1910.

SCHWEDTMAN, F. C., and J. A. EMERY: Accident Prevention and Relief. An investigation of the subject in Europe, with special attention to England and Germany, together with recommendation for action in the United States of America. New York, 1911.

TOLMAN, W. H.: Safety. New York, 1913.

In addition, see reports of American Association for Labor Legislation, Bulletins of the United States Department of Labor, Reports of State Commissions on Employers' Liability mentioned in Appendix II, and files of special journals, such as " Safety Engineering."

Welfare Work:

CADBURY, EDWARD: Experiments in Industrial Organization. London, 1914.

COOK, E. WAKE: Betterment. Individual, Social and Industrial. New New York, 1906.

MEAKIN, BUDGETT: Model Factories and Villages. New York, 1906.

SCHOMERUS, FRIEDRICH: System of Employment at the Karl Zeiss Works at Jena.

TOLMAN, W. H.: Social Engineering. A record of things done by American Industries employing upwards of one and a half millions of people. New York, 1909.

United States: Department of Labor, Bulletin Employers' Welfare Work. Washington, 1913.

In addition, see files of American Federationist, the latter for the workers' point of view. A good deal of literature on the subject of welfare work may be found in periodicals.

Dangerous Trades and Diseases of Occupations:

DAMMER: Arbeiter Wohlfahrt. Stuttgart, 1903.

ALBRECHT: Handbuch der Gewerbe Hygiene, etc.

BROUARDEL: Hygiene Industrielle. Paris, 1908.

PATISSIER: Traité des Maladies des Artisans et de celles qui resultent des diverses professions. Paris, 1822.

TURNER, THACKRAH: The Effects of the Principal Arts, Trades and Professions on Health and Longevity. London, 1832.

EULENBERG: Handbuch der Gewerbe Hygiene. Berlin, 1876.

HIRT: Die Krankheiten der Arbeiter. Leipzig, 1871.

ARLIDGE: The Diseases of Occupations. London, 1892.

THOMAS OLIVER: Dangerous Trades. London, 1902.

THOMAS OLIVER: Disease of Occupations. London, 1910.

WEYL: Gewerbe Hygiene: 8th Vol. of the Handbuch der Hygiene.

HALFORT: Entstehung, Verlauf und Behandlung der Krankheiten der Künstler und Gewerbetreibender. Berlin, 1845.

LEGGE AND GOADBY: Lead Poisoning. New York, 1912.

LAYET: Hygiène des Professions et des Industries. Paris, 1875.

RAMBOUSEK, I.: Industrial Poisoning. London, 1913.

THOMPSON, W. G.: The Occupational Diseases. New York, 1914.

APPENDIX II

A PARTIAL LIST OF THE MORE IMPORTANT INVESTIGATIONS INTO WORKING CONDITIONS AUTHORIZED BY THE FEDERAL AND STATE LEGISLATURES.

(This list covers only investigations relating to factory conditions: such as industrial accidents, occupational diseases, minimum wage, work of women and children, factory inspection and fire protection. It does not include investigations made of immigration, employment bureaus, work in mines or on railroads, trade disputes, arbitration, etc.)

United States:

1900 Report of the Industrial Commission. Washington. 17 Vols.

The report covers immigration, prison labor, industrial disputes, arbitration, conditions and growth of manufactures and commerce, labor legislation, etc. Vols. 7 and 14 are the only ones dealing with factory conditions.

1909 Report on the condition of women and child wage earners in the U. S. Washington. 19 vols.

Report of investigation into conditions in the textile, glass, ready made clothing, cotton, men's ready-made clothing, metal trades and laundries, etc.

Connecticut:

1913 Report of the Commission to Investigate the conditions of wage-earning women and minors. Hartford, 1913, 297 p.

Contains report and recommendations of commission and account of an investigation covering health, sanitation, accidents, wages and hours in relation to child and women workers in certain typical industries., viz, in the manufacture of cotton, silk, corsets, metal and rubber articles, and the conditions of women in alteration rooms in cloak and suit departments of department stores.

Illinois:

1911 Report of Commission on Occupational Diseases. Springfield. 13 pl. 219 p.

Contains report and recommendations of commission and an account of original and thorough investigations into lead, brass, zinc, carbon monoxide and compressed air diseases, occupational deafness, etc., in the State of Illinois.

555

1911 Report of Employers' Liability Commission. Springfield. 249 p.
Contains statistics of accidents in coal mining and on steam and electric railways, their causes and economic results and treatment by the courts.

Iowa:

1912 Report of Employers' Liability Commission. Des Moines. 250 p. 3 pts.
Part I contains some account of industrial accidents in Iowa and Part II a report of the evidence given at the public hearings.

Kentucky:

1911 Report of Commission to Investigate the Condition of Working Women in Kentucky. Louisville. 55 p.
Contains report of Commission with recommendations and account of three months' investigation into 186 industrial establishments in Kentucky.

Massachusetts:

1866 Report of Special Commission on Hours of Labor and Conditions and Prospects of Industrial Classes. Boston. 66 p.
The first labor commission in the United States to make a special report. The report is based on replies received to 1000 circulars sent out by the commission, and on evidence given at eight public hearings held chiefly in the evening to accommodate workingmen. Contains interesting material on child labor, hours of labor and non-enforcement of labor laws.

1911 Report of Commission to Investigate the Inspection of Factories, Workshops, Mercantile Establishments and other Buildings. Boston. 112 p.
Contains investigation of methods of industrial inspection in Mass. Valuable criticisms, conclusions and recommendations.

1911 Report of the Commission on Minimum Wage Boards. Boston. 326 p.
Contains account of investigation into four representative women's trades, viz., department stores, candy factories, laundries, and cotton mills, and statistics based on 6900 wage schedules, 4672 personal and domestic reports. 91 establishmest in 18 localities were investigated.

1912 Report of Commission on Compensation for Industrial Accidents. Boston. 322 p.
Contains statistics of one year's industrial accidents in Massachusetts.

Michigan:

1911 Report of Employers' Liability and Workmen's Compensation Commission. Lansing. 152 p.
Contains statistics of industrial accidents, causes, results, in the State of Michigan.

New Jersey:

1913 Report by the Employers' Liability Commission of the State of New Jersey. Trenton. 21 p.

Statistics gathered by commission cover accidents, court records and compensation for accidents occurring during one year in the State of New Jersey.

New York:

1910 Report by the Commission to Inquire into the Question of Employers' Liability and other Matters. Albany. First report. 271 p.

1911 (The same).

Second report. Causes and prevention of industrial accidents. 116 p.

Third report. Unemployment and lack of farm labor. 245 p.

Fourth report. Review of the decision of the Court of Appeals, March 24, 1911, declaring the Compulsory Compensation Act of 1910 unconstitutional.

1912 Preliminary report of the Factory Investigating Commission. Vol. 1. 837 p.

Contains account of investigation made into the fire hazard in factories in New York State, general sanitary investigation, women's trades, lead poisoning in New York City, tenement house manufacture, work in bakeries and foundries.

Vol. II. 986 p. Evidence taken at public hearings of commission.

Vol. III. 1986 p. Evidence continued.

1913 Second Report of the Factory Investigating Commission.

Vol. I. 395 p. Covers report of Commission on administration law, the fire problem, manufacturing in tenements, canneries, child labor, night work of women in factories, bakeries, general sanitary conditions, accident prevention, dangerous trades, foundries, employment of women and children in mercantile establishments.

Vol. II. 1340 p. Contains reports of original investigations and statistics on above topics.

Ohio:

1910 Report by the Commission to inquire in the question of Employers' Liability and other matters. Columbus.

Part I. 404 p.

Part II. 444 p.

Part III. 37 p.

Part I contains report of special investigation into economic effects of accidents to married men resulting in partial or total disablement or death in industrial occupations in Ohio.

Part II contains report of evidence taken at public hearings.

Part II contains text of act proposed.

Pennsylvania:

1838 Report of Select Committee appointed to visit Cotton and other Factories to Inquire into System of labor, particularly Employment of Children.

This report, though brief, is interesting, as the Committee seems to have been the earliest appointed to investigate child labor in America.

1912 Report of Industrial Accidents Commission. Harrisburg. 53 p.

Report based on data gathered by the department of factory inspection.

A PARTIAL LIST OF THE MORE IMPORTANT DEPARTMENTAL COMMITTEES AND REPORTS IN ENGLAND DURING THE NINETEENTH CENTURY.

1816 Report of Committee appointed to Enquire into the State of the Children Employed in Manufactories.

1831 Report of Select Committee on Factory Children's Labour.

1833 First Report of Commissioners on Employment of Children in Factories. Second Report.

1843 Supplementary Report of Commissioners on the Employment of Children in Factories.

1840 Reports from Select Committee appointed to inquire into the operation of the Act for the Regulation of Mills and Factories.

1843 Children's Employment Commission: Second Report, Trade and Manufactures.

1857 Report to Select Committee of the House of Commons on Bleach and Dye Works.

1861 Report of Commission on the state of Children employed in Lace the Manufacture.

Reports of Commissioners on Employment of Children and Young Persons in Trades and Manufactures not already regulated by law, viz., Six Reports, 1863-1868.

1876 Report of the Commissioners appointed to inquire into the Working of the Factory and Workshops Acts, with a view to their consolidation and amendment.

1882 Report of Alexander Redgrave, H. M. Chief Inspector of Factories, upon precautions which can be enforced under the Factory Act, and to the need of further powers for the Protection of Persons employed in White Lead Works.

1888 Reports from the Select Committee of the House of Lords on the Sweating System.

1893 Reports of the Royal Commission on Labour.

1893 Report from the Departmental Committee on the various Lead Industries; with Recommendations and Suggestions.

1896 Report of the Departmental Committee appointed to inquire into and report upon certain miscellaneous Dangerous Trades.

1897 Second Report on certain Dangerous Trades.

APPENDIX III

SUGGESTIONS FOR THE ORGANIZATION AND EXECUTION OF EXIT DRILLS.

Organization and Duties. All factory exit drills should be subject to the direction of a supervisory organization constituted as follows: chief engineer of exit drill, floor chiefs, room captains, stairway guards, searchers and inspectors.

Chief Engineer of Exit Drill. Should be someone whose position would command respect and insure compliance with all orders and instructions relating to the drills.

He will have general charge of all matters pertaining to exit drills, practice maneuvers and organization, and will designate all persons to fill the positions above mentioned. He will fix the time for making drills and rigidly enforce measures of discipline for failure on the part of any employe fully to observe all the rules and requirements; by personal inspection he should see that overcrowding in workrooms, or elsewhere, is prevented, and that sufficient space is given to aisles and passageways to permit quick access to all of the exits.

Floor Chiefs. Care should be exercised in the selection of these men or women, as upon them largely depend the efficiency and success of the drills. Where department foremen (or women) or factory superintendents possess the requisite qualifications their selection is to be preferred. It is important, however, that they have the trust and confidence of their employes generally, with a fair degree of self-possession and capability of speaking the language of the operatives.

The floor chief shall have immediate charge of all employes or operatives employed on his floor in all matters pertaining to exit drills. He shall be held responsible for the enforcement of all rules and will report to the chief engineer any employe who willfully neglects their proper observance.

He shall see that each movement corresponding to the alarm signal is promptly and properly executed and shall personally supervise the sounding of the general building alarm on his floor. He shall be further responsible for the condition of all aisles and passageways, and will see that chairs, benches and stock are promptly removed to insure unobstructed passageways.

When, by pre-arrangement in drill practice or as a result of actual fire, it may be necessary to depart from the regular instructions as regards selection and use of exits, such change will be at the sole direction of the floor chief.

Room Captains. Whenever floors are subdivided into two or more rooms the floor chief will be assisted by the room captains. For floors of large area, the floor captains should designate a supervisor for every fifty employes, to assist in maintaining the necessary control and discipline. For these latter

559

positions, it may frequently be found desirable to make selections from the forewomen.

Room captains should be chosen from those highest in authority, preferably a foreman or work boss. The same general care in their selection should be exercised as indicated for the floor chiefs.

They should perform the same general duties in their respective rooms as are prescribed for the floor chief, subject to the latter's direction and supervision, excepting that they shall have no authority to change the assignment of exits, nor sound the general building alarm unless under direction of the floor chief.

Stairway Guards. For these positions men are to be preferred; they should be strong and alert, capable of acting quickly in emergencies. Two men selected from each floor should be assigned to each exit or stairway.

Guards are to be subject to the orders of the floor chief or room captains, and shall see that the march from the rooms and in descending the stairway is orderly and without crowding and at uniform speed, with careful observance of spacing between files. They shall be especially watchful of persons stumbling or falling to prevent trampling, and no conditions should be allowed which require a halt after the exit march has started.

Guards shall be stationed as follows: One guard on the room side of the door leading from the room, who shall see that the door is opened promptly after the first signal and is kept open until all the occupants have left the room and then that it be closed, and one guard on landing midway on staircase descending to the next floor below. Where stair exits have sharp bends or are poorly lighted, additional guards should be provided as required. All the foregoing officers should have a first and second assistant to help in the general work and to take charge, by seniority, in case of the absence of the officer.

Searchers. There should be at least one man and one woman searcher on each floor with alternates. They should be cool-headed and strong.

Searchers should immediately after the signal visit the toilet rooms and any room in which there may be occupants who cannot hear the signal. They must look out for any people who may become hysterical and faint.

Inspectors. An inspector selected from among the employes should be appointed to examine each morning the condition of all stairways, fire escapes and roof exits, if any, and to report immediately to the chief of exit drill any obstruction found thereon or any other unusual condition. In large establishments where many are employed, or where the public is present, such as in department stores, the inspector should be uniformed, preferably with fire-department experience. He should make regular rounds of the building and register on an approved watchman's clock.

He shall also see that all doors leading to stairways or exits open outwardly in such a way as not to obstruct the passageway, and will immediately report any found locked or obstructed to the floor chief or chief engineer.

During the winter season attention should be given to any existing fire escapes where exposed to accumulations of ice or snow, and, whenever so found, immediate steps should be taken for its prompt removal.

In addition to the above, provision should be made for a daily inspection and test each morning of the alarm system and of all signaling devices; report thereof to be made to the chief engineer.

Drill Exercise. Exit drills should be held as often as necessary, depending upon the design of the building, the character of the industry, intelligence of employes, etc., and should include everyone in the building. The employes should always be dismissed at night by the regular test signal.

It is advisable that the alarms announcing the drills for each trial should originate on different floors, in order to give different people an opportunity to learn how to act and have the signal sent when they discover a fire, and to afford practice in changing the order of precedence for possession of stairways or fire escapes, if the design of the building requires the latter to be used; excepting that the line of march may be so arranged as to take advantage of the additional time required in the descent of those from the upper floors, by dismissing such of the lower floors as would not delay the egress of the former.

A further exception to the rule should be made where buildings are divided by fire walls having protected openings, which would allow the transfer of all the occupants on a given floor in the fire section to an adjoining section on the same floor in the building, or by means of doors or a balcony to adjoining buildings, or where provision is made for ascending to roof exits that may lead to a safe retreat, either on or in an adjoining building.

In assigning stations, the first consideration is to man the aisles leading to each exit from the fire district and to prevent pushing and overcrowding. As far as possible, the aisle guards will endeavor to effect line formation, in order that the approach to the exit may be as orderly as possible. At all times special consideration should be given to women and children.

Employes who are not members of the section in which they may find themselves at the time of the test, upon the first signal should be at attention and assemble for the line formation. Where the public is present and fire conditions permit, the line should be led off to other exits than those to which the public may be crowding.

Drill practice for tests should closely approximate military precision. It should be orderly and without confusion, and the movements should be simple and as few in number as possible. All movements should lead in the direction of the exits and follow in response to gong strokes.

The first alarm will consist of a series of strokes on a single-tap gong (twice repeated), indicating the floor from which the alarm is given. Upon the first stroke of this alarm all employes will immediately cease work, rise, and as far as possible shut off power to machines.

Upon the first stroke of the drill gong each operative will remove the stock, chairs or benches nearest him in the aisles, placing same either under or on top of the work table or machine. Before the sounding of the second stroke all aisles and passageways should be cleared of obstructions and the operatives should stand ready for line formation, which should be announced by the second stroke.

The next movement should be to march to the door of exit passage in single or double file. If in double file, couples should link arms for mutual support, the women using a free hand to raise their skirts to prevent tripping themselves or those in their immediate rear, especially on the stairs, and each file will move forward, observing a uniform distance between couples to prevent touching. The line should start on motion signal of either the floor chief or room captain, and continue on to the stairway and descend, being subject only to the signals of the stairway guards.

No employe or other persons should be permitted to attempt to secure clothing or street apparel from locker or cloak room.

Drill exercises should aim to bring into practice as often as possible all of the signals as mentioned, to insure against possible misunderstanding at a critical time.

Upon reaching the street the line should be led away to a safe distance to prevent crowding and confusion around the exit, and for this purpose one of the room chiefs or test supervisors from the first or nearest street floor should be assigned to the duty of leading the line away from the building.

Elevator attendants should be instructed to take cars immdiately upon the first sound of the building alarm to the floor indicated and hold themselves subject to the orders of the floor chief. In high buildings of the fire-resistive type, the operator should be instructed to take his elevator into the fire zone and receive passengers, and then if conditions favor such a procedure, discharge them only a few floors below the fire zone. Employes should be instructed to leave at that point and go down the stairways. If this procedure can be carried out much valuable time and many lives may be saved. The usual difficulty, however, is that all stairways and halls are crowded so that the elevators must run to the ground.

NOTE. The practice of holding separate exit drills for each room or department of a building, unless in sections cut off by standard fire walls, is believed to be a serious mistake, not alone for the single-tenant factory, but in particular for the omnibus-tenant factory, where jurisdiction over employes is divided and where operatives of two or more separate employers are required to use the same avenues of egress. For drill purposes, every omnibus factory building should be considered as a unit and the suggestions and recommendations herein made applied to the building as a whole.

Assignment of Exits. The assignment of exits will depend primarily upon their number, capacity and location and to some extent on their arrangement. An exit discharging horizontally into another building or into another section of the same building which is cut off by a fire wall having standard protected openings will accommodate as many persons as a separate and exclusive stairway of the same width for each story, and with the possibilities of danger greatly reduced.

Where conditions permit, it would be desirable in drills to use the regular entrances for exit purposes on account of their familiarity to the employes constantly using them. In their selection, however, consideration should be given to possible exposure by local hazards, such as proximity to heating and power plants and any hazardous processes or locations connected with the premises. It is also important in arranging the regular exits to allow one or more, if possible, as entrances for firemen. The assignment of exits for different floors should first be based on approximate estimates of their relative discharging capacities, then as a result of actual tests based on these estimates, the distribution to each exit can be revised so that the time consumed will average about the same for all. In these trials every available exit, including those reached by way of the roof, should be considered.

Frequently the arrangement of exits may be such as to permit a safer and more rapid dismissal from an upper floor by using the regular exits to one of the lower floors in order to reach an exit discharging on another side of the building. Combinations of this kind should be utilized wherever possible

Signs to indicate location of all stairways, fire escapes and other exits should be displayed in the main aisles throughout building. For this purpose it is believed that the hollow iron sign with the letters cut in each side, against a white background, are the most effective. These signs may be illuminated for use in any dark sections of the building.

Notification. For the purpose of sounding a general building alarm, each building should be equipped with an electrically operated alarm system. Connected in circuit with this system there should be one or more electro-mechanical gongs or horns on each floor, of suitable size to insure being heard above the noise of occupancy, such as moving machinery. The gongs on each floor should simultaneously indicate by strokes the floor from which the alarm is given, which should be twice repeated.

The use of the box stations should be restricted as far as possible, in order to confine their use to the floor chief or his assistants, as conditions may require.

All alarm gongs used as exit drill signals should be used continuously for other than drill purposes in order to insure their being in good condition and to keep the employes accustomed to their use, also to prevent the nervous shock of a first unfamiliar gong tap, which might unfit a person for immediate emergency action.

For the information of all employes, notices should be posted in each room giving full instructions in all matters pertaining to the drills. These notices should be printed in the respective languages of the employes.

The power-plant engineer, upon the first signal of the building alarm, should be instructed to shut off power to machines and shafting throughout the building, excepting in cases where it would affect the operation of the fire pumps, elevators or the lighting system.

A time and place for discussing drills with floor captains, etc., should be frequently arranged so that errors and improvements in drill can be pointed out and discussed.

INDEX